Chemicals
on the
Internet

Gulf Publishing Company
Houston, Texas

Chemicals *on the* Internet

a **directory** *of*
industry sites

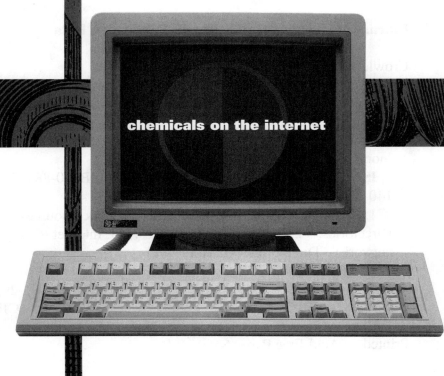

chemicals on the internet

William R. Crowley

This book is dedicated to my mother, Mercedes Crowley Dust.
She gave me the freedom and the understanding to
enjoy chemistry, even while she watched me set the toolshed
(read "makeshift chemistry lab") on fire about once a week
with an experiment gone astray.

Gulf Publishing Company
Book Division
P.O. Box 2608, Houston, Texas 77252-2608

10   9   8   7   6   5   4   3   2   1

Library of Congress Cataloging-in-Publication Data

Crowley, William R.
    Chemicals on the Internet / William R. Crowley.
        p.   cm.
    Includes indexes.
    Contents: v. 1. Organic chemicals and petrochemicals—v. 2.
Inorganic chemicals and minerals.
    ISBN 088415-139-5 (v. 1 : alk. paper). — ISBN 0-88415-
140-9 (v. 2 : alk. paper)
    1. Chemical engineering—Computer network resources—
Directories.   2. Web sites—Directories.   3. Internet (Computer
network)—Directories.   I. Title.
TP184.C48   1997
025.06′66—dc21   96-29505
                                                                        CIP

Printed on Acid-Free Paper (∞)

CONTENTS

ACKNOWLEDGMENTS...vi

INTRODUCTION..vii

ORGANIC AND PETROCHEMICAL COMPANIES.......1

SERVICE AND SUPPLY COMPANIES.........................53

ASSOCIATIONS AND SOCIETIES...............................94

GOVERNMENT SITES...114

COLLEGES AND UNIVERSITIES...............................130

MAGAZINES, BOOKS, AND NEWSLETTERS..............147

CHEMICAL RESOURCE PAGES...............................167

MISCELLANEOUS SITES OF PARTICULAR INTEREST

      MSDS SITES...185

      PATENT SEARCHING......................................192

INTERNET SEARCH ENGINES.................................197

WHITE PAGES, SOFTWARE, AND OTHERS..............204

INDEX..210

ACKNOWLEDGMENTS

This book could not have been prepared without the help of my wife and friends and some individuals who preceded me on the Internet and collected many of the sites you will read about in this directory. My heartfelt thanks go to my wife, Kay, who has already forgotten more about online browsers and Internet connections than I will ever learn. Her experience with Internet shareware and various browsers, and her patience with my long hours in front of the monitor were both invaluable in the completion of this effort. Her ability to show me new shortcuts without laughing at me for having forgotten them from the previous week speak mountains to her patience.

My thanks also go to Ms. Lynn Allen who stepped in at the last minute to help with the final editing and cleanup so that we could meet the publisher's deadline.

Many thanks to those who have gone before and created various resource pages of chemical links on the Internet. The WWW Virtual Library of Chemical, Chemical Engineering and Waste Water Technologies was very helpful in steering me to the best sites. The Newsgroups sci.chem, sci.chem.engr, and other sources of information also led me to many good sites.

The chemical industry is extremely difficult to get one's arms around. Should I limit the book to just petrochemicals? Should I include custom manufacturers and specialty chemical companies? How about commodity chemical brokers? What about metals, biochemicals and pharmaceuticals? My thanks here go to William Lowe, Editor-in-Chief, and Joyce Alff at Gulf Publishing for forcing me to keep the scope under control.

INTRODUCTION

This directory is designed to save both the seasoned Internet traveler and the novice web adventurer their most precious asset . . . time. Use this directory just once and you will have more than recovered your cost in time saved.

As anyone who has surfed the net for more than one day knows, the clock seems to magically take on a life of its own while you are online and seconds turn into minutes, minutes into hours, and lunch breaks into after-work hours. The Internet, and more recently, the World Wide Web, is one of the most fascinating and seductive phenomena to enter our lives in many years.

For the searcher of organic and petrochemical information, this directory may help prevent wasted efforts surfing the net for that tidbit of information needed to finish the project. Look in the directory first. Use the index and select the site that most fits your need *and go directly there* without searching or drilling down yet another 150,000-page index of sites.

This book contains a disk with an Internet "hotlist" or bookmark file in HTML (HyperText Markup Language) format. This file includes all the sites listed in the book. You should sign on to the Internet, open your Internet browser, then open this file in the browser. Use your browser's "find" or "search" feature and keyword search for the site you want. A single click on the name of the site with your mouse will take you to that site on the Internet.

If you need the MSDS (Material Safety Data Sheet) for a particular product, open the hotlist with your browser. Then use the "search" feature and input "MSDS." That should take you to that section in the hotlist; then go to the site you want and click on it. You can retrieve your target in less than three minutes. If you are preparing for a big meeting with a chemical company, go to their site first and catch up on the latest press releases and financial reports; check out their products and plants; see what they are telling the

Internet world. You may be the most knowledgeable person at the meeting.

The Internet provides us with a whole new way of doing business and collecting the information we need to do it better. Hopefully this directory will be of help in that change process.

If you are in the chemical industry and involved in research, engineering, manufacturing, marketing or sales, there is something here for you.

What's in this directory?

This directory began as a collection and review of Internet sites for the petrochemical industry. It quickly became apparent that it is very difficult to get one's arms around the petrochemical industry . . . where does it start? . . . where does it end?

As my friend Dr. Geoff Dolbear said in his newsletter *The Freebie,* "more than a few people seem to be confused by the term *petrochemical.*" He goes further to tell us "to understand petrochemicals, start with the understanding that an immense list of everyday items start life as some fraction of petroleum. The list includes virtually every synthetic fiber and plastic, and most of the nitrogen fertilizers. It includes rubber for tires and the latex in paints. Most of the products are made in great tonnage, and they touch every phase of our lives."

He's right, of course, but this directory will not include the entire scope of petrochemicals. Its focus includes organic chemicals and petrochemicals, but not petroleum. Here's how the chapters developed and what they include.

Chapter One—Organic and Petrochemical Companies

This chapter includes the home page, or Web site, of those companies that either manufacture, market, distribute, or trade organic chemicals. We start with Advanced Chemical Design and end with Zhuhai Skyhigh Chemicals Co., Ltd. I found companies that fit my criteria all over the world from China to France and from Chile to Canada. Each listing provides either the company's comments about the page or their company or, in some cases, I have given my subjective review of their information. Many companies include product specifications and MSDS on their pages. Others will take orders online. This is the information they want you, their customers, to know about them.

Chapter Two—Supply and Service Companies

These are the companies that provide services to the chemical companies. These companies range from large engineering and construction companies that design and build chemical plants to consultants and process troubleshooters. They might provide pumps and valves, highly technical instrumentation, corrosion protection, software, or laboratory glassware. Again the listing summarizes what the companies are saying about their services.

Chapter Three—Chemical Associations and Societies

From the Air & Waste Management Association to the World Association of Theoretically Oriented Chemists, these organizations are the ones that keep the organic chemical personnel up-to-date with the latest changes in the industry. Here you will find information about each organization and its purpose. Many have newsletters that you can read online. A few have membership lists available so you can see who belongs and, of course, meeting announcements are available on their sites.

Chapter Four—Government Sites

Government agencies throughout the world participate in the chemical industry through regulation or assistance. In this chapter you can find most of those agencies' home pages. You can contact government employees for assistance online, or view their guidelines and reports. The national laboratories of the United States are included here and most provide reports of interest to chemical personnel. You can find the latest OHSA regulations and in-depth reports from the EPA and much more here.

Chapter Five—Colleges and Universities

There is no way I could have included all the colleges and universities with either a chemistry or chemical engineering department. Instead, I tried to identify those with a particularly good Web site that discussed something of interest to the organic chemical industry. The range goes from "bucky balls" to a Molecular Monte Carlo.

I included many sites that have VRML (virtual reality modeling language) available. Some of these will let you create a molecule, then look at it in three-dimensional space, turn it around, and maybe even go into it. Some of these sites are truly amazing and were definitely not around when I struggled through Organic Chemistry 301!

Chapter Six—Magazines, Books, and Newsletters

Many full text or abstracts of your favorite chemical magazines can be found here. Magazines for the process engineer and for the R&D chemist are listed in this chapter. Go here and read from those you have never heard about or review articles being presented for publication. The gamut runs from the popular magazine *Nature* to the highly technical *Journal of Computer-Aided Molecular Design*. We can all learn things at these sites, and they are constantly being expanded and updated.

Chapter Seven—Chemical Resource Pages

Many of these sources will become favorites on your Internet browser bookmark list. These are the sites that some call "meta-indices." They contain hundreds of links to subject-related (in this case organic chemicals) sites on the Internet. They are similar to this directory, only they are online. You will also find the home pages to the big information retrieval databases such as STN and Dialog here.

Chapter Eight—Miscellaneous Sites of Particular Interest

MSDS Informational Sites

Here you will find collections of MSDS (Material Safety Data Sheets) from around the world. Most sites are fully searchable. Some are listed by chemical name, others grouped by company. After trying a few of these, you should never be without the MDSD you need.

Patent Searching

These sites are your connection to the world of patents. You can search most of the patent offices of the world using these links.

Chapter Nine—Internet Search Engines

If you can't find it in the directory or on the disk, go here. Knowing that I could never give you everything about organic chemicals and with the realization that any Internet directory is out-of-date before it gets printed, I included my favorite search engines. With these you can find just about everything there is on the Internet. Remember to always read the hints or help file of any search engine before you undertake a search. They all function differently and require different commands to get the best results.

Chapter Ten—White Pages and Other Sites of Interest

If it didn't fit anywhere else, I put it here. Find market reports on the petrochemical industries of Korea and Indonesia and an explanation of all those Internet error messages you keep getting. Read the background on the Nobel Prize for chemistry. Don't miss the fantastic Periodic Table listed here.

No, it was never like this when I went to school.

Here's the Procedure

When you need information, first decide who might have it, then consult the directory and use the index to find them. There are about 650 sites listed in the book. If you don't find it there, check the disk and use your browser's "find" or "search" feature to search by keyword up and down the hotlist. If you still can't find what you need, try Chapter Seven, Chemical Resource Pages.

If you still don't have your information on your screen, go to Chapter Nine, Internet Search Engines. Before you take off on a wild goose chase, read the report at the site called "Best search engines for finding scientific information in the Internet."

Have fun.

Bill Crowley

Organic and Petrochemical Companies

These are links to the manufacturers, marketers, brokers, traders and distributors of organic and petrochemical products across the world. The spectrum covers the largest multi-national petrochemical companies to the small independent custom chemical manufacturer.

Advanced Chemical Design

http://www.coolworld.com/
shopping/advanced

BOROTHENE is a non-flammable, very high solvency alternative to 1,1,1 Trichloroethane and chloro-fluorocarbons. Based upon new halogenated hydrocarbon chemistry that has low toxicity and outstanding cleaning power at a low cost. BOROTHENE does not affect aluminum, magnesiurn or ferrous metals as well as most plastics and elastomers. Works extremely well in vapor degreasers and ultrasonic cleaners. BOROTHENE will work for any application that 1,1,1 had been used for in the past. Economical and Efficient Vapor Degreasing with BOROTHENE Solvent From Advanced Chemical Design.

Links
Detailed Information Page • Order Page

Aktol

http://www.aktol.com/aktol.html

Through the combined resources of our Engen Refinery and the Exxon Chemical Distributorship, Aktol is able to offer the most comprehensive range of solvents and fluids in Southern Africa. From traditional solvents to the very latest high-tech performance fluids, Aktol is able to deliver. Aktol is proud of its sales and distribution infrastructure in Southern Africa. The strong product focus gives customers direct access to specialist advice and laboratory facilities to customize products tailored to their needs. It is geared to provide a high level of service in the domestic market and in exports to both African and overseas companies.

Links
Customer Service • First into the future • Health, Safety and Environment • Quality

Akzo Nobel

http://www.akzonobel.com

Akzo Nobel ranks among the top 10 chemical companies in the world. In 1995 sales revenues exceeded $13 billion. The company employs 70,000 people in 50 countries. Head offices are located in Arnhem, The Netherlands with North American corporate services located in Chicago, Illinois. Many business units of Akzo Nobel trace their origins to the 18th and 19th century. In paints and coatings the Sikkens brand was established in 1764 in Groeningen, the Netherlands. Sulfuric acid was first produced in Amsterdam in 1835 by the Ketjen family. In North America many surfactants were produced by Armour & Co., founded in 1860 and a number of industrial chemicals produced by Stauffer in the 1880's. Today the company has 28 business units, each operating with a great deal of autonomy.

Links
About Akzo Nobel • Products/Business Units • Investor Information • Latest News

Aldrich Chemical Company

http://www.sigma.sial.com/aldrich/aldrich.html

Beginning with one product and a single-page catalog, Aldrich has grown into a worldwide supplier of over 37,000 products. We have expanded our product offering to include laboratory equipment and books as well as information. Our catalog is, in fact, a "Handbook" containing a wealth of information which our customers use and appreciate. Much has changed at Aldrich since its humble beginnings in a small Milwaukee garage. We serve customers from facilities in Milwaukee and Sheboygan, Wisconsin and in Allentown, Pennsylvania. In addition, Aldrich continues to expand geographically with subsidiaries, affiliates, and sales offices at strategic locations in Europe, Asia, the Middle East, South America, Mexico and Canada.

Links
A Message from the President • General Information • Searchable Online Aldrich Catalog • Specialty Product Lines • Topics of Interest • Aldrichimica Acta

AllChem Industries, Inc.

http://www.allchem.com/

Leadership in the fields of petrochemicals, water treatment products and international trade places AllChem as one of the top chemical trading groups in the USA. In addition to industrial chemicals, we have growing commitments to the food, pharmaceutical and specialty chemical industries. AllChem maintains contacts with over 30,000 consumers, suppliers and traders of chemicals throughout the world. Through this network we track production, demand and price movements in the major chemical markets. Using this information and our many years of global experience, AllChem is well equipped to be your primary chemical source. AllChem has been active in the chemical import, export and domestic distribution business since 1982. We maintain warehouses throughout the USA and have affiliates in all the major countries of Europe, Latin America and the Far East. We have packaging and drumming facilities and can supply chemicals in LTL, truckload or bulk quantities. Our business is evenly divided between U.S. sales and worldwide trade operations.

Links
Chemical Bulletin Boards • Current Price Indications on Select Chemicals • Product List • Material Safety Data Sheet • Overview of AllChem Operations • Conferences • Industries Served • Nations with Business Activities • Shipping Schedules

AlliedSignal Inc.

http://www.allied.com

Established in 1985 through the merger of Allied Corporation with The Signal Companies, Inc., AlliedSignal began taking shape more than 70 years ago. Allied Chemical & Dye Corporation was formed in 1920 as an amalgamation of five American chemical companies established in the 1800s. Signal was organized in 1928 as a regional gasoline company in California with oil drilling activities. Today, AlliedSignal is an advanced technology and manufacturing company serving customers worldwide with aerospace and automotive products, chemicals, fibers, plastics and advanced materials. With $14.3 billion in sales, the Company ranks among the top 75 of the Fortune 500, and is one of the 30 companies in the Dow Jones Industrial Average. Our business is comprised of three sectors: Aerospace, Automotive and Engineered Materials.

Links
Corporate Information • News • Financial Information • Aerospace Sector • Automotive Sector • Engineered Materials Sector • Feature Report

AlliedSignal Plastics

http://www.asresin.com

Search for specific plastic resins according to the needs of your applications. If you know the Resin Grade, you can search for additional information. To get info on the different industries we serve, check out Markets. Get the details on our 48 Hour Delivery program. It's all part of the AlliedSignal Advantage.
To learn the basics of the industry, visit The AlliedSignal Plastics Encyclopedia. Resin Overview and Production Technique Overview are just a few of the documents that will be available to help you understand the production process.

Links
What's New • Place Your Order • Search • Markets • 48 Hour Delivery • AlliedSignal Advantage • Troubleshooting Tips • Encyclopedia • Industry/World News

American Chemicals Company, Inc.

http://uc.com/acci/default.htm

A full line Chemical, Solvent, Oil, Lubricant and Specialty product distributor. American has served industry since 1940. It represents many of the major chemical producers of the United States in numerous world wide resources. American Chemicals Company, Inc. offers a wide variety of chemical products in quantities ranging from bulk tank trucks to 55 gallon drums and tote tank containers down to small research and development quantities.

Links
Products and Services • Commodities and Solvents • Oils and Lubricants • Chemical Specialty Products • Research & Development

Amoco Chemicals

http://www.amoco.com/
what_we_do/chem/01_chems.html

The Chemicals sector is the fastest growing segment of Amoco Corporation. In 1994, Chemicals accounted for approximately 45 percent of Amoco's total revenues of $30.4 billion. A testament to the sector's growth is found in its capital budget for 1995 -- $900 million. That's an increase of more than $400 million over the previous year, and the 1995 figure does not include projects financed through Amoco investments in joint ventures around the world. Much of the Chemicals sector's growth is due to Amoco's status as the world's largest producer of purified terephthalic acid (PTA), the preferred raw material for the manufacture of polyester. Popular end-use products containing polyester include fabrics, cassette tapes, microfilm, tire cord, and a wide assortment of plastic containers. Amoco is also the largest producer and consumer of paraxylene, a chemical feedstock used to make PTA. With PTA and paraxylene facilities and investments in the United States, Europe, the Pacific Rim and Latin America, Amoco is well-positioned to capitalize on increasing global demand for polyester products.

Links
Chemical Feedstocks • Chemical Intermediates • Polymers • Fabrics & Fibers • Chemicals Development and Diversification • detailed flowchart •

"Onstream Magazine" • "Explore Our World" • "What We Do" • "Master Index" • Amoco Corporation

Anzon

http://www.polysort.com/anzon

Anzon offers the broadest range of antimony-based polymer additives in the industry plus formulated flame retardants and smoke suppressants. No one else has so many ways to accommodate your polymer, process, environmental needs and application requirements. And if a standard product falls short, Anzon can tailor-make a new one that better meets your requirements.

Links
About Anzon • Product Guide • Flame Retardants and Smoke Suppressants • Hygenic (Dustless) Products • Chemical Products • Products for the Glass and Ceramics Industries • Catalysts • Chemical Intermediates • Friction Modifiers, Lubricants and Pyrotechnical Applications

Applied Chemicals

http://www.apchem.com.au/

Applied is an Australian specialty chemicals company operating in the areas of: Manufacturing, engineering & non-road transport; Automotive; High performance lubrication management; Natural resources extraction & processing; Laundry & catering; Food & beverage processing and; Paper production.

Links
Company Information • Product Ranges

Argus Chemicals

http://www.texnet.it/argus/argus.html

Argus Chemicals is a Rare and Fine Chemicals manufacturer settled in Vernio, north of Florence, since 1987. Coming from a strong industrial organic experience we started to produce on lab/pilot scale rare and otherwise unobtainable products out of common commercial catalogues for pure and applied research. So, with increasing experience, we pointed out some specific areas of greater interest such as: Organophosphorus compounds; Homogeneous/heterogeneous catalysts; Asymmetric synthesis. We produce in the mentioned areas "tailored" products on request, or manage research programs on the basis "no product, no money". Our customers are usually public and private research centers, in Italy and abroad.

Links
Background • Catalogue • Inquiries and suggestions

Asha Nitrochem Industries

http://www.iin.com/asha/index.html

Asha Nitrochem Industries Limited-- Manufacturer of high quality industrial grade Nitrocellulose Products, All grades and viscosities of Industrial grade Nitrocellulose ES (R/S) and SS Grades, Ethanol, Isopropanol, Butanol, DBP, and other Plasticizers WET grades 18-20 cps to 5-6 sec or higher viscosity grades.

Links
Asha Nitrochem Industries - Quality Nitrocellulose (India) • Goodhope International Inc.

Ashland Chemical Company

http://www.ashchem.com

Ashland Chemical Company is a diverse specialty chemical manufacturer. Ashland Chemical Company is also a leading distributor of chemicals and plastics. This combination leads to the company's high potential as a single-source supplier...simplifying customer communication...allowing vendor reduction...providing a wide range of products. We encourage you to contact Ashland Chemical Company for more information about our product lines.

Links
Products by Industry • Communications • Environment, Health & Safety • What's New • Ashland • Valvoline • Guestbook

Ausimont USA

http://www.ausiusa.Inter.net

Part of a multi-billion dollar international enterprise, Ausimont participates in a specialized chemical technology that benefits widely diverse interests worldwide. This technology, pioneered by Ausimont, focuses on fluorochemistry. Fluorochemicals, while offering a balance of useful properties, are particularly noted for their exceptional resistance to other chemical agents and environments that attack and degrade lesser materials. Applications which exploit the special characteristics of fluorochemicals range from durable coatings for architectural components to chemical process vessels and piping, from jacketing for electrical wiring to lubricants. In part, Ausimont's technical advantage in this field draws on the resources available through its link to

Montedison, a key member in the $30 billion Ferruzzi enterprise headquartered in Milan. Montedison invests annually some $350 million in research and development, a significant portion devoted to fluorochemistry. Capitalizing on this base, Ausimont has developed and marketed a family of fluoro-based chemical products that offer high performance in selective applications under difficult conditions. To supply the growing technical markets for its products, Ausimont operates high-capacity production facilities here and abroad. Domestic plants are located in Thorofare, New Jersey and Orange, Texas.

Links
PVDF • ECTFE • CFC Replacement • Blowing Agents • MFA/PFA • Elastomers • Lubricants • Fluids • Ausimont Quality Vision • etc. etc.

Baker Performance Chemicals

http://www.bhi-net.com/bpci/

Baker Performance Chemicals Incorporated is the specialty chemical division of Baker Hughes Inc., and as a service leader, BPCI offers the stability of a large corporation with local company reliability. BPCI markets specialty chemicals that solve problems for customers involved in various industrial processes. The first full service, specialty chemical company with a Web site. In our site you will find a comprehensive summary of the products and services we offer. The latest additions include: Baker Performance Chemicals division wins Hibernia contract; We have a new edition of our electronic newsletter, Synergy; We've added several new sections of information to our Aquaness Chemical division site; Baker

Industrial Chemicals is featuring the HPC-11 Hydrogen Permeation Monitoring System and Sulfix hydrogen sulfide abatement products for refineries and petrochemical plants.

Links
Baker Performance Chemicals • Hibernia • Synergy • Aquaness • Baker Industrial Chemicals • HPC-11 • Sulfix • Baker Performance Technologies

BASF Group

http://www.basf.com

The BASF Group of companies have more than 100,000 employees worldwide that manufacture approximately 8,000 products from sites in 39 countries. Headquartered in Ludwigshafen, Germany, BASF Aktiengesellschaft (AG) was founded in 1865 as Badische Anilin- & Soda-Fabrik AG. BASF Corporation and its affiliates in Canada and Mexico are the NAFTA member of the BASF Group, with headquarters in Mount Olive, New Jersey. BASF Corporation and its affiliates in Canada and Mexico have approximately 16,500 employees and 40 major production sites in the NAFTA region. BASF supplies a wide range of chemical products for the entire manufacturing process -- from raw materials and auxiliaries through precursors and intermediates to finished goods. We also produce various consumer products such as pharmaceuticals and audio/visual cassettes. But there's a lot more information on our company, our products and our services on this web site.

Links

Acrylic Acid and Monomers • Products
• Amines • Press Releases • Cosmetic
Chemicals • About BASF Corporation •
Oxo Products • Markets • Plastic Mate-
rials • Ecology • Plasticizers • BASF
Worldwide Operations • Carpet Recy-
cling • Search • Job Center

Bayer AG

http://www.bayer-ag.de/bayer/
english/0000home.htm

The Bayer Group is an international
chemical and health care company with
some 143,000 employees in 140 countries. With annual sales of more than
DM 44 billion and a profit of DM 4.1
billion (1995), it is considered one of
the world's leading chemical companies. Bayer is a diversified, international chemical and pharmaceutical
company. We offer our customers a
wide variety of products and services in
areas ranging from health care and
agriculture, through engineering materials and specialty chemicals, to
photography and graphic systems.
Bayer is research-based and is aiming
for technological leadership in its core
activities. Our goals are to steadily increase corporate value and continuously
generate a high value added for the
benefit of our stockholders, our employees and the community in every
country in which we operate. We believe that our technical and commercial
expertise involves a responsibility to
work for the common good and contribute to sustainable development.
Comprehensive environmental protection, maximum safety, high product
quality and profitability are all equally
important corporate objectives. Our
"Guidelines for Responsible Care"
serve as the framework in which we set

out to achieve those objectives. Bi-
lingual English/German.

Links

Company • Business • Employees •
Facts • Environmental Protection •
Principal Locations • Culture • News •
Link of the day

Beximco Chemical Division

http://www.beximcorp.com/html/
chem.html

With 12,000 people in employment and
widely diversified activities ranging
from shrimp cultivation to gamma
irradiation of food and medical products, from construction to fine chemical
production, BEXIMCO with its 25
companies is the largest private sector
business conglomerate in Bangladesh.
Beximco Chemical Division with its
annual turnover of Tk. 1.87 billion (US
$47 million) in 1994 is perceived as the
flagship of the Beximco Group. Products and services offered by Beximco
Chemical Division are the trend setters
in the country. The Chemical Division
is comprised of the following business
activities: Beximco Pharmaceuticals
Ltd. (Formulation & Basic chemical);
Beximco Infusions Ltd. (Formulation);
Pharmatek Chemicals Ltd. (Basic
chemical); I&I Services Ltd.
(Distribution & Trading).

Links

About BEXIMCO • News • The
Chemical Division • Investing In
BEXIMCO • Financial Reports • Em-
ployment Opportunities • Photo Album

BP Chemicals

http://165.121.20.76/bischem.html

BP produces and markets a wide range of chemical products throughout the world and maintains a strong global position in the licensing of its leading manufacturing technologies. The Chemicals business operates major manufacturing plants in the UK, France and United States and, through a series of joint ventures, has world class production facilities in Korea, Indonesia, Malaysia and Germany.

Links
Forward to Exploration Expertise • BP Homepage • Tell Us What You Think • Search

Brown Chemical Co., Inc.

http://www.brownchem.com/

Today Brown Chemical is a major Regional Distributor, with 36 employees and third generation management. It has outgrown its beginnings in Paterson and expanded to an additional facility in Oakland, N.J., which now consists of the corporate Headquarters and general warehouse space of 45,000 square feet. This is also the location of Brown's Kosher White Room packaging facility, perhaps one of the finest in the region. The company still maintains its Paterson location, which houses bulk storage tanks and packaging lines. Paterson has approximately 30,000 square feet and 90,000 gallons of bulk storage. The customer base has risen from approximately 10 when the company was started to over 1000. Seven Sales Representatives service this customer base, which is scattered over a 100 - 150 mile radius of northern New

Jersey. Today Brown direct - sells, distributes or packages over 1500 products representing 35 major chemical manufacturers.

Links
About Us • Our Services • Company Profiles • Product Information

Buckman Labs

http://www.buckman.com

Buckman Laboratories is a specialty chemical company serving the pulp and paper, water treatment, leather, coatings, agricultural, wood treatment industries worldwide. K'Netix(sm), The Buckman Knowledge Network, brings Buckman associates in over 80 countries together to share knowledge in solving customer problems through creative chemical treatment technologies and technical service.

Links
About Buckman Laboratories • What's New • The Buckman Fundamentals • K'Netix(sm) • Locations • Markets Served • Value Added Services • Employment Opportunities • Buckman's Micro 101

Calgon Corporation

http://www.calgon.com

Calgon is a leading producer and supplier of specialty chemicals and a provider of related services for water treatment, papermaking, cosmetics, surface treatment and specialty biocides for various other industrial applications. Calgon is headquartered in Pittsburgh, Pennsylvania and employs approximately 1,300 people worldwide.

NEW! Calgon Software Demo • Message From Our President • General Company Information • Short History of Calgon Corporation • Products • Responsible Care • Power Industry • Industrial Skin Care Products • Calgon Corporation News • Upcoming Events • Technical Support Resources • Calgon Offices

Canamex: Chemical Specialties

http://140.148.80.2:80/chemical/canamex/

Canamex, manufacturer with the highest share in the chemical specialties market in Mexico. Manufacturer of chemical specialties, surfactants, resins, polyesters, insecticides, emulsifiers, detergents, antistatics, pyrethroids, polyethylene glycols, dispersants, wetting agents, foaming agents, chemical products. Bilingual page (also Spanish)

Links
About Canamex • How to contact us • Español

Catalytica Inc.

http://www.catalytica-inc.com/

Catalytica is developing and offering to its customers advanced products that use the company's proprietary catalytic technologies to yield economic and environmental benefits by lowering manufacturing costs and reducing hazardous byproducts. Catalytica is currently focused on applying its technologies to two primary areas: improving production of pharmaceutical intermediates and developing advanced combustion systems to reduce emissions generated by gas turbines. Catalysis is essential in the production of many industrial and consumer products.

Links
Catalytica Combustion Systems • Catalytica Fine Chemicals • Catalytica Advanced Technologies • XONON Flameless Combustion System • Fine Chemicals • Consulting and R&D Services • History • Scientific Advisors • Patents • Investor Information • News Releases • Job Opportunities

Cayman Chemical Company

http://caymanchem.com/

Cayman Chemical Company supplies nearly 1,000 innovative and affordable products to meet the needs of scientists worldwide. We provide the research community with an extensive line of assay kits for the measurement of eicosanoids, cyclic nucleotides, cytokines, adhesion molecules and nitrate/nitrite. Moreover, we offer a broad range of quality biochemicals including eicosanoids, nitric oxide reagents, and a variety of related lipids, fatty acids, enzymes, cDNA probes, antibodies and custom antibody production for research applications.

Links
Cayman Worldwide • Online Catalog • News and Special Features • Customer Assistance • Technical Support • New Cayman Chemical Catalog

Chang Chun Petrochemical Co., Ltd.

http://www.asiapacific.com/taiwan/changchun

Product manufactured by this Taiwan chemical company: Polyvinyl Alcohol, Hydrogen Peroxide, Glacial Acetic Acid, Butyl Acetate, Epoxidized Soyabean Oil, Antioxidants, Stabilizer for PVC, Polyvinyl Butyral, Hexamine, Trimethylol Propane.

Links
Taiwan • AsianNet Home Page • Vitalic Home Page

Chemfab Corporation

http://www.chemfab.com

Chemfab Corporation is an international advanced performance materials company that develops, manufactures and markets a broad range of high-performance industrial products based on its expertise in flexible fluoropolymer composite materials. Upon manufacture, the composite materials we make perform under the toughest conditions -- chemical, electrical, temperature, mechanical -- yet retain their "flexibility" or "pliability" and surface release (non-stick) properties. That's why we call these materials "Flexible Composites". Worldwide end-use applications are in electronics, environmental, food processing, architectural, aerospace, communications, chemical processing, protective clothing and many other markets.

Links
Now In Brazil! • Also in China • Technical Developments From

CHEMFAB • Financial (Edgar SEC Filings) • Listing • About Chemfab

Chemsol

http://www.chemsol.com

Chemsol, A chemical solutions company from Ralrube, Inc. Chemsol Inc. was created in 1992 to supply the 300+ Military Spec chemical products to all markets except the GSA. In a short time, Chemsol Inc. has become recognized and sells to foreign governments, general manufacturing, aviation, defense and export industries. Customers call Chemsol Inc. whenever they need Military Spec products. With the manufacturing arm of Ralrube Inc., Chemsol can also supply mil-spec chemicals with hazardous packaging suitable for all modes of transportation including IATA air requirements. Our 10,000 square foot plant is GSA and FDA approved. All products are suitably labeled and bar coded. All shipments contain an MSDS, certificate of conformance or test report per the relevant specification. Quality control that is constantly scrutinized by the U.S. government and industry.

Links
Mil-Spec Chemicals • Featured Chemicals • Quote Request • Company Mission • Cleaners • Waxes/Polishes • Corrosion Preventatives • Adhesives & Sealants • Lubricants • Paints/Coatings

Chevron Chemical Company

http://www.chevron.com/operatns/ccc/index.html

Headquartered in San Ramon, California, Chevron Chemical Company manufactures and markets a variety of industrial chemicals in 80 countries worldwide. Through its U.S. Chemicals Division and its International Group, the company produces and markets petrochemicals, including benzene, cumene, cyclohexane, paraxylene, ethylene, propylene, normal alpha olefins (NAO), polyethylene, styrene and polystyrene. Chevron Chemical deploys the leading technology in aromatics production. The company's Aromax technology produces higher yields of benzene at lower cost than conventional methods, while its Eluxyl technology produces high-purity paraxylene at a cost among the lowest in the industry. The company holds a commanding NAO market position, is a leader in the production of linear and low-density polyethylene, and is a major producer of high-density polyethylene and polyethylene pipe. The Oronite Division's deposit-control gasoline additives are recognized as world market leaders. Oronite manufactures and markets lubricant and fuel additives worldwide, with principal offices in Houston, Paris and Singapore. The division has additive plants in Brazil, France, Japan and Louisiana, and joint-venture plants in Madras, India, and Mexico City.

Links
Home • Operations

Chinese Petrochemical Corp.

http://cpc.com.tw/cpcwww/
intro/econts.html

When the Chinese Petroleum Corporation was officially founded in Shanghai in June, 1946, it took over the facilities of former Oil and Mining Bureau in Kansu, Shihchuang, and in the Northeast of Mainland China as well as re-

lated petroleum facilities in Taiwan. All investing funds were from the national treasury, therefore, it is a 100% state-owned enterprise. After the communists took over the China Mainland, CPC moved to Taiwan along with the central government, and relocated its headquarters to Taipei. It has been under the jurisdiction of the Ministry of Economic Affairs since. CPC is assigned the task of the exploration, production, refining, storage, transportation, and sales of petroleum products and the manufacturing and supply of petrochemical raw materials in Taiwan. The capital amounts to 87 billion NT dollars, with 21,000 employees on the company's payroll.

Links
Introduction • Exploration & Development • Preliminary Oil Treatment • Overseas Oil Exploration • Oil Refining • Petrochemical Production • Transportation and Marketing • LNG Importation and Supply • Research and Development • Pollution Prevention & Environmental Protection • Industrial Safety and Health • Human Resources • Main Products

Chromophore, Inc.

http://www.chromophore.com/

Chromophore is a manufacturer of polymers and small molecules for use in nonlinear optics, as fluorescent biological markers, and as temperature calibration standards. In addition to our catalog items, we offer custom synthesis of new materials, custom manufacturing of known materials, consulting, and a wide array of analytical and computational services for users of chromophoric materials.

Links

nonlinear optics • fluorescent biological markers • temperature calibration standards • Information • Chemical Structure of the Poly-Orange Tom-1 Toluenediisocyanate Polymer • Poly-Orange Tom-1 Toluenediisocyanate • NLO Table of Contents • DAST • DANS • PNA • MNA • urea • Nonlinear Optical Materials • Biological Markers • Liquid Crystalline Materials

Ciba Giegy AG

http://www.ciba.com/

Ciba Giegy is a leading worldwide biological and chemical group, based in Switzerland, dedicated to satisfying needs in healthcare, agriculture and industry with innovative value-adding products and services. We strive to achieve sustainable growth by balancing our economic, social and environmental responsibilities. Empowered employees and a flexible organization support our commitment to excellence. The philosophy of striking a balance between our economic, social and environmental responsibilities is Ciba's Vision 2000. Since its introduction in 1990, it has become a major strategic factor in securing our future success and simultaneously, in consolidating the company's leading position. The Vision calls upon all employees to assume a greater role in the management of the company through empowerment, leadership and teamwork.

Links

Vision • Financial • News • Pictorial History Tour • Merger • Feedstocks

CONDEA Vista

http://www.condeavista.com/

CONDEA Vista Company, headquartered in Houston, Texas, is an integrated producer of commodity and specialty chemicals, employing about 1,400 people. CONDEA Vista's products include linear alcohols and derivatives, polyvinyl chloride resins and compounds, polymer blends and alloys, detergent alkylate, high-purity alumina and other industrial chemicals. CONDEA Vista has an approximate 10% share of the U.S. market for vinyl, the second-largest volume plastic in the country. And we are among the world's largest producers of biodegradable detergent alkylate, used to make household laundry and dishwashing detergents and industrial cleaners. Besides these consumer products, CONDEA Vista's materials are found in products that people use every day, such as shampoos, cosmetics, hand creams and other personal care products, agricultural and textile chemicals, automobile interior trim, pipe, pipe fittings, home siding, wire and cable coatings, catalysts, ceramics, recycled paper, waterless hand cleaners and printing inks. CONDEA Vista is part of the global chemicals operations of RWE-DEA AG, a major German company with activities in oil and natural gas exploration and production, oil refining and marketing, as well as chemical manufacturing. CONDEA also includes CONDEA Chemie GmbH, Hamburg, Germany; CONDEA Augusta, Milan, Italy; and D.A.C. Industrie Chimiche S.p.A., Milan. Together, we have 20 manufacturing sites in Europe and the U.S. and 10 sales offices in countries around the world offering a wide array of products.

Links
Our New Company Identity • Where
We're Located • Company Overview •
What's New at CONDEA Vista • What
We Make • Other Great Chemical Sites
• Our Environmental Commitment

Conoco LiquidPower Flow Improver

http://www.conoco.com/liqpow/
index.html

Representing a new generation in pipeline operating efficiency, LiquidPower
flow improver is the first drag reduction product that truly competes with
energy. Its proven polymer formulation
reduces frictional pressure drop so effectively, selected pump stations or
pumping units can actually be shut
down without reducing pipeline
throughput. As the graph below illus-
trates, that can save you hundreds of
thousands of dollars annually in energy
and maintenance costs, as well as allow
you to take advantage of potential Demand Side Management incentives.
What's more, LiquidPower flow improver allows pumps, motors, parts and
supplies from off-line pump stations to
be used at other operating sites, saving
capital costs. Like traditional flow im-
provers, LiquidPower flow improver
can be used to increase throughput to
meet variable or seasonal market demands. It can help reduce operating
pressure while maintaining pipeline
design capacity. It can also help prevent or delay capital expenditures for
additional pumps, pump stations or
looped piping segments. And because
LiquidPower flow improver is up to
four times as effective as other drag
reducers, it's much more cost-efficient
to use.

Links
Conoco LiquidPower Flow Improver •
MS-DOS P.U.M.P. Software • Conoco
Home • About Conoco • Environment •
News • People • Products

The C. P. Hall Company

http://www.polysort.com/cphall

The C. P. Hall Company is a leading
supplier of plasticizers and performance additives to the polymer industries, worldwide. The company's products are used extensively in rubber,
plastics, adhesives, coatings, personal
care and specialized industrial applications. The company is both the major
producer of polyester polymeric plasticizers and specialty ester plasticizers in
the U.S. as well as a significant distributor and reseller of plasticizers and
additives for its target markets in the
U.S. and internationally. The company's corporate headquarters,
technical service center and
international operations are located in
Chicago. Domestic markets and customers are served through four regional
centers and local warehousing operations. Production is carried out at three
manufacturing facilities in the U.S.

Links
Products • About C.P. Hall • Locations
• Corporate Headquarters • Technical
Service Center • International Opera-
tions • Regional Centers • Manufactur-
ing Facilities • Esters for Industry •
Product Lines and Tradenames • Plas-
ticizer List

Cron Chemical Corporation

http://vellocet.insync.net/
~cronchem/cron0a2.html

Cron Chemical Corporation has provided over 50 years of service to the South Central United States as a distributor of the finest quality chemical raw materials. Cron Chemical Corporation supplies a wide variety of materials from the world's leading manufacturers: Prime Pigments; Functional Pigments; Specialty Chemicals; Filtration Products. Cron Chemical Corporation offers its customers the following: On time delivery; Custom solvent blending and packaging; All shipments DOT compliant with HAZMAT certified drivers; Our own fleet of tractor trailers, flatbeds, and tankers.

Links
Prime Pigments • Functional Pigments • Specialty Chemicals • Filtration Products • Containers • On time delivery • Custom solvent blending and packaging • All shipments DOT compliant with HAZMAT certified drivers • Our own fleet of tractor trailers, flatbeds, and tankers

Cron Chemical Group

http://vellocet.insync.net/
~cronchem/

The Cron Chemical Group is comprised of three affiliated companies: Cron International; Cron Chemical Corporation; Magnolia Chemicals and Solvents, Inc. Each dedicated to providing customers with the very highest quality products and unmatched service. The Cron Chemical Group is backed by the strength and stability of our parent company, Amalgamated Metals PLC, a multi-national company headquartered in London. Cron International represents many of the world's largest chemical companies and serves the continental United States with a full array of chemical products including Potassium Chlorate, Sodium Chlorate Powder, Paraformaldehyde, and Pentaerythritol. Cron Chemical and Magnolia Chemicals and Solvents, Inc. serves the South Central United States with a full line of Prime Pigments, Functional Pigments, Specialty Chemicals, Filtration Products, Solvents, Silicates, Surfactants, Containers, and other industrial chemicals from the United States' leading manufacturers. Services include solvent packaging, custom packaging, custom product blending, and 24 hour service.

Links
Cron International • Cron Chemical Corporation • Magnolia Chemicals and Solvents, Inc. • Information Request • Download Cron Presentation

Cron International

http://vellocet.insync.net/
~cronchem/cron0a1.html

Cron International was formed to provide the U.S. market access to the products of major European chemical manufacturers especially products with limited or no U.S. production. Cron represents some of Europe's largest producers of potassium chlorate, sodium chlorite powder, paraformaldehyde, and pentaerythritol. These European manufacturers include: Derivados Forestales S.A.; Formol Y Derivados, S.A.; S.A. Polialco; Aragonesas.

Links

Derivados Forestales S.A. • Formol Y Derivados, S.A. • S.A. Polialco • Aragonesas • Products Included

Degussa

http://www.degussa.com/

The Chemical Group offering value-adding chemicals and services, consists of the Peroxygen Chemicals Division, the Feed Additives Division and the Organic Fine Chemicals Division. The Pigment Group comprised of the Carbon Black Division, the Chemical Catalyst Division, the North American Emission Control Catalyst Division and the Silica Division, adds performance and value to its customers' products. The Group provides high quality products for a broad range of applications. The Metal Group in close partnership with its customers, develops and produces high-tech precious metal products which meet precise specifications for electronic and metallurgical applications. The Metal Group consists of the Electronic Materials Division, the Precious Metals Division, the Refining Division and the Metallurgy Division. The Dental Division produces high quality alloys and solders, porcelains, merchandise and equipment.

Links

The Chemical Group • The Pigment Group • The Metal Group • The Dental Division • Products By Industry

Dojindo Laboratories

http://www.dojindo.co.jp

Welcome to Dojindo Laboratories, the world of ultra high quality reagents! Dojindo's Company history dates back to the establishment of the Dojindo Pharmacy in 1910's by Keiji Ueno. Since then Dojindo has been making products to back up the progress of scientific research. Today Dojindo produces over 800 well-known products used by research organizations in most disciplines. Many of these products were developed jointly between Dojindo staff and outside researchers. Dojindo strives to expand its ability to analyze the future direction of science by maintaining continued interest in new research activities as well as improving its information-gathering network.

Links

Search products information • What's New • What is Dojindo Laboratories • Catalog request • Dojindo News Letter • Products • How to Order • Special Offer for Bulk Supply • Cyberscientists • Chemical Dojin

Dow Chemical Company

http://www.dow.com/

The Dow Chemical Company is the fifth largest chemical company in the world, with annual sales of more than $20 billion. The company provides chemicals, plastics, energy, agricultural products, consumer goods and environmental services to customers in almost all countries around the world. Dow operates 94 manufacturing sites in 30 countries and employs about 39,500 people who are dedicated to applying chemistry to benefit customers, employees, shareholders and society. Dow is the world leader in the production of olefins, styrene and aromatics. This segment encompasses procurement of fuels and petroleum-based raw materials as well as the production of olefins, aromatics, styrene and cogenerated power and steam for use in the company's operations.

Links
About Dow • News Releases • New Businesses • Emulsion Polymers • Working at Dow • Specialty Chemicals • STYROFOAM • Liquid Separations • INVERT* Solvents

DSM in North America

http://www.dsmna.com/

DSM is a highly integrated industrial group whose main activity is in chemicals and materials. The DSM Group comprises a large number of companies, most of which are based in Europe and the United States. The Group's head office is in Heerlen (Netherlands). DSM currently has annual sales of around $6 billion and employs about 17,000 people, 10,000 of whom are based in the Netherlands.

Links
What's Hot • About DSM N.V. • DSM N.A. Overview • DSM N.A. Companies

DuBois Paper Technologies

http://www.dubois-paper.com/

Welcome to DuBois Paper Technologies--As your online DuBois Representative, let me be the first to welcome you to our site on the World Wide Web. My job, and the job of every DuBois representative, is to make certain you are completely satisfied with your DuBois experience. We accomplish this by providing superior programs and personalized service for all your pulp paper mill cleaning and biological control needs. Our web site gives more information on the wide

variety of products and services available to you, our customer. Our efforts are supported by our parent company, Unilever, a worldwide leader in cleaning research and technology.

Links
Unilever • What's New? • General Information About DPT • DPTCustomer Support • Health and Safety Programs • DPT Products • DPT Laboratory and Analytical Services

DuPont

http://www.dupont.com

DuPont is a science and technology based global company of people who make products that make a difference in everyday life. Our goal is to be the most financially successful, socially responsible, customer-focused chemical and energy company in the world. Our history began nearly 200 years ago in Wilmington, Delaware. Today we do business in more than 70 countries. Our science and technology networks, manufacturing plants and customer service centers bring thousands of products to people across the planet.

Links
What's New • In Today's Edition • DuPont Stock at a Glance • Investment Planned for Pontypool DACRON • DuPont Is One of the Top Users of Information Technology • Conoco Aids Azerbaijani Victims of Disease and War • About DuPont • DuPont at a Glance • DuPont Career Opportunities • DuPont Mexico • DuPont News Releases • DuPont Views • Financial Information • DuPont Safety, Health and the Environment 1995 Progress Report • Science & Technology • Global Company • People • Products • Every-

day Life • News • Search • Browsing Tips

Dynamic Enterprises Ltd.

http://www.carbon60.demon.co.uk/

We are a high technology company specializing in the third allotrope of carbon - the fullerenes, or "buckyballs". The novel properties of these polycarbon supercages are receiving intense interest from the scientific and industrial world. This interest has created a demand for supplies of the pure fullerene materials. In early 1993 a group of scientists and engineers formed Dynamic Enterprises Ltd (DEL) with the aim of developing new, low-cost methods for production of these expensive polycarbon supercages. Today, DEL is the only UK-based company supplying high purity fullerenes to research laboratories and industry at competitive prices.

Links
Fullerenes • High Purity Fullerenes • Prices • Study • Experiment

Eastman Chemical Company

http://www.eastman.com/

Eastman Chemical Company (NYSE: EMN) is a leading international chemical company that produces more than 400 chemicals, fibers and plastics. The company does not sell consumer products, but Eastman supplies billions of pounds of products to industrial customers for use in the manufacture of hundreds of items consumers use every day. Eastman polyethylene terephthalate (PET) plastic is used in containers for beverages, foods and toiletries. Several brands of tools, toys, toothbrushes

and eyeglasses feature products made from other Eastman plastics. Eastman products are in fabrics, floor coverings, paints and other coatings, computers, automobiles, pharmaceuticals, foods, cigarette filters and chemical intermediates. Founded in 1920 as a unit of Eastman Kodak Company, the small operation in Kingsport, Tenn., was established to produce two basic chemicals for Kodak's photographic business. After 73 years as a Kodak unit, Eastman Chemical Company was spun off Jan. 1, 1994, and is now an independent public company whose shares are traded on the New York Stock Exchange. While Kodak is Eastman's largest single customer, Eastman has more than 7,000 customers worldwide. Eastman's sales in 1995 totaled $5.04 billion.

Links
About Eastman • Financial Information • Products & Marketing • Employment • What's New • Search

Ekonol Polyester Resins

http://www.ekonol.com/

Manufactured by The Carborundum Company, Ekonol Polyester Resins are homopolymers based on p-oxybenzol repeat units and are linear thermoplastics. They are highly crystalline polymers but have no observed melting point even at up to 900 - 1000 degrees F. Flow and creep are virtually non-existent below their crystal-crystal transition temperature of 625 degrees. Ekonol Polyesters have a density of 1.44 gm/cc. Ekonol Polyesters possess a compressive strength of 15,000 psi.

Links

Introduction • Ekonol Polyester T-101 Resin • Ekonol Polyester M-102 Resin • PTFE Blends - Catalog • Material Safety Data Sheet

Elf-Aquitaine (France)

http://www.elf.fr/en/index.html

Elf Aquitaine is the number one French industrial company, and also one of the world's ten leading petroleum groups. It operates in four main areas: oil exploration and production, refining and distribution, chemicals, and health and beauty through its subsidiary Sanofi, one of the world's twenty leading pharmaceutical groups.

Links

Exploration and Production • Refining and Distribution • Chemicals • Health And Beauty • Elf Aquitaine in Brief • Files • Events

Epsilon Chimie

http://www.epsilon-chimie.cci-brest.fr/

Born from top University Research, EPSILON CHIMIE offers you a team of scientists, highly skilled in the theory and practice of organic synthetic chemistry. Contractual Research, Multistep Synthesis, Technological survey, Structural analysis. Our mission is to fit to all your needs under quality, quickness and secret preoccupation.

Links

Epsilon Chimie • Online Catalog • Structural Analysis • Useful links • Chemical Shifts • Clipart • Available for 100g - 1 Kg - 10 Kg - 100 Kg • University Research

Ethyl Corporation

http://www.ethyl.com/

A global company, Ethyl occupies a unique position between the automotive and petroleum industries. Ethyl develops, manufactures and blends performance-enhancing fuel and lubricant additives. The company markets these products worldwide to refiners and others who sell petroleum products for use in transportation and industrial equipment. Ethyl additives increase the value of gasoline, diesel and heating fuels as well as lubricants for engines, automatic transmissions, gears and hydraulic and industrial equipment.

Links

Ethyl additives meet or exceed performance standards • Ethyl has facilities around the world • The customer comes first • Up-to-date announcements from the company • The fuel additive that helps reduce smog • Leadership in the industry

Farchan Laboratories

http://www.farchan.com/

Since 1945 Farchan Laboratories has been a world leader in supplying organo-acetylene compounds for Research and Development. Other services now include processes for many Organo-Silicon compounds, along with Custom Synthesis and Contract Research. Farchan Laboratories is dedicated to providing the highest quality research chemicals. Access our Research Chemicals Catalog through our searchable database.

Links
The History of Farchan Laboratories • Company Profile • Search Our Research Chemical Catalog • Semi-Commercial Products

Ferro Corporation

http://www.ferro.com/

Established in 1919 as a manufacturer of porcelain enamel frit, Ferro is now a producer of specialty materials for industry, including coatings, colors, ceramics, chemicals and plastics. Ferro's major markets are building and renovation, major appliances, household furnishings, transportation, industrial products, packaging and leisure products. Ferro has had an international presence since 1927, when it initiated operations in Canada, followed by Great Britain and Holland. Over the years, the Company expanded further into Europe, Latin America, Australia and the Far East. Thus, a global perspective has influenced the organization's philosophy and management throughout most of its business history. The Company's strong worldwide status stems from its current manufacturing presence in 22 countries and its leading position in market segments within each country and regional area. Ferro products are sold in over 100 countries.

Links
Electronic Materials Division • Grant Chemical Division • Filled and Reinforced Plastics

Fiberite, Inc.

http://www.olworld.com./olworld/mall/mall_us/c_busfin/m_fiberi/

Since its inception in 1948, Fiberite, Inc. has grown to become the world's largest supplier of advanced composite materials and a leader in thermoset molding compounds. Our products serve many markets. From aircraft and automobiles to transformer bushings and welding equipment, Fiberite has material solutions. Fiberite composites excel where your applications require superior mechanical, thermal and/or electrical characteristics. If used in place of metals, Fiberite materials can reduce weight, reduce heat transfer, and eliminate machining. If used in place of thermoplastics, Fiberite molding compounds can improve thermal/chemical resistance and enhance dimensional stability--particularly at elevated temperatures.

Links
Thermoset Molding Compounds • Polyimide • Silicone • Sheet Molding Compounds • Phenolic • Prepregs (Broadgoods, Tape and Tow) • Carbon • Glass • Kevlar

Fina Corp

http://www.fina.com/

Fina is an integrated multinational petroleum and chemical company. Fina is active in exploration and production of oil and gas; refining, distribution and marketing of petroleum products; manufacturing and sales of plastics, lubricants, base chemicals and oleochemicals. PetroFina is an international oil and chemical group active in all sectors of the oil industry.

Finapolis is a virtual city. Its buildings contain information about our industry, products and services. There are three routes into Finapolis. 'Fina in Business' provides access to more information about our industrial activities, while 'Fina for You' focuses on everyday life. The third strand, 'Fina in my Country' will be launched shortly.

Links
Fina in Business • Fina for you

Firestone Synthetic Rubber & Latex Company

http://www.polysort.com/firesyn/

Firestone Synthetic Rubber & Latex Company is a division of Bridgestone/Firestone, Inc. and is headquartered in Akron, Ohio at 381 W. Wilbeth Road. Our world-scale ISO 9002 registered plants are located in Lake Charles, Louisiana and Orange, Texas. Firestone's unique anionic polymerization technology allows for production of high purity, high molecular weight polybutadiene and a wide range of block, random and vinyl modified styrene/butadiene copolymers. Statistical process control is used in every step of our operation.

Links
Bridgestone/Firestone, Inc. • Company Background • Product Applications • Technical Bulletins

Fisher Scientific

http://www.fisher1.com/

The catalogs listed below are complete electronic versions of their printed counterparts. Each catalog offers an intuitive table-of-contents navigation tool, full-text searches, as well as part number, page number, and manufacturer searches. Almost 100,000 quality Fisher Scientific products and 10,000 images are represented here in over 4,000 catalog pages. You can search for any MSDS from our popular database within the Fisher Chemical and Acros Chemical catalogs.

Links
ProcureNet • The Fisher Catalog 95/96 • Fisher Safety America 95 • The Fisher Chemical Catalog 95/96 • Fisher What's New Catalog • Acros Chemicals Catalog 95/96 • Ordering • Directory • Locations • Employment

Flexsys

http://www.polysort.com/flexsys/

Welcome to Flexsys, the largest world wide producer of accelerators, insoluble sulfur, antidegradants, and specialty chemicals for the rubber industry. We are pleased to have you visit our site and invite you to browse through it. Flexsys, now celebrating its first year anniversary, was formed as a joint venture company by combining the rubber chemicals businesses of Monsanto and Akzo Nobel in May, 1995. That means we primarily focus on serving the rubber industry. This focus allows us to support the rubber industry through continual investments in our products and processes and through technical development. As the first major evidence of our commitment we have announced plans to invest in new 4-ADPA manufacturing technology (4-ADPA is a key intermediate used to make PPD antiozonants). This project will result in a significant reduction of the waste we generate compared to our use of current industry manufacturing technology.

Links

Monsanto • Akzo Nobel • new 4-ADPA manufacturing technology • What's New • Product Guide • Message To Our Customers • President's Message

Fluka Chemical Company

http://www.sigma.sial.com/fluka/fluka.html

The Fluka Catalog contains nearly 18,000 products of which 2,000 are new. We continue to add new products to help our customers with their total scientific requirements. Our products include chemicals, biochemicals, laboratory equipment and books.

Links

Message from the President • General Information • The Fluka Quality • The Fluka Catalog • New Products • Product Line Overview

FMC

http://fmcweb.ncsa.uiuc.edu/

FMC Corporation is one of the world's leading producers of chemicals and machinery for industry, agriculture and government, FMC participates on a worldwide basis in selected segments of five broad markets: Industrial Chemicals, Performance Chemicals, Precious Metals, Defense Systems, and Machinery and Equipment. FMC operates 115 manufacturing facilities and mines in 24 countries.

Links

About FMC Corporation • Investor Relations • News Release Library • Global Capabilities • Product Information and Brochures • FMC Environmental Honor Roll • FMC Foundation •

Consulting Services • Planning Your Career with Us

FPPF Chemical Company, Inc.

http://www.fppf.com/

This company supplies a number of fuel and lubricant treating chemicals. See the links below.

Links

Diesel Treatments • Antifreeze Recycling Chemicals and Systems • Home Heating Oil Treatments • Gasoline Additives • Conditioners • Lubricants and Cleaners

GE Plastics

http://www.ge.com/plastics/index.htm

An early pioneer on the World Wide Web, GE Plastics was the first materials producer to establish a site providing a broad range of in-depth technical information to serve the plastics industry. Within these pages, you will find a wealth of technical data and guidance pertaining to engineering plastics design, processing, and performance. Our goal is to deliver the highest level of information-based value to our visitors.

Links

What We Do • Products • GE Plastics News • Living Environments • Thermoplastics Education • Tech Tip of the Week • GE Select • GE Home Page

GE Specialty Chemicals

http://www.ge.com/specialtychemicals/

A division of General Electric Corporation, GE Specialty Chemicals includes Phosphite Antioxidants,

Modifier Resins, Additive Blends. Enhancing polymer performance to help resin manufacturers and compounders by providing: Design for higher value; Meet the demands of new applications; Reduce material costs; Improve quality

Links
GE news • GE products & services • Who We Are • What We Offer • Product Information • GE business finder

Glidco

http://www.millenniumchem.com/main/mchgld.htm

Glidco is one of the world's leading producers of chemicals derived from crude turpentine, a natural pine tree extract. Glidco sells over 300 specialty chemicals based on torpene chemistry, used for fragrance, flavour, pharmaceutical and industrial applications. Approximately 80% of total sales are for aroma chemical use.

No links

Goodyear Chemicals

http://www.goodyear.com/cgi-bin/chemhome.pl

For over 50 years, Goodyear Chemical has met the needs of customers in a variety of markets, from automotive to paper to textiles to footwear. To better acquaint you with the variety of raw materials supplied by Goodyear Chemical, this new directory is divided into groups to help you select information on materials that apply to your specific situation.

Links
Polymers • Sunigum Acrylate Terpolymer • Chemigum Nitrile Rubber - Acrylonitrile Butadiene Rubber • Chemigum HR • Chemigum Powder • Chemigum Carboxylated • Chemigum "80 Series" • Plioflex • General Purpose E-SBR • Budene Solution Polybutadiene Rubber • Natsyn Polyisoprene Rubber • Solflex Solution SBR • Pliolite Rubber Reinforcing Resins • Polymer Standards

Grupo Petropol S.A. de C.V. (Mexico)

http://spin.com.mx/~mbuschbeck/eng2.html

Grupo Petropol is one of only 5 direct dealers from PEMEX , having a warehouse of up to 2.5 million Lts. cap. and having future plans for expansion, figuring in the top petrochemical Mexican industry and dealership. Please feel free to leave an E-mail for any contact information. below is a list of the just some of the products we are ready to supply. (Bi-lingual Spanish)

Links
Pemex • Products

Harris Specialty Chemicals, Inc.

http://www.hsc-ss.com/index.html

Harris Specialty Chemicals, Inc. is a manufacturer of specialty construction products and systems for the construction industry and specialty fluorine and silane chemicals for the pharmaceutical and electronics industries. HSC's principal products are: Decorative coatings for waterproofing concrete and masonry; Expansion joint systems; Compression seals, bearing pads, and traffic bearing membrane systems for roadways and bridges; Epoxy concrete repair and overlay systems; Specialty flooring; Wall systems; Anti-corrosive pipeline coatings. HSC has 16 manufacturing plants in North America and Europe and sales offices throughout the world.

Links
Who We Are • Organization • Markets • Press Releases • Product Releases • Fact Sheets • HSC Products • Contact HSC • About PCR • Commercial Products • Electronic Catalog • Customer Service • Patents & Papers • Environmental

Hoechst

http://www.hoechst.com/

Welcome to Hoechst, a world leader in pharmaceuticals and chemicals. We are an international network of innovative and customer-oriented companies that are among the leading suppliers in the fields of industrial chemistry, pharmaceuticals and agriculture. We set our sights on long-term partnerships with customers. In order to recognize our customer's needs swiftly and flexibly, we have organized our company into business units operating in close proximity to customers. Hoechst is committed to promoting the concept of "sustainable development". This challenges us to open up market opportunities with innovative and environmentally advantageous products and processes.

Links
Who we are • Progress Report • Publications • Press Service • Investor Relations • Career Opportunities • Research & Development

Hoechst Celanese Corporation

http://www.hcc.com/

Hoechst Celanese manufactures and markets a diversified line of chemicals, fibers and film, specialty materials and technical polymers and advanced technologies, primarily to industrial customers. AgrEvo Canada is breaking new ground in crop protection and plant biotechnology. Hoechst Celanese announced in 1994 major expansions to maintain its leadership position in worldwide production of acetic acid and vinyl acetate monomers (VAM). These products are used to make adhesives, fibers, paints, plastics and many other products that play an important role in daily life activities. To establish a strong local presence in the rapidly growing Asian market, the company plans to construct a VAM plant in Singapore. Targeted for completion in 1997, this plant will have capacity to produce 330 million pounds per year of VAM, enabling Hoechst Celanese to deliver faster, more dependable service to customers in that region. For example, in China and Malaysia a ready supply of VAM will meet continually increasing demand from these countries' paint, plastics and fibers industries.

Links
Our Word, Our People, Our Work • About Hoechst Celanese • Right Now • Who We Are • Where We Are • In Depth • At A Glance • Search

H&S Chemical Co. Inc.

http://www.cris.com/~Hschem/

H&S Chemical has been Manufacturing, Researching and Developing Specialty Chemicals Since 1983.

Links
Chloramine-T • Trichloromelamine • Hydriodic Acid • Methyl Fluoride • Difluoro Acetic Acid • DDCP • Optishield (Specialty Corrosion Inhibitor)

Hukill Chemical Co.

http://www.hukill.com/

At Hukill Chemical, our commitment is to servicing our customers. Historically this commitment has been exhibited by our willingness to try innovative approaches to solving chemical problems and our flexibility in responding to the service requirements of our customers on a timely basis. For over 45 years Hukill Chemical has served industry with: Distribution of chemical products from major chemical manufacturers; Custom chemical processing; Solvent recycling (reclamation); Simple and fractional distillation; Solvent drying; Custom blending and formulating of industrial solvents and acids; Disposal of hazardous and non-hazardous waste materials through approved facilities; Thermal destruction of solid wastes through approved facilities; Blending of waste materials for supplemental fuels conversion.

Links
Distribution • chemical processing • recycling (reclamation) • distillation • drying • blending and formulating of industrial solvents and acids • Disposal of hazardous and non-hazardous waste materials through approved facilities • destruction of solid wastes through approved facilities • Blending of waste materials for supplemental fuels conversion.

Huls America Inc.

http://www.huls.com/

Huls America Inc. provides high quality colorants, biocides, raw materials and additives for architectural and industrial coatings; intermediates and fine chemicals for the pharmaceutical, cosmetics, photographic, agricultural and food industries; specialty polymers for adhesives, coatings and engineering thermoplastics; silanes and silicones for use in pharmaceuticals, adhesives, coatings, plastics and weatherproofing; methacrylate monomers and polymers; synthetic lubricants for industrial applications; surfactants; and heat transfer fluids. Huls America and its Canadian and Mexican business units employ about 1,000 people in North America. In 1995 the company's annual revenues were $525 million.

Links
Products, Major Trademarks • The company at a glance and Associated Companies • Facilities and Manufacturing Operations • Employment Opportunities • Upcoming Trade Shows • Recent Press Releases

Ichemco - Chemicals & Specialties

http://www.wms.it/ichemco/ingl.htm

ICHEMCO s.r.l. was established in 1979 with the aim of offering specialty products joined with an excellent service to well defined industry segments.

We started with a wide range of products for pressure sensitive applications, continuing with products for adhesive, textile and leather finishing , etc. Today ICHEMCO develops, produces, and markets internationally general and taylor-made products for (see links).

Links

Pressure Sensitive Adhesive Product List • Adhesive products (Hot-Melt, Solvent, Waterborne) • Textile finishing (Flame Retardants, Hydrophobic Agents, etc.) • Leather finishing • Rubber and Plastics • Laboratory Testing

ICI

http://www.demon.co.uk/ici/

ICI is one of the world's largest chemical companies. We make paints, industrial chemicals, materials and explosives. We have a portfolio of over 8,000 products and more than 200 manufacturing facilities in over 30 countries worldwide. Our strategy is to focus on core businesses which through market leadership, technological edge and a world competitive cost base, create value for our shareholders. We are committed to reaching standards of quality and service which our customers regard as better than our competitors. We are promoting the continuous improvement of safety, health and environmental performance throughout all our operations. We seek the highest standards of our products and processes through our traditional strengths in research, technology, manufacturing, engineering and through the involvement of all our employees worldwide.

Links

ICI Principal Addresses • ICI Environmental Report 1994 • ICI Safety, Health and Environment Challenge 2000 • Safety, Health, Environment Policy • ICI Dulux Customer Pages • Macco Adhesives (part of ICI Paints in the USA • ICI Australia Online • ICI Acrylics Inc. • ICI Polyester

Industrial Services International, Inc.

http://www.cais.com/cytex/isi/tsorb.html

Terra-Sorb® Superabsorbent polymers are solid, water swellable, cross-linked, polymers designed to absorb water or aqueous solutions. The product swells and forms a tight gel that holds water molecules, even under pressure. Industrial Services International, Inc. (I.S.I.) was formed in 1976 to promote the use of superabsorbent polymers. Superabsorbent polymers are materials that absorb hundreds of times their weight in water. One kilogram of these materials can absorb over 300 liters of water. The materials are inert and consequently do not alter the liquid that they absorb. These materials are by far the most absorbing substance in existence offering a low cost alternative to conventional absorbents in many applications. The company is the primary marketing arm for a single technology manufacturing facility located in the Carolinas here in the United States. I.S.I. is unique in its ability to provide unparalleled technical support to identify and manufacture unique specialty superabsorbent polymers for industrial and commercial customers. Today 60% of the company's sales are into agricultural applications with the balance used in non-agricultural applications.

Links
Agricultural Applications • Non-Agricultural Applications

Interchem Corporation

http://www.interchem.com/

International Technical Polymer Systems, Inc. is seeking international licensing agreements for the manufacture and/or marketing of its new line of inorganic polymeric modifier "systems". This line of products, marketed under the name "INTEC," represent cutting edge technology and is unlike any other modifiers in the marketplace today. Royalties and patent licensing available on a country or specific customer basis. ITPS will provide all manufacturing know how and raw material support in addition to exclusive marketing agreements. Licensing available for the rubber or plastics markets. Polymer testing at independent, internationally known testing labs along with factory trials have shown products proven in EPDM, natural rubber (and reclaim), SBR, silicone, nitrile and fluoroelastomer rubbers. In plastics: nylon, PVC, polyethylene, and polypropylenes and polycarbonates. The line of INTEC products is non-toxic, reduces production costs, and leads to quality improvements. INTEC is commercially available and being sold throughout the U.S. to over 35 rubber and plastic customers in only 18 months from product introduction. INTEC also inhibits carcinogenic nitrosamine generation during rubber production. Because of this feature, the product has demonstrated the potential for anticancer drug therapy and various

antibacterial and antifungal medicinal applications with significant market potential.

Links
Notes from the President and Chairman • About Sales & Marketing • News and other information • Suppliers • ACS Dobfar • Seloc • UCB • IMPACT Search Service • Interchem Locations

International Technical Polymer Systems

http://www.polysort.com/itps/

International Technical Polymer Systems offers the polymer world a new technology of non-toxic, rubber and plastics additives. The new world of additives, where the only restriction is your imagination. ITPS, Inc. Goes Worldwide To Serve You Cutting edge inorganic polymer modification technology available for exclusive manufacturing licensing and/or marketing opportunity. International Technical Polymer Systems, Inc. is seeking international licensing agreements for the manufacture and/or marketing of its new line of inorganic polymeric modifier systems. This line of products, marketed under the name "INTEC" represent cutting edge technology and is unlike any other modifiers in the marketplace today.

No links

IQM QB Quimic (Mexico)

http://www.iqm.com.mx/

We are a group of Mexican companies in the inorganic and organic chemical business, committed to quality and superior service to its customer base.

Links
Industrial Quimica de Mexico S.A. de
C.V • Quimic S.A. de C.V. • QB
Quimicos S.A. de C.V.

JLM Industries, Inc.

http://www.niicorp.com/jlm/

JLM Industries, Inc. is the parent organization of three main affiliates: JLM
Marketing, Inc.; Olefins Marketing,
Inc.; JLM International, Inc. Building
on its worldwide reputation as am ethical, responsible marketer of petrochemicals and plastics, the JLM companies provide transportation and ter-
minating expertise and services for
bulk liquid and gaseous chemicals. In
addition, JLM functions in a sales and
marketing capacity for domestic and
international petrochemical producers,
including both joint venture partners
and suppliers. Incorporated in 1986,
JLM Industries was formed as a succes-
sor to two international chemical trading and distribution companies. Today,
JLM boasts a world-wide network offices and subsidiaries, built upon long-
term relationships with producers and
suppliers. In keeping with JLM's
growth and restructuring, the company
moved its corporate offices in 1993
from Stamford, Connecticut to new
facilities in Tampa, Florida.

Links
JLM Marketing • Olefins Marketing •
JLM International • JLM Terminals •
Quality Service • JLM Locations •
Quality Service Pledge

Kalama Chemical Inc.

http://www.kci-freedom.com/

Kalama Chemical, certified to ISO
9002, is a diverse manufacturer of specialty, fine and commodity chemicals
and a leading world producer of certain
flavor/fragrance compounds and pre-
servatives. Kalama Chemical endeavors
to maintain quality production in an
environmentally sound atmosphere,
while paying attention to its neighbor-
hood through Responsible Care® including Community Outreach and
CAER® projects.

Links
General Information • Product/Sales
Information • Technical Information on
Product Line

Kediachem

http://www.atw.fullfeed.com/
~kediachm/

The KEDIACHEM group is involved
in manufacturing and project consultancy in the fields of pharmaceutical
intermediates, pesticide intermediates
and leather chemical intermediates.
Established in 1972, the group has concentrated on innovative chemistry for
the development of specialty chemicals.
Multinationals and Small Scale Industries have alike depended on us for
timely delivery, commitment towards
quality and competitive prices.

Links
Manufacturing • Project Consultancy •
The Director - Marketing

KMCO

http://www.kmcoinc.com/

KMCO began in 1975 as a small distillation unit, specializing in custom chemicals. Since that time, owner Artie McFerrin, has seen KMCO grow into a ninety-acre facility specializing in complex reactions, distillations and the manufacturing of specialty chemicals. KMCO has a vast array of synthesis equipment to utilize to meet the customers' needs. Reactor metallurgies include carbon steel, stainless steel, glass and Hastelloy. The customer can also utilize KMCO's pilot facilities for research and product development. Our carbon and stainless steel distillation equipment can be run in the batch and continuous mode. Our laboratory distillation equipment allows us to simulate the customer's distillation project with a great degree of accuracy. KMCO enjoys being the industry leader in glycol reprocessing, and continues to strengthen its position in the processing of olefins, amines and alcohols. KMCO continues to offer services other than synthesis and distillation. Some of these services are drying deodorizing, and color removal. Combining these services with our synthesis and distillation capabilities allows KMCO to offer customers capabilities that specifically fit their needs.

Links
KMCO Company Overview • KMCO Guiding Principles • Health, Safety & Environment Principles • Antifreeze Information • Brake Fluid Information • Custom Processing Information • Intermediates & Oil Field Products Information • Custom Processing Facilities Information • Obtaining a KMCO MSDS • KMCO Company Overview

K. R. Anderson Co., Inc.

http://www.kranderson.com/

Incorporated in 1968, K.R. Anderson Co., Inc. provides the industry with the most comprehensive line of specialty manufacturing materials in the West. Applications for K.R. Anderson Co., Inc. products can be found in virtually every industry, from mold making through the most complex electronics manufacturing process. Our company is currently in the process of posting our product lines on the web. We will eventually put up general information, MSDS's and data sheets. Some have already been posted. We are now a stocking distributor for Pace Incorporated soldering, reworking, and repair systems and fume extraction systems.

Links
About Us • New Info • Product Lines • Pictures • Product Name • Product Properties

Kumho Petrochemical Co.

http://camd1.kkpcr.re.kr/kumho/kumho.html

Kumho Petrochemical Co. manufacturers SBR (Styrene Butadiene Rubber); S-SBR (Solution Polymerized SBR); BR (Polybutadiene Rubber); HSR (High Styrene Rubber); NBR (Acrylonitrile Butadiene Rubber); SBR LATEX (Styrene Butadiene Latex); BD (Butadiene); AP (Alkyl Phenol) and Carbon Black

Links
KKCL(Korea Kumho Chem. Lab.) • Kumho Group • Polymer Chem • Bio-Chem • telnet to our computer

Lancaster Ltd.

http://www.lancaster.co.uk/

If you need to know about a product - talk to the team that made it. Lancaster manufactures most of the material we sell and our chemists have practical, indepth knowledge of the widest range of chemistry. A dedicated technical support centre in the UK are ready to process your inquiry. We can offer valuable advice on product performance and utilization. Direct fluorinations of complex molecules are rarely satisfactory due to the extremely reactive and non selective nature of elemental fluorine and many other electrophilic fluorinating agents, which are also often highly corrosive and/or toxic. The use of building blocks in which the fluorine atoms are already present allows the required pattern of fluorination to be introduced in a predictable manner. Some recent uses of fluorinated intermediates are shown.

Links
Update '96 Catalogue • Lancaster Lecture • Action Online • Information

Linkers Far East Pte Ltd.

http://www.singnet.com.sg/
~linknet/

Linkers (Far East) Pte Ltd is a distributor and an international trader of Industrial Chemicals & Plastic Raw Materials regularly serving markets of South East Asia, Indo China, China, Indian Subcontinent and Australia/New Zealand. We also supply the spot requirements of several customers in Europe, USA and the Middle East with chemicals produced in Asia, Europe, China and South America. Incorpo-

rated in Singapore in 1982, Linkers is now ranked within the TOP 40 companies specializing in Chemicals in Singapore (among whom include many multi-nationals). With offices in Indonesia, Thailand, Vietnam, Pakistan, Sri Lanka, Bangladesh and India, our customers not only in these countries but also elsewhere are assured of speedy and efficient services and quality materials at competitive prices.

Links
Industrial Chemicals • Acrylic Acid & Acrylates Monomers • Solvents • Plasticizers • Plastic Raw Materials • Resins • Branch Offices

Lomas International

http://www.lomas.com/

Lomas International is a specialty chemicals and minerals distributor serving the coatings, inks, plastics, rubber, adhesives, soaps and textile industries.

Links
Products and Services • NACD Affiliation • ISO9002 Certification • Product Specifications & MSDS Requests • Worldwide Connections

Lubrizol Corporation

http://www.lubrizol.com/

For almost 70 years, we've been building a company that applies advanced research and development to the formulation of high-performance specialty chemicals for transportation and industrial systems worldwide. One of our strengths has always been our ability to work as partners with our customers and to form mutually rewarding strategic alliances with companies related to our core business. As you browse our website, think about areas where we can work together. And remember, there's nothing we like better at Lubrizol than tackling a tough technological challenge.

Links
Welcome • Industry Related Sites • What's New • Products and Services • Career Opportunities • Publications • Investor Relations

Magnolia Chemicals & Solvents, Inc.

http://vellocet.insync.net/ ~cronchem/cron0a3.html

Magnolia Chemicals & Solvents can provide custom packaging of a wide selection of chemical products - from pints to 55 gallon drums to tote tanks to bulk tank trucks. Magnolia can supply custom packaging of paint thinners, lacquer thinners, and custom solvents, blended to your specifications or our own stock formulations - with your label or ours. Magnolia Chemicals & Solvents has served the Gulf Coast area since 1961 with a comprehensive inventory of chemical raw materials for (see links).

Links
Oil and Gas Service Industries • Chemical Process Industries • Paint and Coatings • Chemical Compounding • Metals Processing

Melamine Chemicals, Inc.

http://www.melamine.com/

Melamine Chemicals, Inc. is one of only two producers of melamine in the Western Hemisphere and is one of the three largest producers in the world. Formed in 1968, Melamine Chemicals supplies approximately 60% of the North American merchant market and also enjoys substantial international sales. The corporation's headquarters are located adjacent to the Mississippi River near Donaldsonville, Louisiana.

Links
ISO 9002 Certified • The Melamine Home • Applications • Products • Personnel • Technical • Customer Service and Orders • Quality Edition Newsletter • Melamine Molecule • Press Release Page • The Melamine House • General Application Information • Laminates • Molding Compounds • Adhesives • Coatings • Fire Retardant • Analyses Information. • Technical Data Sheet • Material Safety Data Sheet • Packaging Information

MER Corporation

http://www.Opus1.COM/~mercorp/

Materials and Electrochemical Research (MER) Corporation is devoted to high technology materials and electrochemical research and development with emphasis on advanced ceramics, intermetallics, reinforcements, composites, coatings and fullerenes. MER was started in 1985 with SBIR contracts as its primary business. In 1986, MER entered into a joint venture with a foreign international chemical corporation with MER as the managing partner to commercialize aluminum nitride ceramics. After building the joint venture into a research, development and production operation, MER sold its interest to Montedison in mid 1988. MER has built state-of-the-art research, development and small scale production facilities for performing contract R&D and production demonstrations. Extensive cooperative efforts between major universities and international corporations have been a hallmark of MER's research and development activities.

Links
History • Capabilities • Future • Fullerenes and Nanotechnology • Coatings • Reinforcements • Electrochemical Systems • Powders • Joining

Merck KGaA

http://www.merck.de/

We are a leading European group in pharmaceuticals, laboratory business and specialty chemicals with a strong commitment in North America and the growing markets in South East Asia. Merck has its own representations in 45 countries and 63 production plants in 30 different countries. (Bi-lingual German).

Links
Essentials • History • General Organization • Local Representation • Pharmaceutical Field • Laboratory Business • Specialty Chemicals • What's new • Press Releases • Employment Opportunities

Methanex

http://www.methanex.com/

Methanex is the world's largest producer and marketer of methanol. Methanol is produced primarily from natural gas and is a basic chemical building block that is used to manufacture formaldehyde, methyl tertiary butyl ether ("MTBE"), acetic acid and a va-

riety of other chemical intermediates which form the foundation for a large number of secondary derivatives which, in turn, are used in the manufacture of a wide range of products. Due to the diversity of the end-products in which it is used, methanol demand is influenced by a broad range of economic, industrial and environmental factors. Methanex operates strategically located methanol production facilities in North America, New Zealand and Chile and sources additional methanol produced by others in the United States, Europe and Trinidad. Methanol produced by Methanex and sourced from other producers is sold by Methanex through an extensive global marketing and distribution system which has enabled Methanex to become the largest supplier of methanol to each of the major international markets.

Links
Corporate Reports • Financial Highlights 1993-1996 • Methanex at a Glance • Shareholder Information • Methanol Markets

Miwon Petrochemical Corp.

http://mpc.co.kr/

Miwon Petrochemical Corporation has been producing synthetic resins such as PS, SAN, ABS, EPS, E(PE/PS) and Engineering plastics as well as PPG for Urethane intermediate material, as a Korean pioneer in this field since establishment of its PS plant at the Ulsan Petrochemical Complex in Korea in 1972.

Links
Miwon Petrochemical • News • Products

Mobil Chemicals

http://www.mobil.com/

Our petrochemicals business improved most dramatically as stronger industry fundamentals yielded improved margins. Polyethylene prices, which began strengthening in the fourth quarter of 1994, rose rapidly in the first half of 1995, driven by tight industry ethylene supplies coupled with strong demand. Prices in the second half softened, however, as supply increased and demand weakened. Paraxylene prices rose steadily throughout the year as worldwide supplies remained tight and as demand remained strong. Petrochemical sales volumes were higher, reflecting increased output from the Singapore petrochemical complex and our petrochemical joint venture in Saudi Arabia.

Links
Summary of Goals, Major Projects, and Accomplishments • Manufacturing Facilities/Plant Locations • Operations and Developments • Chemical Financial Data • Mobil Home Page • Fact Book Home Page

Monsanto

http://www.monsanto.com/

Monsanto is devoted to discovering, manufacturing and marketing agricultural and biotechnology products, prescription pharmaceuticals, food ingredients and performance chemicals used in consumer products.

Links
Welcome • New Monsanto • New Stuff • Products • Financial • Environment • In The News • Careers • Fun Stuff •

Site Map • Search • Eye On The Web Award • Industry Link Magnet Award • AgView Cool Site Award

Nagase America Corporation

http://www.nagase.com/

Nagase was founded in Kyoto, Japan in 1832 as a trader of dyestuffs. Through the years Nagase has progressed beyond dyestuffs, and is a leader in the development, production, sale and import and export of dyestuffs, chemicals, plastics, and biochemical products as well as attendant machinery. The New York branch of Nagase was established in 1915, and is now known as the Nagase America Corporation. Nagase enjoys a solid reputation as a technology-oriented marketing company. Specifically, we furnish technology, information, and services to complement the individual products and materials that we market. Nagase's special strengths are its technologies accumulated over many years and the special knowledge of its employees. We are thus able to maintain independent information gathering capabilities through which we conduct studies and offer needed technologies to both customers and suppliers. We also bring companies together for product development and production partnerships. Furthermore, we provide product and business development, wide-ranging planning, business proposals, and support and maintenance services.

Links
Export Opportunities • Company Information • Products • Chemicals • Pharmaceuticals • Electronics • Color Formers & Paper • Plastics

Napier International Technologies, Inc.

http://www.intergate.bc.ca/napier/

Napier seeks business partners, agents and distributors around the world to market its' unique line of specialty chemicals. Click on to the product type that interests you, then complete the "Inquiry Profile" and send it to us. We will then contact you with additional information. Biodegradable Products--For a variety of purposes ranging from paint stripping to household cleaning. Forestry Products--Products used by lumber Manufacturers to protect green lumber from mold and sapstain. Algaecide/Mildewcide--An all "All In One" product for removing mold, mildew and algae from exterior structural surfaces.

Links
Biodegradable Products • Forestry Products • Algaecide/Mildewcide • Napier Corporate Information • Inquiry Profile

National Starch & Chemical Company

http://www.nationalstarch.com

National Starch and Chemical Company is a leading manufacturer of adhesives, specialty chemicals, resins, electronics materials and specialty food and industrial starches. National produces thousands of technically advanced products and operates an international network of more than 125 manufacturing and customer service centers, located in 36 countries on 6 continents. The company was founded a century ago as a manufacturer of glue sizings (used to prepare paper and

textiles for printing) and then branched out into industrial adhesives. The commitment to the adhesives business was extended into the refining of starches and then the manufacture of synthetic polymers for new adhesives and textile and cosmetic ingredients.

Links
The Americas • About Our Company

Neste Oy

http://www.neste.com/

Neste is an oil, energy, and chemicals company. Oil refining, marketing, international trading and shipping operations form an integrated oil chain. Neste's most international division, Neste Chemicals, develops, manufactures and markets forest industry adhesives and industrial coatings. In its main products, for example in adhesive resins and polyester gelcoats, Neste Chemicals occupies an important position internationally. The business also includes oxo products and polystyrenes. Fiber reinforced sports and leisure equipment, manufactured by Chemicals' subsidiary Exel, have won worldwide renown for the division Neste is an oil, energy and chemicals company with operations in over 30 countries the world over. (Bi-lingual Finnish)

Links
Neste Oy - kotisivu • Finnish pages • Encyclopedia • Product Files • Neste Financial • Press Releases • Brochures

Neste Resins North America

http://www.neste-resins.com/

Utilizing our resin and formaldehyde plants in Canada, the United States, and Mexico, Neste Resins North America reliably and promptly supplies millions of pounds per day of thermosetting resins to our customers in the wood products, paper, fiberglass, and specialty industries. Our people recognize the critical needs of each customer, and we strive to assure satisfaction in product and assistance. We serve you with over thirty years of experience, as well as the benefits of international ownership that keeps us in touch with worldwide developments in resin research and technology.

Links
Products • Services • Locations

Norlabs Incorporated

http://www.norlabs.com/

Norlabs Inc. is a leading manufacturer of epoxy resins, adhesives, silicone greases and compounds, and one and two part silicones. Norlabs product lines consists of a wide variety of resins, compounds and adhesives. These specialty materials are used by our customers in the manufacture of products in the transportation, utility, aerospace, product assembly, automotive and electronic industries. Norlabs sells directly to industrial customers. Our products are found in many items you see or use every day. From hammers to PC boards to subway cars, Norlabs can provide materials with the performance needed for our customers to succeed.

Links
About Norlabs • Greases and Compounds • Epoxy Resin Systems • One and Two Part Silicones • Quotation • Information

Norsk Hydro

http://www.hydro.com/

Norsk Hydro manufactures the plastic raw material polyvinyl chloride (PVC) at plants in Scandinavia and in the UK. The most important precursor to PVC - vinyl chloride monomer (VCM) - is produced at the company's plants in Norway and Sweden, and is also sold to other manufacturers of PVC in Europe and the Far East. Hydro has a 60% interest in a PVC plant in Singapore, and is busy developing a similar plant in China. For the past few years, Hydro has also gone in for value-added products, for example through interests in the manufacture of PVC compounds and plastic pipe.

Links
Petrochemicals • Second Quarter 1996 • Group information • Quarterly results • Environment • Annual report • Press release • Latest news

NOVA Corporation

http://www.nova.ca/

NOVA Corporation is an integrated operating company sharing best practices and knowledge across all of our businesses. Our beginnings were in natural gas transportation. Our future is in adding value to hydrocarbons in energy-producing regions worldwide, by taking full advantage of the opportunities available across the natural gas value chain. OVA's petrochemicals business is Canada's largest. We are North America's second largest and lowest-cost producer of ethylene, fifth largest and lowest-cost producer of polyethylene and fourth largest producer of polystyrene. NOVA is among the world's lowest-cost producers of petrochemicals products. In addition, NOVA owns a 24.8% interest in Methanex Corporation, the largest and one of the lowest-cost methanol producers and marketers in the world.

Links
NOVA At A Glance • News Releases • 2ND Quarter Financial Results • Our Board of Directors • Our 6 Year Earning Performance • Contacts • Voluntary Challenge • NOVA Chemicals Inquiries

Occidental Chemical Corporation

http://www.oxychem.com/

Occidental Chemical Corporation, or OxyChem, is one of the world's largest producers of chemicals. OxyChem has interests in basic chemicals, petrochemicals, polymers and plastics, and specialty products. The sixth largest chemical operation in the U.S.A., with annual sales of some $5 billion, OxyChem is the country's largest merchant marketer of chlorine and caustic soda, the number one producer of chrome chemicals and the second largest producer of sodium silicates. OxyChem's Petrochemicals business consists of the Olefins & Aromatics division, the Ethylene Oxide & Derivatives division and a pipeline operation. At the heart of this business is ethylene, the world's most widely used petrochemical. We produce 3.6 billion lbs. of ethylene each year, most of which is used as a reliable source of raw material for the company's other products. Today, we continue to emphasize leadership in commodity chemicals. We work to maximize our low-cost position, concentrating on efficiency and

productivity to remain a competitive supplier for the long term. Our unique system of product integration is continually being refined, since it gives us flexibility unmatched by other manufacturers. And, of course, exceeding customer expectations is our overriding concern - everything we do is done with the customer in mind.

Links
Overview • Products • Safety • Service • Education • Issues • About • News

OM Group

http://www.omgi.com/

OMG offers the chemical industry a wide range of technological experience, a global workforce and an extensive background in the manufacture and development of high quality metal powders, carboxylates and inorganic salts. OMG is the result of the merger of two diverse but equally strong companies - Kokkola Chemicals Oy (formerly Outokumpu Chemical Oy of Finland) and Mooney Chemicals, Inc. of the U.S.A. Through multiple raw material sourcing and a unique vertical integration from the base metal or concentrate to the finished metal products, OMG is able to deliver the quality products and total manufacturing control that can only be offered by a complete service supplier. Whether your manufacturing process requires an existing material, a modified product or the development of a new product to meet exacting specifications, OMG provides the material, technology and personnel worldwide to meet your manufacturing objectives. Look to OMG to serve your specialty metal chemical needs.

Worldwide Locations • What's New •
About OMG • Products • Support •
Investment • Search

ORTEC Inc.

http://www.cris.com/~Ortec/

ORTEC is a custom chemical manufacturer located in Easley, South Carolina.
This page shows their reaction
capabilities and process equipment.

Links
Reaction Capabilities • Process
Equipment

Pechiny

http://www.pechiney.fr/som.html

Deux traits dominent l'histoire du
Groupe : le goût pour l'innovation et
l'excellence technique, et la volonté de
se déployer hors de ses frontières. Dès
1911, Pechiney s'installe aux Etats-
Unis. Il s'y implante solidement dans
les années soixante. Européen depuis
l'entre-deux guerres, africain depuis
1954, Pechiney est aujourd'hui en Aus-
tralie, en Amérique latine et en Asie.
Centré sur deux activités principales,
l'aluminium et l'emballage, le Groupe
intervient également dans l'élec-
trométallurgie et dispose d'un réseau
international de vente et de négoce.
(French only)

Links
le groupe Pechiney • les hommes •
chiffres et activities • Pechiney dans le
monde • l'intelligence industrielle •
l'environnement • etc.

Petronas

http://www.jaring.my/petronas/
petronas.html

The implementation of the PGU project
has opened an exciting new business
area for PETRONAS - petrochemical
manufacturing which uses gas as feedstock. PETRONAS has entered into
joint ventures with several multinational corporations to undertake a
methyl tertiary butyl ether
(MTBE)/propylene project in Kuantan,
Pahang and an ethylene/polyethylene
integrated project in Kertih, Tereng-
ganu. PETRONAS also owns and operates a polypropylene plant adjacent to
the MTBE/propylene plant in Kuantan
as well as a methanol plant in Labuan.
PETRONAS has also set up an
ammonia/urea plant in Bintulu,
Sarawak in a joint venture with the
countries of ASEAN. This project,
known as ASEAN Bintulu Fertilizer
Sdn Bhd (ABF) is one of the two projects under the ASEAN Industrial Projects Scheme. Today, ABF has further
extended its supply of urea and
ammonia to the Asia Pacific region. To
further boost the present supply of fertilizer, PETRONAS has incorporated
PETRONAS Fertilizer (Kedah) Sdn
Bhd with the purpose of setting up a
second fertilizer plant. PETRONAS in
a joint venture with Idemitsu of Japan
is also setting up an ethylbenzene-
styrene monomer plant in Johor.

Links
Background • Company Profile • Do-
mestic Activities • Global Ventures •
Latest Updates • Financial Highlights •
General Information • Search

Phoenix Polymers, Inc.

http://www.polymers.com/phoenix.html

Phoenix is an emerging growth company led by a strong, entrepreneurial management team. Incorporated in 1991, the company has gone through stages of product development, start-up and pilot production. We are now undergoing substantial expansion in anticipation of rapid growth. The company currently holds eight US Patents in the fields of compatabilization, reactive compounding, crystallinity of PET and in blends and alloys. The company also holds many foreign patents worldwide and other proprietary manufacturing technologies. Phoenix is a compounder of patented engineering thermoplastic alloys and a supplier of custom compounded engineering materials. The proprietary materials include a family of PC/PET and modified acrylic alloys plus a line of proprietary glass reinforced PET.

Links
Poly-Links • Who we are • Product Guide • Press Release • Employment Opportunities • "The Little Company That Could"

Pilot Chemical Company

http://www.pilotchemical.com/welcome.html

Pilot Surfactants help you work hard and look good---Flexible, Responsive, and Independent. That's Pilot Chemical Company. A leader in surfactant technology for over forty years, we offer a unique brand of flexible, person-to-person responsiveness based on the exclusive advantages of an independent, privately owned company. Our reputation is built on the highest standards of quality and service, and an unwavering focus on you, the customer. Pilot's ability to meet the demands of the specialty surfactants market emanates from our leading process technology, symbolized in our logo. The snowflake represents ice-cold manufacturing technology - one of our many innovative processes that are working for you.

Links
Ice Cold Sulfonation • Surfactants • Personal Care Products • Location

Polymer Composites Inc.

http://www.polymercomposites.com/index.html

Polymer Composites Incorporated (PCI), located in Winona, Minnesota, is the leading manufacturer of fiber reinforced thermoplastic composite materials. PCI's products combine fibers – glass aramid, carbon or stainless steel – with matrix resins – such as nylon, polypropylene, or polyurethane – making new materials with unique properties. They have simultaneously high stiffness and toughness properties, high enough to replace metals in many instances. In addition, parts made from these materials are usually lighter than parts of comparable strength made from other competitive materials. Other benefits include improved fatigue properties, low coefficient of thermal expansion, and corrosion resistance. As a specialist in these materials, PCI sells over 100 different products, as well as a number of custom formulations. They are also manufactured in Germany by Hoechst AG and by licensing agreement at Polyplastics Co., Ltd. in Japan, serving customers worldwide. They are used in virtually every sector of consumer and industrial manufacturing, including automobiles, computers, electronics, appliances, power tools, and sporting goods.

Links
PCI • Technical Support • New • Products

PPG Industries

http://www.ppg.com/

PPG Industries is a global producer of coatings and resins, continuous-strand fiber glass, flat and fabricated glass and chemicals. The company has nearly 50 production facilities in the United States and about 90 worldwide, including subsidiaries, joint ventures and minority interests. The company's overriding philosophy is a worldwide dedication to achieving Total Quality by fully meeting customer requirements and doing things right the first time, every time.

Links
Architectural Finishes Store • Photochromics • 1995 Annual Report • Press Releases • College Recruiting Section • Experienced Job Openings • Industry Resource Locator • Total Quality • Coatings & Resins • Fiber Glass • Flat Glass • Chemicals • Search • What's New • Company • People • Markets • Products • Environment

Pressure Chemical Co.

http://www.presschem.com/

Since 1964, Pressure Chemical Co. has provided unique technical expertise in the development and manufacture of novel organic, inorganic and

organometallic specialties and research materials. Its synthetic capabilities have focused upon extremes - high pressures, high temperatures, high corrosivity or air sensitivity, high purity or other tight specifications as with our monodispersed polymer standards.

Links
Register Now! • Letter From The Chairman • Services • Products • Polymers • Catalysts & Platinum Group Metal Salts & Compounds

Quaker Chemical Company, Inc.

http://www.quakerchemical.com/

Quaker Chemical's global experience and expertise in the world-wide chemical market enables us to offer you superior product knowledge and "know-how". Our qualified staff is prepared to provide you personal support to help you prosper in today's competitive chemical industry. Or, if you prefer, we are also equipped to provide you with your own "turn-key" chemical operation with minimal investment. Quaker Chemical Company has successfully manufactured chemical products for industrial use for over 35 years. However, in today's fast paced world, we also recognize the growing need for consumer products that are readily available for export. Because we recognize that everyone's needs are unique, we have diversified our services to meet this widely different demand. (Bi-lingual Spanish)

Links
Quaker chemical products & labels • Consumer private labels • Custom formulations • Exclusive contracts to your market • Products in concentrated form

• Manufacturing equipment • On site installation of plant equipment.

Quantum Chemical Company

http://www.quantumchemical.com/

Quantum is a leading producer of plastics, chemicals and specialty polymers which cover a broad range of applications that touch many facets of our lives. You are invited to browse through the Quantum web site to explore the chemistry to compete. Quantum can help you meet or exceed your product requirements. Let us show you how we can help you in real time with answers to your needs.

Links
About Quantum • Polyethylene • Specialty Polymers • Chemicals

Quantum Chemical Company II

http://www.millenniumchem.com/main/mchqtm.htm

Quantum Chemical is the largest manufacturer of polyethylene resins in the US. Quantum is also the second largest US producer of vinyl acetate monomer and acetic acid, and a leading producer of compounds and concentrates for plastics, specialty polymers for adhesives, sealants and coatings, wire and cable compounds and tie-layer for multi-layer flexible packaging.

No links

Quimica Anglo Chilena S.A.

http://www.chilnet.cl/qac/

Quimica Anglo Chilena, S.A. manufactures and distributes chemicals and equipment for the mining, pulp and paper, textile, cosmetic, food, shoe and other industries and has production, development, and quality control staff. Our 1995 sales volume was US$ 12 million and we employ 78 people. Our product range covers bulk commodity chemicals, water treatment chemicals, motors, filtration media, specialty chemicals, surfactants, specialty equipment, pumps, process chemicals, dyestuffs, and cosmetics. (Bi-lingual Spanish)

Links
Andean Mining and Chemicals, Ltd.

resinall Corporation

http://www.resinall.com/

resinall® is a manufacturer of hydrocarbon, rosin-based and specialty resins. These products are used as basic raw materials by a broad range of industries, and are produced at resinall's production facilities in Severn, North Carolina and Hattiesburg, Mississippi. Making Specific resins for specific needs is what resinall® does best, utilizing the flexibility of a variety of technologies to solve particular problems for our customers. Technical involvement with our customers allows us to understand their needs and formulate products to their specific requirements. Our ability and our readiness make resinall truly unique in the resin industry.

Links

resinall Hattiesburg • resinall Severn • resinall Capabilities • Product Information • resinall History/information • Information request form • What's New at resinall?

Rhône-Poulenc Environmental Services USA

http://ourworld.compuserve.com/homepages/rhone_poulenc/

Poulenc Environmental Services, Houston Plant, is a customer driven provider of sulfuric acid, sulfur dioxide, and liquid hazardous waste incineration services. We endeavor to exceed the expectations of both customers and stockholders through constant improvement of all our processes. Continuous improvement of communication with all customer and stockholders is a primary goal of our quality effort. Rhone Poulenc Environmental Services was recycling material long before most people had even heard the word. In fact, this facility was the first sulfuric acid recycling, or regeneration, plant in the world. That process was started in 1943, but the plant has been in existence at this site since 1917. It covers 46 acres on the Houston Ship Channel and employs approximately 170 salaried and hourly employees.

Links

Products & Services • Safety, Health & Environmental Issues • Community Relations • Job Opportunities • Slide Show of the Houston Plant • Corporate Home Page • Rhone-Poulenc Surfactants & Specialties North America

Rhône-Poulenc France

http://www.rhone-poulenc.com/

The Chemical Sector's mission is to provide industrial customers with solutions that improve the quality, performance and safety of their products, with a constant focus on safeguarding the environment. The Sector serves a wide range of markets, including the automobile, building, pharmaceuticals, personal care, detergent, electronics, agriculture and food industries.

Links

Group 2nd quarter 1996 results • Safety data sheets server

RJF International Corporation

http://polysort.com/RJF/

RJF International Corporation is a market-oriented manufacturer of engineered polymer products for select specialty markets. RJF supplies customers a versatile line of customized polymer-based products that end up in a spectrum of applications. For example, wall coverings in an exclusive luxury hotel, protective linings in a power plant flue gas scrubber, backlit awnings on a popular restaurant and flooring in the combat information center on board a high-tech Navy ship. With more than seven hundred employees and corporate offices in Fairlawn, Ohio, RJF is organized into self-contained, entrepreneurial business units supported by corporate management and technical resources. As such, each unit knows its market, customers and competition intimately. Engineering excellence, manufacturing quality and dependable, enthusiastic customer service are the hallmarks of each business.

Links

Koroseal and Vicrtex Wall Coverings •
Koroseal Wall Protection • Koroseal
Matting • Polymeric Protective Linings
• Koroseal Specialty Films • Koroseal
Flexible Magnetic Products • Koroseal
Profile Extrusions • KoroKlear Strip
and Sheet Products

RODA Chemical Products

http://www.lag.itesm.mx:80/roda/
ingles.htm

We have the biggest selection on
chemical products for general industry,
agricultural industry, textile industry,
food industry, Agip lubricants and water treatment. More then 3 decades
supports us as a serious and dependable
supplier. (Bi-lingual Spanish)

Links

General Industry • Water Treatment •
Agricultural Industry • Textile Industry
• Food Industry • Agip Lubricants •
Company Profile

RPM, INC.

http://www.rpminc.com/

RPM, Inc. is a manufacturer of industrial coatings and sealants for waterproofing and general maintenance,
corrosion control and other specialty
chemical applications. RPM also
manufactures consumer do-it-yourself
products for the home maintenance,
automotive repair, consumer hobby,
leisure and marine markets. RPM
shares are traded on the Nasdaq Stock
Market under the symbol RPOW. RPM,
Inc. consists of more than 35 Operating
Companies that produce more than 100
leading brand name coatings, sealants
and specialty chemicals. RPM's major

consumer brands include RUST-
OLEUM, BONDEX, ZINSSER,
TESTORS, BONDO and WOLMAN,
while its strong industrial brands in-
clude DAY-GLO, CARBOLINE,
MATHYS, MOHAWK,
ALUMANATION and PLASITE.. The
company's products are sold in more
than 130 countries and are manufac-
tured at 59 plant locations in the United
States, Canada, Europe, China, South
Africa, and Singapore under many
Trade Names.

Links

Link to RPM, Inc.'s News Releases on
PRNewswire • Operating Companies •
Trade Names • 1996 Annual Report •
Updated Stock Quote • SEC EDGAR
Filings • NAIC Green Sheet Informa-
tion • NAIC Green Sheet Order Form •
Share Transfer Agent • The Research
Magazine

Rohm and Haas Company

http://www.rohmhaas.com:80/

Rohm and Haas began in 1909 as a
partnership between innovative chemistry and business. Its origins trace back
to pioneering work in leather tanning
by Dr. Otto Rohm and Mr. Otto Haas.
Today, Rohm and Haas is a manufacturer of specialty chemicals and plastics. Its products are those "invisible"
ingredients that make things work better and last longer. The company's expertise in polymer design and small-
molecule chemistry, along with a tradi-
tion of dynamic customer service, have
made it one of the world's premier
suppliers of specialty chemicals. While
its name may not be familiar to consumers, Rohm and Haas products improve the quality of life in every part of
the world. Its technology is an essential

component in things such as laundry detergents, house paints, industrial coatings, food packaging, computer equipment, automobile taillights, window frames, diapers, motor oils, refined sugar, construction materials, magazines and products for agriculture. Company sales were $3.9 billion in 1995. Rohm and Haas employs approximately 11,670 people. Rohm and Haas is a Delaware Corporation whose stock is publicly traded on the New York Stock Exchange under the ROH symbol.

Links
About Rohm and Haas Company • Businesses and Products • Around The World • Financial Information

ROSS Chem, Inc.

http://www.rosschem.com/

ROSS Chem, Inc. is a manufacturer of Defoamers and Antifoams. Founded in the late seventies, ROSS Chem, Inc. owes its rapid growth and success to the extensive experience of our people in product development, manufacturing, application know-how, and marketing of antifoaming and defoaming agents. Our people are committed to excellence; superior product quality is a goal of everyone. And we are proud of their ability to provide the best products for your needs.

Links
Product Information • Company Information • Ink/Graphic Arts • Paints/Coatings • Adhesives/Glues • Textiles • Pulp/Paper • Waste Treatment • Polymer Processing • Food/Pharmaceuticals • Chemical Specialties • New Products

SAF Bulk Chemicals

http://www.sigma.sial.com/sigma/saf1hp.htm

The SAF Advantage lies in the roots of our parent company, Sigma-Aldrich Corporation. For over 40 years, Sigma, Aldrich and Fluka Chemical Companies have provided high quality organic and inorganic research chemicals, expertise and foresight to customers. This reputation for quality and service has now expanded into bulk chemical manufacturing with SAF Bulk Chemicals. SAF Bulk Chemicals offers over 50,000 products for biotechnology, pharmaceutical and diagnostic manufacturing. We can provide products for every manufacturing phase, from bench top to pilot scale to full-scale production. SAF offers the same quality and service you have come to expect from Sigma, Aldrich and Fluka in a single bulk chemical source. That is the SAF Advantage. SAF's capabilities combine the resources, capacity and production expertise of hundreds of chemists at 15 manufacturing sites worldwide. Through SAF you have access to multiple reaction vessels of up to 1,600 liters and an equipment list that is the most flexible in the industry. Our chemical reaction capabilities range from Acetylation to Zone Refining and just about everything in between. SAF carries over 23,000 preps on file. If you don't see the compound you need, we can custom manufacture it. cGmp and ISO 9001 compliance is available.

Links
SAF Information • What's New from SAF • Manufacturing Facilities • About SAF Bulk Chemicals • What's New From SAF • Literature • Manufacturing Facilities • Technical Service

Samsung Petrochemical Co., Ltd

http://203.255.124.7/Samsung/
Chemicals/SPC.html

Employees: 2,582--1995 Sales: US$1.2
billion Samsung General Chemicals
operates a huge petrochemical complex
at Daesan, Korea that turns out two
million tons of petrochemical products
per annum. These products range from
base olefins to composite resins.
Samsung Petrochemical completed its
third purified terephthalic acid (PTA--a
base material for polyester fabrics and
film) plant in April 1995. As a result,
the company's total annual PTA production capacity is now 900,000 tons,
making Samsung the world's second
largest PTA producer.

Links
Products • About Samsung • News
Flash • Samsung Austin Semiconductor
now recruiting! • Internet Expo • Samsung & Sports

Sea Lion Technology, Inc.

http://www.sealiontech.com/

Sea Lion Technology, Inc. was founded
in 1975, and is located in Texas City,
Texas. The facility is located on a thirty
acre site which is close to many of the
petrochemical complexes in the Gulf
Coast area. Our company's primary
area of business is in the manufacture
of organic specialty chemicals. Nitra-
tion of aromatic compounds comprises
our largest product line.

Links
Company Profile • Services • Regulatory Affairs • Technical

Seidler Chemical Company

http://metropolis.idt.net/~seidler/

A family-owned business in continuous
operation for 100 years specializing in
the repackaging of chemicals in the
size and type of container you want.
covering all your chemical needs and
featuring a diverse product line, along
with custom repackaging, as well as
extensive document, warehousing, and
delivery capabilities with an emphasis
on quality.

Links
Chemicals • Size • Type • Chemical
Needs • Diverse Product Line • Custom
Repackaging • Document • Warehous-
ing • Delivery • Quality

Senson Corporation

http://users.uniserve.com/
~ustech/us_cpp.html

These environmentally friendly rust
preventative products offer the solution
to the EPA's 1995 phase out of harmful
CFC's and Nitrites. Each year billions
of dollars are spent replacing the
equipment damaged by corrosion. In
addition to replacement costs, the costs
of downtime, non-performing equipment and consequent loss of production
attributed to corrosion is enormous.
Corrosion in electrical and electronic
systems is insidious, in that the corrosion is almost invisible. Microscopic
tin whiskers, black wire syndrome, and
metal migration cause intermittent or
permanent systems failure. This corrosion, like the every-day rust we ob-
serve, is predominantly caused by the
environment. Senson Corporation has
developed a range of environmentally

friendly products specifically designed to resist corrosion in the harshest of industrial and tropical environments. Products are designed to be used in three forms: Conformal Coatings; Cleaners; VPCI Powders and Paste.

Links
Main • Press Releases • Lockhart Technologies • More Info

Sentrachem

http://www.senchem.co.za/

Sentrachem, formed in 1967 by the merger of several smaller chemical companies, adheres to a decentralized management philosophy, while the structure of the individual businesses provides flexibility to meet the challenges of a changing operating environment. In 30 years, Sentrachem has grown from annual sales of R35-million to R3,7-billion in 1995, from seven to eight major sites and from 2 000 employees to approximately 6 000. Sentrachem is a major South African and international chemical company with experienced, highly regarded management, leading edge technology and a strong asset base.

Links
Profile • Financial Highlights • Group Structure • Products and Markets • Environmental Statement • Human Resources • Corporate Social Investment

Shaper Chemicals Ltd.

http://chaos.taylored.com/home/shaper/

Founded in 1991 and located in Maharashtra (India), Shaper Chemicals Ltd. has developed a wide range of fine organic chemicals. Its Board consists of internationally renowned scientists and accomplished businessmen. The company also has an in-house Research facility. The types of reactions handled include Chlorination, Halogen exchange, aminations, reduction, condensation, cyclization, etc. Under the guidance of highly qualified and devoted scientists and chemical engineers, the R&D facility has the expertise required in developing new products. We can develop many products on specific demand or on a tie-up basis. Quantities from a few kilograms to a several tons can be produced in our pilot-plant and in our versatile multipurpose plant.

Links
Shaper Chemicals Ltd. • Products Offered

Shell Chemical Company

http://www.shellus.com/Chemical/Welcome.html

Shell Chemical Company's products add quality to your everyday life. From hand soaps to rooftops, we help make the products you use, and depend on, safer and better. See if you can find things along your journey that might be made with Shell products; you might even find a couple of surprises! Eleven Shell Chemical Company business centers, our Responsible Care Program, and What's New are featured in this journey. You can go as deep or shallow as you like ... technical information is available by clicking on a particular business center sign; the journey is designed to let you know about the many products we make that make your life more enjoyable.

Links
Additives • Base Chemical's • Detergents • Elastomers • Polyester • Polybutylene Resins • Pecten Chemicals, Inc. • Resins • Shell Saudi Arabia • Solvents • Business Centers Directory • Shell Oil Home

Showa Chemical Co., Ltd.

http://www.st.rim.or.jp/~shw

Showa supplies reagent grade specialty chemicals. (Bi-lingual Japanese)

Links
Chemical Database • Reagents' Chemical Database • MSDS's Site

Sigma-Aldrich Corporation

http://www.sigma.sial.com/

Aldrich Chemical Company is a subsidiary of Sigma-Aldrich Corporation. Aldrich and the other companies within Sigma-Aldrich (Sigma Chemical Company, Fluka Chemie, Supelco and B-Line) share a Corporate Vision: "We are committed to the success of our customers through science, technology and service." Our Corporate Mission is "To be the preferred supplier of products and services in the market we serve" by offering our customers value through: quality products at competitive prices, unsurpassed service convenience of one-stop shopping (for example, our catalog) Aldrich Chemical Company was founded in 1951 to fulfill the growing needs of research scientists around the world. Our company's motto is: "Chemists helping chemists in research and industry".

Links
Sigma Chemical Company • Aldrich Chemical Company • Fluka Chemika-BioChemika • Supelco Chromatography Products • Sigma-Aldrich International Offices

Sipsy Fine Chemicals

http://www.sipsy.com/

Sipsy produces Pharmaceutical intermediates and bulk Medicinal Drugs and performs multi-step chemical reactions under cGMP conditions. They are experts in Hydride reductions, Hydrogenations and Organometallic reactions. Sipsy performs many Asymmetric chemical reactions as well.

Links
Sipsy, Your Exclusive Partner • Scientific Articles • Newsletters Directory

Southern Chemical Group, LLC

http://www.southchem.com/

Southern Chemical provides an online order blank for it's line of fullerenes. Fill it out and click send, it's that easy.

Links
SCG fullerene catalogue and prices

Struktol Company of America

http://polysort.com/struktol/

A global company with more than a century of specialty chemicals expertise. Inexhaustible technical support. Every minute of every day. For every customer. Struktol Company of America embodies the same impeccable service that has fueled the growth of our parent company, Schill & Seilacher, since 1877. After 100 years of serving specialty product manufacturers in Europe and Southeast Asia, the company opened Struktol Co. Ltd. In Canada as its first North American sales office. The U.S. tire industry beckoned, and the firm answered with Struktol Co., a sales office in Stow, Ohio, near Akron, the heart of the tire business. With a handful of technical experts, we introduced processing and homogenizing agents to tire compounders. Our products gained wide acceptance, and in 1979 we added production facilities in Stow to better serve the unique needs of the tire industry. We also developed a nationwide network of technical sales experts and warehouses to guarantee the immediate service and technical support for which we are well recognized.

Links
Rubber • Thermoplastics • When it comes to making tires • Quality additives for performance • Quality

The SulfaTreat Company

http://www.sulfatreat.com/

Hydrogen Sulfide gas (H2S) removal is our company's specialty. We have a patented process called SulfaTreat which has been rated the best H2S removal process by Gas Research Institute (GRI), an industry research organization. If you are experiencing problems associated with H2S, we may be able to help. Let us know where you are having the problems, and give us the operating conditions. (If you don't know them, don't worry because we can help there too!) We promise you an answer within twenty-four (24) hours. We don't mean just a yes or no answer,

if we can help you, we will tell you all the details, including costs. All this for free! (Tri-lingual Spanish, French, English)

Links
GRI report • Free Demo Software • Free Request for Quotation Form

Sumitomo Chemical Co.

http://www.sumitomo-chem.co.jp/

Established in 1913, Sumitomo Chemical is one of Japan's leading chemical manufacturers, offering a diverse range of products, including basic chemicals, petrochemicals, fine chemicals, agricultural chemicals, and pharmaceuticals. We maintain a worldwide network of subsidiaries, affiliates, and other offices, and our products are sold in more than 100 countries. Sumitomo Chemical's strong basic and applied research programs have yielded numerous products that have gained top market shares in domestic and global markets.

Links
Kandoh Chemical • About the Company • Responsible Care • Our Product • R&D

Sybron Chemicals Inc.

http://www.sybronchemicals.com/

Sybron Chemicals Inc. is an international specialty chemical company that supplies chemical specialties and related technology and intensively services its customers in two large markets: environmental and textile wet processing. The Company's chemical specialties are used to enhance the aesthetic and physical characteristics of textiles during textile preparation, printing, dyeing and finishing. Sybron Chemicals environmental products soften and demineralize water, purify drinking water at the point of use and biologically break down waste matter into harmless components.

Links
Sybron Overview • Product Tables • Interactive Forms • Press Releases • WW Organization • Businesses & Products • Financial Information • News & Press

Synair Co.

http://www.synair.com/

Synair Corporation is a world recognized rubber urethane chemical company specializing in the development and production of resin systems for use in rubber mold making and casting. In technical terms we formulate and manufacture one and two component thermosetting elastomer resins, isocyanate terminated prepolymers, hydroxy terminated curing resins, and engineer custom turn key urethane processing and manufacturing equipment systems. We provide custom and pilot manufacturing toll services to specification for qualifying companies. Synair's repertoire of urethane resins include the Monothane® and Duothane® one and two component casting resin series used in manufacturing products ranging from ultra soft vibration dampening membranes to high speed highly resilient roller coverings for the printing and roller covering industry.

Links
Products • Opportunities • Dealers • Hands On Training • Users • prepoly-

mers • curing resins • Monothane® • Duothane® • Por-A-Mold® • Por-A-MoldTA® • Por-A-Kast® • Clear Kast® • TyrFil® • TyrLyner®

Taiwan Styrene Monomer Corporation

http://www.hhinet.com.tw/tsmc.htm

Taiwan Styrene Monomer Corporation, TSMC, operates two ethylbenzene/styrene plants in Kaohsiung, Taiwan. The first plant was commissioned in 1982 and the second plant in 1990. Consistent with our effort to use the most advanced technologies, the Mobil/Badger Third Generation Ethylbenzene process was commercialized for the first time at TSMC. A p-diethylbenzene plant, based on TSMC's proprietary catalyst and technology, was installed adjacent to an ethylbenzene unit and commissioned in early 1990. Since then it has been expanded to meet increasing demand and upgraded to produce p-diethylbenzene of exceptionally high quality.

Links
Our Products • About Our company

TeleChem International, Inc.

http://www.hooked.net/users/telechem/index.html

TeleChem International, Inc. provides import, export, and distribution services of unequaled efficiency. From our Silicon Valley headquarters, TeleChem coordinates the delivery of a variety of chemical products to a global client base. TeleChem's philosophy dictates the use of a small, highly-skilled multidisciplinary team and places quality above quantity. We keep overhead costs low and pass that savings along to our customers. Our client advocacy approach results in better quality and lower costs. TeleChem's market knowledge empowers our customers with products and information that provide long-range strategic advantage and consistent return on investment.

Links
Suppliers • Products

Thai Petrochemical Industry Public Company Limited

http://urgento.gse.rmit.edu.au/
untpdc/incubator/tha/tpbkk/
trading-centre/standar1.html

The Leophairatana family established TPI in 1978. It has subsequently grown to become an important group of companies engaged in the production of a wide range of essential materials. Today TPI comprises several affiliates, among which TPI Polene Public Company Limited, and TPI Concrete Co., Ltd. are prominent. Administrative offices in Bangkok oversee TPI's extensive operations, while the group's main production facility is situated in Rayong, on Thailand's Eastern Seaboard. In addition, TPI Polene has a cement plant in Saraburi. As a pioneer in the Thai petrochemical industry, TPI was the first producer of low density polyethylene in South East Asia. The company was also a prime supporter of the Thai government's National Petrochemical Public Company Limited (NPC on the Eastern Seaboard and has been a major investor in the project since its inception in the early 1980s. With steady expansion over the past several years, TPI now produces several types of plastic pellets in response to

market demands. These materials have varied and distinct properties which serve a variety of purposes.

No links

Tiger Chemicals

http://www.webworld.com.au/tiger/

Tiger Chemical Company began trading in October 1989 as an importer of chemical raw materials. The activities of the company have expanded significantly over the first five years to a point where over 150 items are regularly sold on an ex-stock basis. Roughly half of the business activity of Tiger Chemicals now consists of locally sourced product to be distributed to our growing customer base. Products were principally imported from Asia but expansion of product range over the past few years has seen increasing quantities of product coming from Europe and the U.S.A. Business activity comprises five main areas: Surface Coatings, Textiles, Detergents, Food and Pharmaceutical and Commodity trading.

Links
Company Profile • Markets • Products • Tiger Search • Future • Inquiry • People • Tech

TRInternational Trading Company Inc.

http://www.tritrading.com/

TRInternational Inc. is an active U.S. trader of industrial chemicals, specialty chemicals and raw materials. TRInternational has well established relationships worldwide for the prompt and efficient sourcing of raw materials. We are able to provide product from multiple origins allowing our customers the freedom to choose the best product to meet specific needs. TRInternational Inc. stocks and warehouses raw materials in USA, Asia and Europe. As a customer driven company, it is our goal to provide the best and most cost effective product available anywhere in the world.

Links
Products • Organization • Services • Why TRI? • Active Markets • TRI Trade Talk

UCB Group

http://www.ucb.be/

The UCB Group is one of the largest concerns in Belgium being a pharmaceutical and chemical Group of world class. The business areas of the Group are currently centered around three industrial fields : the Pharma Sector, the Chemical sector and the Film Sector. Its strategy consists in specializing, after having withdrawn from its more cyclical activities, in ranges of products with high added value, resulting from its own research, in markets where UCB aims to be amongst the world leaders.

Links
Pharma • Chemicals • Films

Ultrafine

http://www.u-net.com/~ultrfine/

Salford Ultrafine Chemicals and Research Limited was founded in 1984 by Dr. Feodor Scheinmann in the Pure and Applied Chemistry Department of the University of Salford, Greater Manchester, U.K. Ultrafine quickly estab-

lished itself as an organization which could synthesize highly complex chiral organic compounds, for medical research purposes. In 1986, due to a steady growth and continued success with the synthesis of all manner of complex organic molecules, Ultrafine Chemicals relocated to Manchester Science Park. From this prime central location, adjacent to the University of Manchester, Ultrafine's team of technical experts gained access to academic consultants and the facilities associated with the largest educational complex in Europe. Since then, Ultrafine Chemicals has continued its expansion into many different areas of Chemistry and Biochemistry. We work as research partners with the major pharmaceutical and fine chemicals companies, academic institutions and government agencies, world-wide. As a company we continue to grow in size. In 1993, Ultrafine moved again into Synergy House on the Science Park, a new much larger building. We now have an 'in house' kg scale manufacturing facility. Hence, this gives us the ability to produce Master Batch Production Records and Standard Operating Procedures required for G.M.P. manufacture of mg to kg quantities of complex, chiral organic molecules.

Links
Capabilities and Catalogue Products • Quality Standards and Client List • Facilities and Custom Synthesis • Reply and Catalogue Request Form

Union Carbide's Investment Recovery Department

http://www.ucarbide.com/#topofpage

Welcome to Union Carbide's Investment Recovery Department Home

Page. This site includes several tables that are best viewed using Netscape. This Internet location contains a periodic offering of surplus property for sale by Union Carbide Corporation. This surplus falls into the following categories:

Links
Chemical Processing Equipment • Material Handling & Construction Equipment • Miscellaneous Equipment

United Chemical Technologies, Inc.

http://www.unitedchem.com/

United Chemical Technologies, Inc. (UCT) develops, manufactures and markets organosilicon compounds used in the clinical testing, pharmaceutical, medical, chemical, research and manufacturing industries. The company was incorporated in Delaware as a private corporation in October 1988 and is headquartered at 2731 Bartram Road in Bristol, Pennsylvania. UCT is the manufacturer of Petrarch® silanes and silicones and Worldwide Monitoring® surface modified organosilicas. Petrarch® specialty silanes and silicones are widely used in a variety of applications, such as pharmaceutical synthesis, elastomers, lubricants or reagents for making surface modified silicas. Over 1,400 silane and silicone compounds are marketed under the Petrarch® trademark, including a line of polysiloxane platinum, zinc, tin and peroxide catalysts.

Links
Petrarch® • WorldwideMonitoring® • Frequently Asked Questions • Website Search Page

WATCON Inc.

http://www.watcon.com/

We provide service oriented Water Treatment programs for: Boilers, Cooling towers, Closed loop systems, All commercial and domestic water concerns, Engineering services for all your water related needs, The latest advances in water treatment technology. Here is our newsletter and information related to water treatment

Links
New Form to Serve You Better • History • Boilers • Cooling Towers • Closed Loops • Equipment • R&D • Newsletter

Wavin BV (Netherlands)

http://www.xxlink.nl/wavin/home.htm

Wavin has over 40 sites in 20 European countries and employs 6000 people. Company's headquarters is in Zwolle, the Netherlands and President is Mr. A.J. Driessen. Technology has played an important role in the development of the company's products and the use and application of plastics in general. Over 550 own patents are safeguarded. Not only has Wavin become Europe's largest plastic processor, it is also Europe's largest plastics recycler. The key to this achievement is continuous improvement exemplified by over 25 years experience in the business, using some 70,000 tons of scrap and post-use waste and turning it into high quality products.

Links
General Information • Financial Figures 1995 • Useful Addresses

Yanshan Petrochemical Corporation

http://www.china-time.com/
manufact/bypc/0004.htm

Beijing Yanshan Petrochemical Corporation is an extra large petrochemical complex in China. It covers an area of 36 square KM with 48,000 staff and workers. BYPC has built 60 sets of petrochemical productive installations and facilities with an annual refining capacity of 9.5 million tons of crude oil and 450,000 tons of ethylene. BYPC can provide over 4.5 million tons of various kinds of oil products to the market each year, and produce 450,000 tons of synthetic organic materials and products such as high-pressure polytene, polypropylene, polystyrene, polyester, cis-polybutadiene. It also produce over 1 million tons of synthetic chemical materials like ethylene, propylene, butylene, oxybenzene, acetone, ethylene glycol, styrene, matacresol, and benzene etc. Moreover, BYPC has an annual processing capacity of 5 million square meters of synthetic carpets.

No links

Yukong

http://www.yukong.co.kr/yukong/
eng.html

Since Yukong's establishment in 1962 as a pioneering enterprise in the integrated energy and chemicals industry in Korea, we have served as the nation's major supplier of stable and economical energy resources, along with a wide range of petrochemical products. Today, Yukong maintains its leadership as the key driving force behind Korea's industrial development. Yukong has actively engaged in worldwide oil exploration and development activities while focusing constant attention on the issue of environmental control. Yukong's expanded commitment to environmental protection, for example, led to the successful operation of our Heavy Oil Cracking & Desulfurizing Unit.

Links
What's New • About Yukong • Business • Products • Subsidiaries • Sunkyong

Zeneca

http://www.zeneca.com/

Zeneca is a leading international bioscience group active in three main areas of business - Pharmaceuticals, Agrochemicals and Specialties - which provide products and services to improve human health, nutrition and quality of life around the world. Our broad portfolio of products includes world-leading cancer therapies (Zeneca is the world's number two in sales of anti-cancer medicines), advanced crop protection products (we are one of the world's top six agrochemical companies) and specialty products including a leading UK low-fat alternative to meat. We aim to maintain a flow of new products which meet customer needs. Recent additions to our range, which will build on the success of our more established products, include three new therapies for prostate, breast and colorectal cancer, and an important new crop protection fungicide.

Links
Zeneca, The Group • Zeneca Pharmaceuticals • Zeneca Agrochemicals • Zeneca Specialties

Zhuhai Skyhigh Chemicals Co.,Ltd.

http://www.ghgcorp.com/ftnet/pubserv1/zhuhai/

Zhuhai Skyhigh Chemicals Co.,Ltd. is specialized in organic pigments, colorants, pigment printing paste, chemical intermediates and fine chemicals.

Links
Company Information • Skyment Pigments • Skyhigh Chemicals • Pigment Printing Paste • Custom Manufacturers • China Chemical News

Supply and Service Companies

These are links to those companies that provide the services and support for the chemical companies around the world. These companies range from large engineering and construction companies that design and build chemical plants to consultants and process trouble shooters. As an example, these companies might provide pumps and valves, highly sophisticated instrumentation, corrosion protection, software, or laboratory glassware.

ABB - Africa

http://mbendi.co.za/ca8xogp.htm

The oil, gas and petrochemical industries face formidable challenges. The pressure is on to boost profits in the face of rising costs, increasing quality demands, proliferating environmental and safety regulations, and increasing global competition from low-wage countries. ABB can help you meet these difficult business challenges. Our advanced technology, industry experience, and process expertise is industry proven - from oil and gas exploration and production to the manufacture of petrochemical and chemical end products. In fact, we can draw on an extensive range of products and services which enable us to offer optimal solutions in terms of technological approach and cost effectiveness. Whether you need a single critical component or a total turnkey facility, look to ABB to be your single source.

Links
Oil and Gas Exploration and Production • Petroleum Refining • Petrochemical and Chemicals/ Plastics Manufacturing • Chemicals and Plastics End Use Manufacturing • ABB Sub-Sahara Africa • The Challenge to the Oil, Gas and Petrochemical Industries • ABB's Oil, Gas and Petrochemical Industries Solutions • Customer Commitment • ABB's Proven Record • Optimizing Multiple Processes • Leading Edge Technologies • A Commitment to Development • Environmental Compliance • Staying on Top of Environmental Regulations • Look No Further Than ABB • Process Engineering and Technology • Process Optimization • Power Generation, Transmission and Distribution • Services • ABB's Strength • ABB - Sub-Sahara Africa (Pty) Ltd.

ABB USA - Chemicals

http://www.abb.com/americas/usa/chemical.htm

From exploration and production to end products, ABB has unmatched expertise for increasing its customers' productivity and profitability. ABB has serviced the hydrocarbon and chemical processing industries for 100 years, providing single components to total turnkey solutions.

Links
Case Studies • Industries • Markets •
ABB USA • Process Control Systems •
Drives and Drive Systems • Environ-
mental Consulting & Services • In-
struments • Process Analyzers • Control
Products • Mass Flowmeters • Indus-
trial Services • Robot Systems • Power
Generation • Power Transmission &
Distribution

Advance Scientific and Chemical Co.

http://www.sawgrass.com/advance

We supply all types of chemical compounds for utilization by Universities,
Corporations and Individuals.

Links
Chemicals • Laboratory Glassware •
Laboratory Instruments

Alpha Analytical Labs

http://world.std.com/~alphalab/

Alpha is a full service environmental
analytical laboratory designed to provide its clients with accurate, precise
and reliable data within the best turnaround time and at the most reasonable
prices. In business since 1985, Alpha
has built an outstanding reputation as
New England's premier laboratory, not
only for the high quality data it generates, but also the extensive services it
provides its clients. We invite you to
learn more about Alpha by exploring
the rest of our World Wide Web site!

Links
Mission • Services/Prices • Facilities •
Certification • A Brief History • Introduction to Our Staff • Internet Resources

American Refractories Company

http://www.compu-tek.com/
american/ref.htm

American Refractories Company -- A
company which handles warehouse and
direct sales to the refractory consuming
industries. George E. Snyder Contractors is the construction division with 40
years of experience.

No links

Analyticon Instruments Corporation

http://www.analyticon.com/
aichome.html

The Information Source for the Analytical Laboratory and Instrumentation
Industry. This site is devoted as a
source of information relating to the
global analytical instrument marketplace. It includes a "Global Manufacturers Directory", a " Product Search
Index", and information about Analyticon and the products we offer. Our
goal is to help you source laboratory
equipment and instrumentation,
manufacturers and suppliers, dealers,
trade shows, organizations and other
industry related information from
around the world.

Links
Manufacturer And Supplier Directory •
Gold Member Internet Sites • Global
Product Source Guide • Trade Shows •
Global Analytical Instrument Cyber-
show • Scientific Supply Houses And
Catalog Dealers • Trade Journals,
Publications And Reports • Organiza-
tions And Scientific Employment
Agents • News Groups • About Ana-

lyticon • What's New • Analyticon
Product Lines • Application
Information • Ordering & Warranty
Information

Anton Paar

http://www.anton-paar.com/ap/

Innovative technologies from our partners at leading universities and international research institutes . Our competence in development and manufacturing of high-precision mechanics and
latest electronics . Our focus on technical support and application know-
how by dedicated specialists. A
worldwide network for sales, installation and after-sales service. Makes us
unique for solving specific problems in
the fields of: (see links)

Links
Density and Concentration Measure-
ment • Rheology and Viscosity • Col-
loid Science • High Precision Tempera-
ture Measurement • X-Ray Structure
Analysis • Sample Preparation for
Trace Element Analysis • Ultra-
Microhardness Testing • Biology and
Medicine

Aquapal

http://www.i-way.co.uk/~janthony/
aquapal.html

Aquapal are currently looking for
agents around the world to sell their
expanding range of products.
Aquapal sells a range of scientific
products including:

Links
Karl Fischer Titrator • Vaporizer •
Consistometer • Moisture Balance •
Trip Switch • Integrator • Tensiometer

• Vacuum Pump • Sieve Shaker •
Reagents • 3 Phase Diagnostic • Particle Distribution Analyser • International Approved Suppliers • customer
profile • Aquapal group

Arnold Equipment Company

http://www.arnoldeqp.com/

Specializing in Buying and Selling
Used Equipment and Machinery for the
Chemical and Related Processing Industries. Our 30,000 sq. ft. warehouse
is located in Cleveland, OH, near the
intersection of Interstate routes 77 &
480.

Links
Explore Our Inventory • Arnold Ap-
praisal Division • Check Out This
Month's Featured Items • Request a
Free Catalog

ARSoftware's Online Catalog

http://www.ari.net:80/ars/

Computational Solutions for the
Chemical Industry -- Welcome to AR-
Software's WWW Catalog
HSC Chemistry for Windows is a
chemical reaction and equilibrium
software package which utilizes an extensive thermochemical database of
over 7,600 compounds. The program
includes 7 different calculation options
for computing Gibbs free energies and
equilibrium constants for reaction
equations, heat and material balances,
equilibrium compositions, formula
weights, electrochemical cell equilibria,
phase stability diagrams, and Eh-pH
(Pourbaix) diagrams. Kinetics numeri-
cally integrates the rate equations for
reversible multistep chemical reactions
to determine the concentrations of the

chemical species in the system as a function of time. The program provides an easy to use interface which allows users to create complex reaction systems by entering the reactions of interest and the associated rate constants. No other input is required by the program. The program formulates the required rate equations from the list of reactions. Graphical output of results can be obtained, and an output file suitable for use in a spreadsheet program is generated

Links
Thermodynamics and Kinetics Modeling Software • Molecular Modeling and Drawing Software • CompuDrug Software • Chemical Engineering Software • Optical Software • Consulting Services • Training Seminars • HSC Chemistry for Windows (version 2.03) • KINETICS (version 1.04) • ChemSage • TAPP • TEP(Thermal Equilibrium Program) • PCMODEL • HyperChem, ChemPlus, and HyperNMR • MOPAC 6.0 • Kekulé • ChemWindows and ChemIntosh • CAD Crystallography • CompuDrug Pallas for Windows • FLO-SERIES and adjunct tools • PROCEDE for Windows • OPTIMATR • TFCalc • Software demos for downloading • Price List

Asahi/America, Inc.

http://www.asahi-america.com/

Asahi/America manufactures and distributes a broad line of corrosion-resistant products, primarily constructed of various types of thermoplastic. We have engineering, custom fabrication and clean room departments to accommodate special needs.

Links
Product Line • Valves and Piping Systems

AspenTech

http://www.aspentec.com

A leading supplier of software and services for the analysis, design and automation of manufacturing plants by companies in the process industries, including the chemicals, petroleum, pharmaceuticals.

Links
Featured Articles • About AspenTech • Products & Services • Technical Resources • AspenTech at ISA/96 • Partnering Solutions • Related Links • Rigorous Crude Unit Optimization • Past Featured Articles • What's New • Feedback • Search

Automated Solutions Inc.

http://www.tiac.net/users/asisales/

ASI is a leader in the field of laboratory automation products and services. ASI has authored numerous publications, chaired symposiums and short courses on this topic. ASI believes one of the secrets of creating great products is to have hands on experience with, and listen to, the users wants and needs. Our newest and most exciting product is CHEMIST'S LabBENCH. An order form for CHEMIST'S LabBENCH is available. We would also be happy to put you on our mailing list so we can keep you informed of future product offerings. You can also request a demonstration copy of CHEMIST'S LabBENCH.

Links
About ASI • Press Releases • Publications • Technical Papers and Notes • Consulting Services • Chemist's Lab-BENCH • Work Center Management

Baker Jardine & Associates

http://www.pipesim.com

Baker Jardine are World leaders in Multiphase Flow Simulators for the Oil & Gas Industry and have been developing state of the art computer software for over 10 years. We supply software and consultancy services to leading companies in the industry

Links
PIPESIM • PIPESIM-Net • PIPESIM-FPT • PIPESIM-GOAL • Consultancy Services • Company Profile • Baker Jardine WorldWide • Latest Features • Spanish • Known Bugs • Reporting Bugs • Suggestions • Sales Information

Bara Environmental Solutions, Inc.

http://www.bara.com/

Helping to bring your Company into OSHA, ISO9000 and ISO14000 compliance.

Links
What does Bara Environmental do? • Available Products, Services and Pricing • Manufacturer's and Distributor's Corner • Examples • Customer Login • Hazard Communications Plan • Hazard Communications Check-list • Hazard Communications Standard • Occupational Safety and Health Administration (OSHA) • Environmental Protection Agency (EPA) • ISO

9000 • ISO 14000 • Safety Online • Bara's Business Associates

Beckman Instruments, Inc.

http://www.beckman.com/

Welcome to Beckman Instruments, Inc. World Wide Web Information Service.

Links
What's New • General Company Information • WorldWide Contacts • Bioresearch • Clinical Diagnostics • Search the Documents on this Service

Bechtel Group

http://www.bechtel.com/

Since 1898, Bechtel has worked on more than 15,000 projects in 140 nations on all seven continents. Its people have mastered every kind of engineering, construction, management, development, and financing challenge imaginable. Today, it is one of the largest and most respected firms of its kind in the world, with a reputation for making things happen: using its mix of skills to bring customers' projects from vision to reality when others cannot.

Links
Who we are • What we do • How we deliver value • Where you can find us • What's NEWS

BetaCyte

http://www.betacyte.pair.com

BetaCyte is an Internet Consultancy, dedicated to assist the Chemical Community with the Internet. As a consultancy, we keep on hearing these questions: Can our organization profit from the Internet? But how do people find us on the Internet? Is it expensive to be on the Internet? Why should we use Beta-Cyte?

Links
WebPage/Catalogue/Journal/Mailing List Setup • Online Marketing • Technical Support • Business Card • Price list • Online Chemistry Journals • Random ChemLink

Brown & Root

http://www.halliburton.com/bar/home.htm

Brown & Root Inc. is one of the world's largest providers of engineering, construction, project management, facilities operation and maintenance, and environmental services for industrial and government customers. The company provides services to refining, chemical and other related process industries; the energy industry, including onshore and offshore oil and gas development; transportation, water, contract mining, electric power, and manufacturing industries, including pulp and paper, pharmaceutical and automotive.

Links
Company • News • Halliburton Home Page

Bryan Research & Engineering

http://www.bre.com/

Welcome to the Bryan Research & Engineering, Inc. BR&E is an engineering company that develops chemical process simulation software for the oil, gas, and chemical industries, in addition to offering consulting services. This home page provides a description of BR&E's process simulation software, access to demonstrations of the BR&E software, information about free training sessions, and information about contacting BR&E.

Links
Company Information • PROSIM • TSWEET • Files • Training • Contacting BR&E • Employment Opportunities • Relevant Links

CambridgeSoft

http://www.camsci.com

CambridgeSoft Corporation, formerly Cambridge Scientific Computing, develops, markets and supports high quality desktop applications for chemists and engineers. The ChemOffice suite integrates our cornerstone product, ChemDraw (chemical structure drawing), with Chem3D (molecular modeling/analysis), and ChemFinder (chemical information management). CS products enable chemists to communicate in the 'language' of chemistry: chemical structures and models.

Links
ChemOffice 3.5 • ChemOffice Pro 3.5 • ChemDraw Pro 3.5 • Chem3D Pro 3.5 • ChemFinder Pro 3.0 • CS MOPAC Pro • CS Catalyst • Register My Software • What's New • ChemFinder Server • CS Products • Technical Support • CS Services • About CS • Free Software • Chem Links • ChemOffice Giveaway • Be a Beta Tester

Capital HPLC Limited Chromatography Columns

http://www.capital-hplc.co.uk/

Welcome to Capital HPLC, Manufacturers of Quality Columns and Accessories for High Performance Liquid Chromatography. Capital HPLC was founded in Edinburgh in 1984 by former academic research scientists from the world renowned Wolfson Chromatography Unit at the University of Edinburgh. Shortly after its conception the company became established as a quality supplier of packed HPLC columns and accessories, with a reputation for quality and service which is second to none. The company's position in the market was strengthened further in the late eighties by its introduction of the world's first fingertight ferruless cartridge system (UCC) which has been highly commended by chromatographers world-wide. This cartridge system which incorporates a unique color coding scheme has been successful beyond all expectations. The company has recently expanded its production capacity by relocating its headquarters to new custom built premises and currently has fifteen employees.

Links
Company Profile • Order Form • Packing Materials • Capital HPLC's New Generation Inert Phases • Inertpak • Neutropak • HPLC Columns and Cartridges • Kromasil • Hypersil • Nucleosil • J'Sphere • YMC • Apex • Partisil • Zorbax • Rosil • Spherisorb • Adsorbosphere • Lichrosorb • Techsphere • Exsil • UCC Cartridge System and Accessories • Narrow Bore Columns • PEEK Fingertight Accessories

CE Instruments

http://ceinstruments.it/

CE Instruments -- a new world of performance perfecting specialized solutions in Gaschromatography, GC-MS, LC-MS, Organic Elemental Analysis, Mercury Porosimetry and Gas Adsorption. CE Instruments (formerly Carlo Erba Instruments), part of the ThermoQuest Corporation, pioneered high resolution capillary gas chromatography and remain ahead of the field in GC, GC-MS, microHPLC, Organic Elemental Analysis, Mercury Porosimetry and Gas Adsorption today with a modern range of instruments exploiting the latest developments in sample preparation, detection and data handling systems.

Links
Gaschromatography • GC-MS • Organic Elemental Analysis • Microstructure (Mercury Porosimeter & Gas Adsorption) • Contact details for CE Instruments specialists worldwide • ISO 9001 Certification • Latest CE Instruments S/W update

C. F. Picou Associates

http://www.challenger.net/local/cfpa/

C. F. Picou Associates, Inc. is an engineering consulting firm providing control system and related engineering services to the refining and petrochemical industries in the areas of: Operations; Technical Service; Planning and Economics; Modeling and Simulation; Project Engineering; Process Computer Applications; Information Systems Software. Our objective is to provide top-quality control system engineering services that directly impact operating efficiency, product quality, and profitability. We provide these services within the framework of specific projects with clearly defined objectives, schedules, and fixed-price terms. Projects range from small scoping studies to major control system modernization and consolidation projects.

Links
Refining • Petrochemical Processes • Major Advanced Control Projects • Interface Logic Algorithm • Dynamic Feedforward Algorithm • Dynamic Multi-Variable Adaptive Control • Intelligent Feedback Algorithms • Advanced Distillation Controls For Light Ends Fractionators • Inferred Property Calculation Software-Distillation Cut Points • LABSYS Modules

Chemical Accident Reconstruction

http://www.Opus1.COM/interi/fox/

Chemical Accident Reconstruction -- Expert Witness and Consultant -- Plastics; Propane; Aerosols; Warning Labels; Water Chemistry; Fires & Explosions; Hazardous Chemicals; Ground Water Testing; Corrosion & Metallurgy; Failure Analysis - Materials; Hot Water & Hot Coffee Burns; OSHA, EPA, DOT Regulations; Nuclear and Fossil Power Plants

Links
Michael Fox, Ph.D

Chemical Leaman

http://www.cltl.com/

Chemical Leaman Tank Lines provides the highest quality bulk motor carrier

transportation and associated services available. We represent the first and final step in our customer's efforts to deliver and receive products consistently. Our services meet or exceed customer expectations at a profitable and competitive price.

Links
Want to track your Chemical Leaman Order? • Who is CLTL • Lots to offer, including Order Track • New & Exciting Events around CLTL • Lots of interesting information here including WhitePapers and Transportation Information! • Find out about the wide variety of Equipment CLTL has to offer • Visit some Industry related sites ranging from logistics to chemicals • Find out about the CLTLs Value Added Services • Looking for something particular, try our Search Page • Come join a Winning Team!

ChemicaLogic Corporation

http://www.chemicalogic.com/

ChemicaLogic Corporation is a management and technology consulting firm. We trouble-shoot operational problems and conduct market research for clients in the chemical process industries. We also develop custom software tools for chemical industry applications.

Links
About ChemLogic • Services • Products • Index

ChemInnovation Software

http://www.cheminnovation.com/

The World's Most Intelligent Chemistry Graphic Program! Chemistry 4-D

Draw ranked the best chemistry drawing program in the latest test conducted by C'T Magazine of Germany (February, 1996). It has many advantages over other competing programs.

Links
Check out the NEW Competitive Upgrade Program • PowerRef • Chemistry 4-D Draw • NamExpert

ChemKey Search

http://euch6f.chem.emory.edu/

ChemKey Search Database -- Organic Synthetic Method Computer Database -- 50,000 References Available.... Are you having difficulty locating an important chemical reference? Are you spending valuable time searching volumes in the library? Let us help you. Keyword searching using Professor Albert Padwa's synthetic method database will save you both time and money. 50,000 references have been collected over a thirty year period from journals that organic chemists traditionally use. Particular attention has been devoted to synthetic methods, heterocycles, reactive intermediates, organometallic chemistry, photochemistry, stereochemistry, theory, asymmetric synthesis and many more. Yearly updates (ca 5,000 new references) are available at an attractive, low cost. Add your own references to the search routine for more personal customized searches.

Links
Free Demo • To order ChemKey Search database

ChemSOLVE

http://www.chemsolve.com/

ChemSOLVE Corp. is a small environmental analytical laboratory located in Austin, Texas, founded in November of 1992, and formally incorporated as a Texas corporation in August of 1994. ChemSOLVE Corp.'s primary business is providing analytical services to industry, government, consulting and engineering firms, and laboratories.

Links
ChemCROSSER • About ChemSOLVE • Surplus Laboratory and Computer Equipment • Our Price List

Chilworth Technology, Inc.

http://www.chilworth.com/

The Chilworth Technology organization has some of the most up-to-date electrostatic and dust explosion research and testing facilities in the World, all accessible via a brand new laboratory and office center in the Princeton Corporate Plaza, New Jersey. Facilities include, high voltage supplies, femtoammeters, electric field and electrostatic volt meters, resistivity / conductivity meters, special electrostatic probes, dust explosion testing equipment , controlled humidity test chambers and many others.

Links
Ask The Experts • Testing Services • Training Services • Consulting Services • Instrumentation • Newsletter • Article Archive • New Courses

Chrompack International

http://www.chrompack.com/

Chrompack International -- A company for chromatography products for GC (incl PLOT) and HPLC, instruments etc. If you're looking for products for (gas) chromatography then you're at the right place! Chrompack supplies chromatography products to customers who set the highest standards. If you want reliable analytical results and durable instruments, Chrompack will meet the challenge. Our product range includes instruments and equipment for chromatographic analyses of chemical substances in gaseous, liquid or solid forms. Gas chromatographs, columns for gas or liquid chromatography, accessories and courses can all be supplied by Chrompack - using the latest technology to provide the highest possible quality at competitive prices.

Links
Capillary Columns For Gas Chromatography • PLOT columns • HPLC columns • Gas-Clean filters • Gas chromatographs and other instruments • Courses • Low Cost Accessories • Product of the Fortnight • Search Program • Hot News • Company Profile • The complete product range

CLI International, Inc.

http://www.clihouston.com/index.html

CLI International, Inc. was established in Houston, Texas in 1982 by Dr. Russell D. Kane. Since then, CLI has grown to become a trusted organization committed to understanding and solving materials and corrosion problems worldwide. CLI provides testing and consulting services, custom fabricated

testing equipment and a unique suite of easy-to-use software for selection of materials and assessment and prediction of corrosion rates. Genera™ is a framework to generate computer-based representations of problems and solutions. It can be used to characterize and represent any application related to the area of Materials and Corrosion such as material selection, corrosion assessment, failure analysis etc. To download a free version of Genera 1.0 beta click on the icon.

Links
Genera 1.0 software • Services & Products • Equipment • Classic Corrosion Photographs • Materials & Corrosion Links

Condux Consulting

http://www.conduxconsulting.com/

Engineering, Marketing, Business & Technology Consultants to the International Chemical and Related Industries, Basic Chemicals, Fine Chemicals, Intermediates & Polymers, Processes, Troubleshooting, Safety, Technology & Markets, Fibers, Film, Engineering Plastics, Commodity Plastics, Elastomers, Membranes, Pigments, Explosives, Agrichemicals, Pharmaceuticals. CONDUX was formed in 1985, from a group of scientists and engineers who had long service as Du Pont's internal consultants. It has grown both in the range of talents it represents and the breadth of its activities in support of its clients. CONDUX now offers over 250 leading professionals formerly with the best known major chemical manufacturers.

Links
About-Condux • What's-New • Expertise-Services

D & S Consulting Engineers

http://fly.hiwaay.net/~ssmith

D & S Consulting Engineers, Inc., a professional engineering services firm, is dedicated to providing high quality services and products for our customers. As a full service technical organization, D & S is capable of performing the entire range of engineering projects for our clients in the chemical and manufacturing industries.

Links
Mechanical • Process • Electrical • Environmental • Software Tools • Clients

Daelin Engineers & Constructors

http://www.daelimen.co.kr/

Founded in 1939, DAELIM Engineers & Constructors is the core business wing of the DAELIM group with 13 affiliates engaging in engineering & construction, petrochemicals, trading, finance, information & telecommunications, motorcycles, concrete, ceramics, hotel & leisure, and real estate. DAELIM Engineers and Constructors has been widely recognized as one of the most reliable engineering contractors in the international market through successful completion of numerous projects for over half a century. With abundant manpower resources of over 1, 400 highly qualified engineering experts and 2, 200 construction specialists, DAELIM has demonstrated its excellent capabilities for feasibility study,

project management, engineering, procurement, construction, start-up operation, maintenance and project financing services in the field of various plant industries, civil, building, and architectural works in more than 20 countries around the world.

Links
Job Opportunity(urgent wanted !!) • Questions and Comments • Daelin Overview • Useful Information

Daylight Chemical Information Systems, Inc.

http://www.daylight.com/

Daylight Chemical Information Systems, Inc. was incorporated in 1987 and grew from the MedChem Project at Pomona College. The invention of the SMILES language, by Dave Weininger, first at the EPA in the early '80s and then Pomona, laid the groundwork for the creation of a new chemical information system. Daylight's mission has been to provide high performance chemical information processing tools to chemists. New software has been developed continually and the list of available and supported software continues to grow. Emphasis has been placed on the "Daylight Toolkit", a set of programming libraries comprising a "chemical information infrastructure", upon which custom applications can be built. The toolkit has been used by both Daylight developers to build supported applications, and by customers to build custom in-house applications.

Links
Press Releases! • Daylight Partners Page • Daylight Website Search

D. B. Western, Inc.

http://www.iceInternet.com/
dbwestern.html

For more than 14 years D. B. Western,
Inc. has been committed to meeting the
needs of tomorrow by offering the best
available technology today. With over
25 plants completed, we are meeting
the challenges of building plants
Around the World.

Links
Company Overview • Formaldehyde
Process • Benefits • Products • Services
• Clients • Companies and Locations

Dedert Corp. Liquid/Solid Separations Division

http://www.nell.com/DEDERT/
ddrtsepr.htm

Dedert Corporation provides a wide
range of alternate technologies for removing liquids from particulate material. We also offer many ways to improve the efficiency of the existing
equipment with either standard accessories or custom designed enhancements. The following are offered
worldwide: Dedert/Reineveld centri-
fuges--peeler-type horizontal-basket
designs for high-capacity dewatering of
fine crystalline or granular materials in
the 2 to 100 micron range...Dedert ro-
tary dewatering screens - improve
screw press performance on products
with high water-to-fiber ratios by partial dewatering...

Links
More product descriptions

Dresser Engineering

http://www.dresserengineeringco.com/

Since 1926, from our headquarters in
Tulsa, Oklahoma. Dresser Engineering
provides complete engineering and
construction services, including project
financing, to the energy industries for
the installation of process facilities and
plants.

Links
Oil & Gas • Refining • Transportation •
Environmental • General • Example

Druck Pressure Expertise Forum

http://www.pressure.com/

Druck is a major world-wide manufacturer and supplier of pressure, temperature and tank contents instrumentation;
including sensors, calibrators and controllers. This site is offered for related
software, application and product data
and synergous topics. Third party contributions are welcomed

Links
Company profile of Druck • Worldwide network of Druck companies •
Pressure • Temperature • Tank Contents • Press Releases for last 6 months
• Application Data • Application Software for PCs • Other related sites &
vendors • Request form for data on
products • Young Engineers event for
1997 • Simple voltage supply, bridge
output sensors • Regulated and ampli-
fied output sensors • Very low pressure
sensors • Current output sensors • Frequency output sensors (RPT) • Laboratory pressure gauges • Process pressure
gauges • Multi-channel readouts •

Multi-function readouts • Barometers • Industrial Calibration • High Precision Calibration • Premium Grade Controllers (from Druck/Ruska) • Deadweights • General Purpose gauges • High Precision, multi-function • Tornado • Civil Aircraft • Military • etc.

Durametallic Corporation

http://www.durametallic.com/

Durametallic is a leader in the design and manufacture of sealing systems for rotating equipment. Founded in 1917, Durametallic Corporation was one of the first companies in the world to realize the significance of the end-face mechanical seal. Today, the mechanical seal is one of the most reliable methods of sealing rotating equipment and they have since become a critical component for the leak-free, low maintenance operation of pumps, mixers, reactors, and other equipment which process large volumes of corrosive, volatile, abrasive, precious, flammable, and other liquids under a wide range of operating conditions. Durametallic is positioned to provide products, parts and service throughout the world. We operate 9 complete regional service centers for manufacturing and repair across the USA and a total of 30 centers worldwide. In addition, we operate over 100 sales offices in 47 countries, including 60 in North America. Check out our WorldWide Locations.

Links
About Durametallic • Company Overview • WorldWide Locations • Durametallic Product Information • DURA SEAL LINE • GF-200 • API 682 Dura Seals • DURA ONLINE Request Form

Dynachem Technologies

http://www.dmv.com/business/dynachem/

Dynachem Technologies is an industry leader in the recycling and marketing of waste products & byproducts; performs services for many fortune 500 companies and large chemical facilities; several distillation processing divisions to recycle many of your waste products; excellent environmental compliance and safety programs; minimizes waste reduction and saves you $$$; toll processing capabilities; purchases many waste products; evaluates waste products at no cost to generator; permitted for industrial and fuel grade alcohols; dsp facility for recovery and distribution of high quality alcohols; marketing and packaging division with years of experience which aids in distribution throughout the united states; transportation provided by railcar or tank truck.

Links
Specializing in the recovery of • What can we offer you? • Industries that we service

Eclipse Software Technologies, Inc.

http://www.eclipsesoft.com/

Eclipse Software Technologies, Inc. specializes in developing software products for regulatory compliance and the environmental industries. Our company began out of a national demand for computer solutions to solve many of the issues resulting from federal regulations on businesses and industries of all sizes and types. All of our products are designed by our staff of expert computer programmers and environmental professionals. Eclipse Software Technologies, Inc. uses the latest in software technology to create powerful, yet easy-to-use software that is simple enough for even the most novice computer user.

Links
Company Info • MSDS Wizard Demo Software • MSDS Scan Wizard Demo Software

Ecodyne Ltd.

http://www.ecodyne.com/

We are one of the world's most experienced water technology companies and have been furnishing systems and equipment worldwide for over 35 years. Headquartered near Toronto, Canada, Ecodyne Limited is one of the world's most experienced water technology companies, and suppliers of water and waste treatment equipment in Canada, and around the world. For over 35 years we have been providing the water treatment industry with complete systems from, which include the treatment of water to potable standards, its purification to industrial and utility boiler feedwater quality; condensate treatment; specialized processes and solids recovery; the cooling of water and waste treatment. Our systems are found in such major industries as Pulp and Paper, Oil and Gas, Chemical and Petrochemical, Mining and Primary Metal, Food and Beverage, Nuclear and Conventional Power Generating Plants and in many municipal water treatment plants.

Links
Ecodyne Ltd. • Our products • Contact Information

EMAX Solution Partners

http://www.emax.com/

EMAX Solution Partners specializes in the integration of chemical information and systems to speed productivity at major corporations.

Links
Your SAP-EHS Questions Answered • Events Calendar • Chemical Information Solutions • Career Opportunities • Industry Groups Web Page • EMAX Publications • Environment Today / EMAX Industry Survey Results

Environmental Laboratory of the Pacific

http://www.ipbd.com/ipbd/el_pacific/el_pacific.html

Environmental Laboratory of the Pacific, Inc. (E.L. Pacific) is a full-service, analytical laboratory committed to chemical testing and analysis of a wide variety of environmental and industrial samples. E.L. Pacific, a Hawaii-owned business, commenced operations in 1986 and became incorporated in 1992. The 4,000 sq. ft. state-of-the-art facility is located close to the Downtown/Airport Business District in Honolulu, Hawaii. E.L. Pacific's scope of services includes BTU evaluations, drinking water analysis, field sample collection, ground and surface water studies, RCRA hazardous and industrial waste characterizations, recycled oil analysis, soil and sludge evaluations, and underground storage tank investigations. Services are available throughout the Hawaiian Island chain and the Pacific Rim.

Links

Statement of Qualifications • Review
Fee Schedule

EXSYS, Inc. Expert System Software & Services

http://www.exsysinfo.com/index.html

EXSYS software tools are used for
building probabilistic, knowledge-based
expert systems. Expert systems also
called "knowledge-based systems are
computer programs that use expertise
to assist people in decision-making, in
performing a wide variety of functions.
EXSYS Inc. believes the most efficient
way to build expert systems is to have
the experts themselves create them. Our
goal has always been to make tools that
are easy to use, but also with the
flexibility and capability to handle real-
world problems. EXSYS, Inc. was
founded in 1983 and is one of the long-
est lived expert system companies on
the market. EXSYS, Inc. is completely
devoted to helping people develop
problem-solving applications. Expert
systems are not just add-ons at EXSYS;
they are our only business. EXSYS
software has proven itself in a wide
range of real-world problems with over
11,000 users worldwide. EXSYS products are selected as the tools of choice
by both novices through professional
knowledge engineers.

Links

About EXSYS • What are Expert Sys-
tems • EXSYS Products • EXSYS
Applications • Your Application •
FREE EXSYS Demos & Docs •
EXSYS Tech Support • EXSYS Infor-
mation Request • EXSYS Forums •
EXSYS Hot News • Search EXSYS •
TECOM AI Technology Symposium •
Getting Started Manual •   Congres-

sional Symposium • WIN a fully featured version of EXSYS RuleBook!!
($1495 value) • DuPont purchases
world site license from EXSYS

Fiveash Data Management - Reference Spectra, Chemical Information

http://www.intaccess.com/fdm/

FDM provides Reference Spectra Databases, Books and Chemical Information
including FTIR, Raman, C13 NMR,
Proton NMR, Heteroatom NMR,
UV/VIS, FTNIR, and Mass spectra. We
have chemical information in the areas
of polymers, surfactants, solvents, organic and inorganic compounds, drugs,
and natural products.

Links

FTIR • Raman • C13NMR • VP-FTIR •
Mass Spec • HNMR • FTNIR • UV/VIS
• Heteroatom NMR • Natural Products
& Drugs • Polymers, Plastics &
Coatings • Surfactants • Chemical In-
formation • Electronic Handbooks on
CD-ROM • Atomic Emission • Con-
version Software • Network Licenses •
Formats • Database Indexes • Academic
Pricing • What's New

Fluent Incorporated

http://www.fluent.com/

Headquartered in Lebanon, New
Hampshire, Fluent Inc. develops and
markets Computational Fluid Dynamics (CFD) software for use on PCs,
workstations, and supercomputers.
Combining ease-of-use with robust,
reliable, physicals models, FLUENT,
first introduced in 1983, gained rapid
acceptance in the marketplace and is
today the most widely used CFD soft-

ware in the world. Our sister companies, Fluent Europe, Fluent France and Fluent Deutschland, serve the European CFD markets. In Japan the sales, marketing and support are handled by our joint venture partner, Ryutai Consultants. Fluent Inc. has distributors for its CFD software products in Korea (ATES), Australia (CANCES) and India (FCI).

Links
Information about Fluent Inc. • CFD Software Packages • CFD Applications • World Wide Offices and Software Distributors • Hints and Tips for our Software Users • Customer Training • Press Releases • Trade Journal Articles • Employment Opportunities • Newsletters • Request additional information about Fluent Inc. products • Fluent Inc. Hardware/Software Partners • Fluent Inc. Usenet CFD Network Archives

Fluid Data, Inc.

http://www.fluid-data.com/

Fluid Data is a leading supplier of online process analytical instrumentation serving the chemical, petrochemical, oil and gas, power, and other industries. Fluid Data, Inc., a unit of Elsag Bailey Process Automation N.V., is a process analytical company that manufactures gas chromatographs, sulfur analyzers, octane analyzers, and other systems for the chemical and petroleum industries. Please select from the following topics for additional information.

Links
Description and short history of Fluid Data • News releases • Employment Opportunities • Dataline Newsletter • Product information • Customer sup-

port • Elsag Bailey Home Page • Excel V Gas Chromatograph • Sulf-Tane® • InfraTane® • TVP-1000 Vapor Pressure analyzer • 8280 Hydrocarbons-in-Water monitor • FLO-CAL High Speed Calorimeter • Py-Gas sample conditioner

GraphPad Software. Intuitive Software for Science

http://www.graphpad.com/www/welcome.html

GraphPad Software creates intuitive programs that simplify scientific graphing, curve fitting and statistics.

Links
Prism Description • Your Complete Solution For Scientific Graphing, Curve Fitting And Statistics • Instat Description • The World's Easiest Statistical Program • Update To Prism 2.01 Free Of Charge • Special Offer For Students: Buy Prism 1 For Only $89 • free trial version of GraphPad Prism to analyze and graph your scientific data • Nonlinear Regression • Analyzing Radioligand Binding Data • GraphPad radioactivity web calculator • Technical articles • etc.

Hanjin Shipping

http://www.hanjin.com/

Hanjin Shipping Co., Ltd. started the industry with only one 750TEU class full container vessel and a determination for sea transportation in 1977. Since then, we have steadily gained our position as a global container liner with our main service in the Trans-Pacific, world's largest trade route. Following the 1988 merger with Korea Shipping Corporation, we rapidly diversified with vigorous investments in introducing series of new vessels along with opening of our exclusive container terminals and etc. Meanwhile, we revamped our bulk sector extending into new areas of conventional, tramper, and specialized tanker services. Today, HJS is emerging as a highly competitive global carrier, providing a fully integrated world-wide transportation system to customers. Serving over 60 countries and with 120 offices world wide, Hanjin Shipping links countries around the world to deliver optimum service, anywhere, anytime.

Links
What's New • About the Company • Service Guide • Sailing Schedule • Equipment Specifications • Global Office Listings • HANPAS Purchase System • Hanjin BBS • Hanjin Group

Hewlett Packard

http://www.tmo.hp.com/

Hewlett-Packard is the world's leading supplier of test and measurement products and services. HP T&M has helped make engineers' jobs easier for over 50 years. The total number of datasheets available for online viewing is now over 1000. Be sure to browse our collection of product data sheets, complete with product photos, features, specs and ordering information for products that meet your needs.

Links
Quick Burst Cable Modems • Basic Instruments Online • HP 8485D High Sensitivity Diode Power Sensor, 50 MHz to 26.5 Ghz • Interactive Models from the T&M Application Notes Library • Gamelan Best Java Award • T&M News, August 1996 • Telecom-

munications News, April 1996 • Online Newsletters and Events • Service and Support • Product Information • Microwave and RF computer-aided design software • Internetwork monitoring software • data sheets, complete with product photos, features, specs and ordering information • HP Basic Instrument Catalog where you'll find high-performance instruments at affordable prices • application notes by title, subject or publication number • About Test and Measurement

Highway Transport

http://www.hytt.com/

Founded in 1948 in Knoxville, TN, Highway Transport, Inc. is a quality driven company committed to excellence, safety, and total customer satisfaction in over-the-road transportation of liquid specialty chemicals. Utilizing a state-of-art fleet and highly trained personnel, Highway Transport provides liquid chemical transportation throughout the United States and Canada, and offers interline service to Mexico.

Links
Information about our equipment • Let us submit you a rate quote • Sales Information • Join our team

Hitachi Instruments, Inc.

http://www.hii.hitachi.com/

Hitachi, known worldwide for innovative technology, assists researchers to find solutions to their scientific instrument requirements. At Hitachi Instruments, Inc. (HII) we are committed to designing, manufacturing and providing the highest quality scientific instruments available. Headquartered in the "capital of Silicon Valley", San Jose, California, HII supports thousands of satisfied customers with reliability proven products ranging from Clinical Blood Analyzers, analytical instruments, such as UV/VIS Spectrophotometers, Atomic Absorption (AA), High Performance Liquid Chromatography (HPLC), Fluorescence, electromagnetic instruments (NMR and Mass Spectrometers), High Efficiency Diffraction Gratings, and Electron Microscopes (SEM, TEM, and CD-SEM).

Links
Who we are • Product Information - About our Products • Service and Support Information • What's New • Latest Press

Hyprotech

http://www.hyprotech.com/

We're a software company that develops, markets and supports process simulation software for the Chemical and Hydrocarbon processing industries. Our corporate and development offices are located in Calgary, Canada, but we operate through an international network of Offices and Agents covering every geographic region of the world. Hyprotech, in conjunction with our technical alliance partners, provides modelling applications covering essentially the entire scope of process engineering. If you want to get product specific information, go to the "Integrated Engineering" page and work from there.

Links
Updated Agenda • Corporate Services • Product Listings • Integrated Engineering • Offices and Agents • Papers • What's New • Application Examples •

Training Courses • On Display • Employment Opportunities • Hyprotech FAQ • HYSIM • Conceptual Design • Process Design • Dynamic Modelling • Polymers • Equipment Design • DCS • FTP Site

ICIS Online

http://www.icislor.com/

ICIS-LOR provides market coverage on the price, supply and availability of chemicals world-wide. We supply this information via the World-Wide Web and the Internet as well as by direct dial up via modem. You can view and evaluate samples of ICIS weekly polyethylene reports for the USA, European and Asia-Pacific markets free of charge. For further information please view the Online brochure.

Links
Chemical products • Prices available upon request from your nearest ICIS-LOR sales office • Open a new account

Indigo Instruments

http://ds.internic.net/indigo/index.html

We are pleased to offer our wide selection of science related equipment. We have been on the Web at this location since 94.10.01. Stay tuned for more product announcements in the near future.

Links
What's New • chemistry clipart • optical equipment • tuning forks • dental knives and spatulas • magnets • Hobby and Biology Tools • Magnifiers • Molecular Models • Sets • Kits • Components • Optical Equipment • Photo CD's • Scientific Glassware • Software • 3D

Molecular Modeling • CD Clip Art •
etc.

The Indus Group, Inc.

http://www.indusgroup.com/

The Indus Group, Inc. provides
Enterprise Management Software Solutions for Process Industries worldwide. INDUS enables customers to
improve operating efficiencies, reduce
costs, and comply with governmental
regulations.

Links
Products • Services • Technology • The
Indus World • Indus News • User
Group

Intergraph International Online

http://www.intergraph.com/

Intergraph Corporation develops,
manufactures, sells, and supports
computer systems for the Technical
Desktop -- the combination of compatible technical applications and personal productivity tools in a single
desktop computer. Hardware products
include workstations, servers, scanners,
and plotters. The company's integrated
software applications are used for computer-aided engineering, design,
analysis, manufacturing, publishing,
and earth sciences such as map-
ping/geographical information systems.
A member of the Fortune 1000, Intergraph is the world's largest company
dedicated to supplying interactive
computer graphics systems.

Links
What's New • Products and Services •
Customer Services • User Groups • In-

ternational Home Pages • Search our
Website • Intergraph News • About
Intergraph • ANA Tech Division • In-
terCAP Graphics Systems • Intergraph
Computer Systems • Intergraph Federal
Systems • Intergraph Public Safety •
Intergraph Software Solutions • Op-
tronics Division

Jandel Scientific Software

http://www.jandel.com/

Jandel Scientific was established in
1982 to create microcomputer based
software tools for scientists. The company was founded by Dr. John J. Osborn, Dr. Richard Mitchell and a talented group of computer engineers.
Both Dr. Osborn and Dr. Mitchell are
former directors of the Institute for
Biomedical Engineering in San Francisco. Jandel began manufacturing and
selling graphics software for the Apple
II and Commodore 64 computers in
1983. These forerunner products led to
the release of the first IBM PC version
of SigmaPlot in 1985, which quickly
became the industry's leading package
for publication-quality scientific
graphics. Since then the product line
has expanded to include products for
scientific graphics, statistics, data
analysis, image measurement and gel
analysis.

Links
What's New • The free version 3.03
update is now available • Technical
support • Graph of the Month • Application • Products • About Jandel

JEOL USA, Inc.

http://www.jeol.com

JEOL USA is part of a world community of JEOL subsidiaries and sales agents. JEOL USA is responsible for sales of JEOL equipment in North America, Central America and South America. We welcome viewers from anywhere in the world and we hope you will find things of interest to you here, but you should note that some of the information and instrument configurations that we speak about will not be applicable to you. Also please visit our Canadian Sales Representative's site (Soquelec, Ltd.).

Links
Quick Index • About Us • Our Products • Other Services • Our Location • Info Requests • Related Links • Announcements • Documents

Johnson Screen Co.

http://www.johnsonscreens.com/pchem.html

Catalytic reforming, ammonia conversion, hydrodesulphurization, isomerization and styrene dehydrogenation are typical processes using Johnson screens. In these and other processes, the ability of Johnson screens to withstand high temperatures and pressures is especially valued

Links
Chemcial/Petrochemical Processing • Radial Flow Systems • Scale Traps • Outlet Baskets • Support Grids • Header/Lateral Assemblies • Who and Where are We? • What is Johnson Screens?

KCC Corrosion Control Co.

http://www.kcccontrol.com/

Your Single Source For High Performance Corrosion-Resistant Systems. KCC is a leading technology corrosion control coating and lining manufacturer who specializes in high performance tank linings, secondary containment coatings, flooring, and equipment grouts. We handle the most demanding chemicals conditions in industry providing corrosion control and spill containment as well as the highest performance foundation grouting products.

Links
About KCC Corrosion Control • Table of Contents • Feedback Form

KEMCO

http://comp2000.com/Kemco

Krueger Engineering and Mfg. Co. designs and manufactures a complete line of custom shell and tube exchangers for the petrochemical, refining and gas processing industries. Our engineering staff and plant personnel have the capabilities to design and fabricate these exchangers to meet the full range of temperature, pressure and alloy requirements, as well as all construction codes. Our "Outline of Facilities" confirms the ability to meet your requirements. KEMCO's record of performance in providing the petrochemical, refining and gas processing industries with quality heat transfer products and service is best demonstrated by our customer referral list and repeat business records.

Links
A Word from the President • History •
Organization • Petrochem, Refining
And Gas Processing Units • Specialty
Items

Ketema Process Equipment

http://www.ketema.com/pec/index.html

We are a leading provider of Process
Equipment to industry. Our products
include Centrifuges, Filter Dryers,
Horizontal Palte Filters, Mixer Dryers
and Outstanding Aftermarket Service

Links
Process Equipment Company • New
Products • Centrifuges • Filtration
Products • Filter Dryers • Dryers • Af-
termarket Products • Fabrics

Khem Products, Inc.

http://www.khem.com/khem/

A Chemical Inventory, Waste, and
MSDS Database on your PC! Khem
modules are a group of relational database programs that can be used collectively as a complete Chemical Management System or separately as a
stand-alone support system. Each
module assists the user in the areas of
chemical inventory, waste tracking, and
material safety data management.
K.P.I. has re-evaluated it's approach to
the compliance issue by providing universal tools that will serve as a foundation for regulatory
compliance world wide. Modules have
been placed in shareware and are currently available for downloading and
evaluation.

Links
Khem Admin • Khem Search • Khem •
Khem Waste • Khem Setup • Khem
Label • Khem Report • Purchase Cost •
Registration • Company Profile

Lanxide Coated Products

http://www.ravenet.com/lanxcoat/

Welcome to the Lanxide world of advanced composite materials, where
Lanxide Coated Products announces
the latest, cost-competitive, customer-
ready material: Titanium Carbide-
Coated Graphite. Titanium carbide
(TiC) is one of the hardest materials yet
discovered. TiC-coated graphite components demonstrate exceptional resistance to wear, corrosion and oxidation
in a wide variety of environments.
Lanxide Coated Products uses a unique,
proprietary coating process to manufacture components with controlled composition, thickness and mechanical
properties The combination of a
ceramic coating and a graphite substrate utilizes the engineering advantages (low density, high stiffness, re-
fractoriness and durability) of both
materials, yet remains readily machi-
nable into complex shapes at low cost.
The as-coated surface has exceptional
metallic brilliance and additional pol-
ishing upgrades it to optical quality.

Links
Chemical • Electronics • Fiber • Glass •
Metallurgical • Paper • Lanxide Corpo-
ration

Larox Group

http://www.larox.fi/

Larox is a world leading manufacturer
of pressure filters and pinch valves. On

the following pages you will find more information on Larox and it's products.

Links
Larox Group today • Larox News • Solid/Liquid Separation • Larox Valves • Larox office addresses and phone numbers

Lightnin-Mixers

http://206.214.17.19/LIGHTNIN/

From a modest beginning in the 1920s as a design and engineering firm, LIGHTNIN has grown to become the world's leader in mixing technology and the world's largest company devoted to the manufacture of industrial mixing equipment. LIGHTNIN has two manufacturing sites in the United States. The main office, research and development, and manufacturing operations for the LIGHTNIN Systems Division, which produces larger fixed-mounted top, bottom and side entry mixers, and smaller size mixer lines such as laboratory and portable mixers, is at 135 Mt. Read Blvd. The Wytheville Division in Wytheville, Virginia, supports the Rochester products with the production of speed reducers and gear drives, a major component of the large process units.

Links
News from Lightin • Company Background • Lightin Rep Locator • Product Information • Technical Information

Liquid Transport Corp.

http://www.liquidtransport.com/

Liquid Transport CRP has a long history of bulk transportation industry leadership. We take pride in our sixty years of safe, quality service to chemical manufacturing customers throughout the U.S. and around the world. You can trust that products will be handled responsibly...delivered on-time and on-spec while minimizing distribution risk.

Links
Corporate Overview • Our People • Safety & Compliance • Quality Systems • Facilities, Equipment & Services • Logistics Management

Louisiana Chemical Equipment Co.

http://www.lcec.com/

Louisiana Chemical Equipment Company, a premier used process equipment dealer, has grown into one of the world's largest used process equipment dealers with an online searchable database of over 14,000 individual parts listed by categories and over 25 acres of process equipment including a thirty two thousand square foot warehouse full of compressors, pumps, plastics equipment, and other used process equipment. Our online interactive Used Equipment Database is among the best in the world

Links
Company Profile • Merits of Experienced Equipment • Success Stories • Catalogue • How to Order • Valves • Staff • Chemical Plant • What's New

MAGMAR Associates, Inc.

http://www.dca.net/clients/magmar/

MAGMAR Associates has been providing commercial and technical liaison services relating to the chemical and allied industries to its clients since 1987. Unlike others in the industry, MAGMAR does not issue multiclient studies. MAGMAR's services are assignment oriented -- not project oriented. MAGMAR provides a very unique service to its clients in that we respond to their needs on an individualized basis. MAGMAR has the capability to report on virtually any subject relating to the chemical and allied industries. Between key contacts in the industry and U.S. Government, and our in-house database search specialists, we have been able to efficiently and effectively respond to our clients' needs in a timely manner.

Links
Subjects • Contact

Marley Cooling Tower

http://www.marleyct.com/

Welcome to the Marley Cooling Tower home page. We design, manufacture and market water cooling towers or power generation, industrial, refrigeration and HVAC markets throughout the world. Like the earth itself, cold, clean water is the lifeblood of your building, manufacturing process or plant. If you've walked beside a waterfall, you know the remarkable cooling efficiency of water. Marley tower puts that cooling efficiency to work. Since Marley's founding in Kansas City in 1922, our customers have come to rely on our engineering expertise to provide solutions for their heat exchange requirements.

Links
HVAC/Industrial • Reconstruction • Power • World Locations

MBA Labs

http://www.neosoft.com/~mbalabs/

Analytical testing services for industry, government, and the public. Est. 1968.

Links
Computer Programming • Ask the PC Guy

MDL Inc.

http://www.mdli.com

Welcome to MDL, the leading supplier of integrated scientific information management systems, databases, and services used worldwide in pharmaceutical and chemical companies and in industries that use chemical products.

Links
Tell me more • Academic Researchers: Have we got a package for you • ISIS 2.0.1 • Now you can seal your electronic records • Scientific Information & Management • Combinatorial Chemistry • Lead Optimization • Chemical Locating and Purchasing • Environmental, Health, and Safety • High Throughput Screening • Synthetic Chemistry • Application Development

Mettler Toledo - Balances & Instruments

http://www.mettler-ta.com/home.html

One of the oldest established companies for balances and weight determining instruments.

Links
Take a chip off the old cost • Get a free documentation printer • Your Old Instrument Is Worth Up To $ 3,000 •

New • Tradeshows • Document Library • Thermal Analysis • Products • Accessories • Services • Where to Buy

Miller Transporters

http://millert.com/index.html

Miller Transporters' experience in chemical transportation stretches back to 1952, when H. D. Miller Sr. purchased his first stainless steel trailer. As one of America's remaining full-service carriers, Miller applies this same experienced professionalism to the many other materials we transport.

Links
Miller Transporters Inc. • Miller Intermodal Logistics

Millipore

http://www.millipore.com/

Millipore is a multinational corporation that develops, manufactures and sells a broad range of purification products to the microelectronics manufacturing, biopharmaceutical manufacturing and analytical laboratory markets. Company headquarters are in Bedford, Massachusetts, and Millipore employs 3200 people in seven manufacturing plants and more than 30 subsidiaries and sales offices around the world. Through this vast network, Millipore sells its products in more than 100 countries. In 1995, Millipore sales totaled $594 million. Sixty-six percent of sales came from outside the United States, Canada and Latin America. Twenty-nine percent of sales was to the microelectronics manufacturing market, 29 percent to the biopharmaceutical manufacturing market, and 42 percent to the analytical laboratory market.

Links
What's New • Catalogues • Tech Support • Local Offices • Ordering • Careers • Search • About Millipore • About Millipore • Investors • Annual Report • Employment • Foundation • Milligram • Seminars • Hyperfilter • Applications • Case Studies • Hyperfilter • Filtration • Training • Applied Microbiology • OEM Healthcare • Lab and Research • About Lab Water

MMC International Corp.

http://www.oettco.com/mmc.html

MMC International Corporation manufactures vapor control valves, quick coupling flanges, product sampling equipment, and product measurement instruments which meet or exceed the standards for "intrinsically safe" equipment set by governments and certifying agencies around the world. MMC's primary products include Cam-Lock flanges, vapor control valves, deck covers, oil-water separators, cargo UTI measurement devices, high level alarm systems, gas samplers, product samplers and related items for the maritime petroleum and chemical transport industry as well as land-based petrochemical facilities. One of the oldest and most experienced firms of its kind, MMC is widely acknowledged for its history of technological innovation and the dependability of its products.

Links
Product Lines • WorldWide Sales & Service Locations • General Company Background

Molecular Probes

http://www.probes.com/

Molecular Probes is committed to being the leading provider of novel fluorescent reagents and techniques that advance scientific and biomedical research world-wide. Supplying superior products and services, together with achieving customer and employee satisfaction will be the driving forces of our organization.

Links
Molecular Probes • Product Literature • What's New • How to Contact Us

Molecular Simulations Inc.

http://www.biosym.com/

Molecular Simulations Inc. (MSI) is the leading provider of scientific simulation software and services. Founded in 1984, our computational chemistry software is used by scientists, experimentalists, and engineers at the world's foremost R&D facilities to organize scientific data, share information, and develop, analyze, and simulate novel compounds and processes. MSI employs over 260 staff worldwide, including more than 130 Ph.D. scientists who are recognized experts in their respective fields. The company is headquartered in San Diego, with an R&D facility in Cambridge, England, and support and sales offices worldwide.

Links
About MSI • Contact Us • Events Hotline • Job Opportunities • Navigating Our Site • Sales Offices< • What's New • Products and Services • By Application Area • Product Listings • WebLab • Research Applications •

Training • Technical Support • Graphics Gallery

The Nest Group Home Page

http://world.std.com/~nestgrp/

We consider ourselves a "value-added" distributor. We are focused on electrophoretic and chromatographic separation and scale-up of proteins, peptides and nucleic acids. It is our only business, allowing us to offer you: Technical expertise in the isolation and purification of proteins, peptides and nucleic acids-"a resource that you can't get from a book; New, unique and sometimes unconventional materials and approaches when traditional methods fail; Responsive service for your questions and problems; Rapid delivery from a large inventory of both standard and odd size HPLC columns from a variety of manufacturers.

Links
Company Profile • Products & Prices • Idea Book • Personnel • Mol. Biol. WWW sites • Chemistry WWW sites • What's New • Literature Request Form • Application Guides and Protocols

Nicolet Instrument Corporation

http://www.nicolet.com/

Nicolet is the industry leader in Fourier transform infrared (FT-IR) and Fourier transform Raman (FT-Raman) spectroscopy products. Nicolet Instrument Corporation manufactures and sells the highest quality Fourier transform infrared (FT-IR) and Fourier transform Raman (FT-Raman) instrumentation in the world. These techniques identify and quantify unknown chemical compounds and are useful for inspecting product quality, determining sample composition and investigating material properties. Nicolet introduced its first Fourier transform infrared spectrometer in 1976 and is currently the world market leader for FT-IR. Our instruments are used throughout the chemical, pharmaceutical, polymer, petrochemical, food and energy industries, as well as in government and university laboratories.

Links
What's New • Who is Nicolet? • Nicolet Products • Applications • Events, Seminars and Trade Shows • Nicolet Contacts • Relevant Links

Nutter Engineering

http://www.nutter1.com/

Nutter Engineering is a leading supplier of mass transfer products and services worldwide. We produce a wide array of fractionation trays, random and structured packings, liquid distributors, and associated tower internals. This broad spectrum of products allows us to meet virtually any process requirement throughout the chemical, refining, petrochemical and gas processing industries. Nutter Engineering can also provide turnkey capabilities through Nutter Field Services. Nutter Field Services specialize in the installation of tower internals and other tower services. Nutter products are manufactured and marketed worldwide from our operations in Tulsa, Oklahoma, USA and in Bilston, West Midlands, UK.

Links
Company Information • Products & Services • Case Studies • Engineering Specialists • What's New

Odor Management Inc. - Refinery & Petrochemical Processing

http://www.odormgnt.com/odor.i.html

Oil refineries and petrochemical plants may generate large volumes of odor from the processing and refining of different fuels. Sulfides, mercaptans and hydrocarbon compounds are all closely related to the oil industry. The odors generated from these compounds are of a high nuisance value and generally create concern among local air boards and the public. ECOSORB may be used in a variety of areas around a refinery. These areas usually include water treatment facilities, sludge ponds, sulfur recovery units and API separators. During tank cleaning and maintenance operations, portable dispersion systems can be used in the immediate work area to control odorous emissions. ECOSORB can be directly injected into flues and stacks and may be used as a substitute scrubbing solution in some applications.

Links
Case Studies • Physical Data • Dilution • Simplicity • Packaging • Pricing

OI Analytical

http://www.oico.com/default.htm

OI Analytical is dedicated to bringing you the very finest in analytical instrumentation. Whether it be gas chromatography, microwave digestion, extraction, or site monitoring, this web site has been designed to answer questions you may have about our company, products, and services. The Company's mission is to be a leading supplier of instrumentation used for the analysis of impurities in water, soil, air, and other matrices. The Company serves environmental and non-environmental markets.

Links
Products • Technical Support • Application Notes • Order Information • OI WorldWide • Current Events • Employment Opportunities • Company Information • ICR • Seminar Information

OMNI North America

http://www.omniez.com/

Logistic Services, Liquid & Dry Bulk Transportation Specialists. OMNI's single source routing program will narrow your base of transportation carriers. We set up and maintain: carrier compliance, selection, routing, bid process, undertake risk management and provide single contract maintenance on all inbound and outbound bulk distribution. When you outsource to a single carrier, you are limiting your resources. If your company is serious about sole sourcing their bulk distribution, then you will benefit from an unbiased industry perspective by contracting with a non-asset based entity that specializes solely in bulk commodities. All modes of transport, with convenient routing options are available through OMNI North America's EZ Access online system. A well-experienced industry leader in Bulk Traffic Management since 1982.

Links
Isotank • Members of OMNI • Non-Members • Hazmat Database • Diesel Fuel Pricing • More OMNI Links

OmniTech International, Ltd.

http://www.omnitechintl.com/

Consultants to the chemical and process industries worldwide, providing engineering, research and marketing research services. Provide manufacturing, profit improvement services, staffing and quality services to general manufacturing.

Links
To the chemical and process industries • To small and mid-sized general manufacturing • To offshore firms with (or seeking) U.S. interests • Industries served • Product and process expertise (examples • Project case histories • Client list • Browse our latest newsletter

Orion Research, Inc.

http://www.orionres.com/

This year, as Orion Research celebrates the thirtieth anniversary of the invention and commercialization of the Ion Selective Electrode (ISE), our goal is to build the world's best source of electrode-based measurement information available on the World Wide Web. We will also use this site to supply Orion Customers and Dealers with timely information on new products, upcoming seminars and participation in major scientific conferences.

Links
Search the Orion Web Site • Contents • What's New • Press Releases

Oxford Molecular Group

http://www.oxmol.co.uk/

Founded in 1989, Oxford Molecular Group PLC is a leading developer and marketer of computer-aided chemistry and bioinformatics software. The Group has four major operating divisions: Oxford Molecular Ltd., computer-aided molecular design software; IntelliGenetics Inc., bioinformatics tools and related services; CAChe Scientific Inc., computer-aided chemistry software; The Drug Design Division, integrated drug design services. Many of the Group's products have originated in the worlds' finest research laboratories. The Group forms a bridge between university research and industry which facilitates the transfer of software and experience from academe to the marketplace.

Links
Industrial Applications of Quantum Mechanics • Oxford Molecular Group History • Latest News Releases • Product Information • Download Gene-Works Demo Now • International Contact Information • Product Support • Collaborations • Science Showcase

Papros Inc.

http://www.papros.com/

PAPROS INC. is a company engaged in the efficient application of robust computerized systems for the Chemical Industry and Environmental Planning in the areas of material handling, material and personnel safety related issues, specifically Environmental Impact Studies, Hazard Mitigation, Risk Assessment, Risk Reduction, Emission Inventory Planning and Reports (CA

AB 2588 etc.). We specialize in obtaining permits from the County, State and Federal agencies. PAPROS INC. will help you in your efforts to reduce pollution by risk reduction, hazard identification and mitigation and safety related training. We will help you in your efforts to comply with the regulations imposed upon you by Federal, State and County agencies and in obtaining and updating permits from these agencies. Our advanced customized assistance in computerizing your efforts in the direction of environmental protection will be of immense help for you. Call us for news of software products from us in developing your own MSDS databases from your datasheets on existing paper records for online access rather than relying on other online services.

Links
Company information • Corporate mission of Papros Inc. • Products • Services • Newsletter • Calendar • Internet-MSDS • Public education on household toxics

Park Scientific Instruments

http://www.park.com/

From nanoscale to macroscale, our microscopes let you explore the Nanosphere™. Scanning probe microscopy (SPM) is the powerful, new surface imaging method for researchers in science and industry who routinely study the surface properties of a wide range of materials at the nanometer scale. Since 1988, Park Scientific Instruments has been dedicated exclusively to the advancement of scanning probe microscopy, manufacturing high quality, full-featured SPMs that operate with our easy-to-use, Windows® based software.

Links

A Practical Guide to Scanning Probe Microscopy • What's New • Carbon Fiber in Epoxy Matrix • Phase Detection Data Sheet • Compliance and Phase Image of Graphite-Epoxy Composite • Live Cell Movie!!! (Netscape Browsers only) • Silicon Ultralevers™ • Silicon Nitride Microlevers • Tipless Silicon Ultralevers • What is scanning probe microscopy • What is Autoprobe? • Autoprobe M5: A fully integrated SPM system • Autoprobe CP: A modular SPM system for your laboratory • Scanmaster® PSIs Closed-Loop scan correction system • Autoprobe SA: A flexible easy to use SPM • AutoprobeVP: True atomic resolution UHV AFM/STM • Park Scientific Instruments' full line of SPM cantilevers •

Perkin-Elmer

http://www.perkin-elmer.com/

Perkin-Elmer is the leading worldwide supplier of analytical, bioresearch, environmental, and process analytical systems for research, analysis, quality assurance, and related applications.

Links

Perkin-Elmer Corporate Center • Perkin-Elmer Divisions • PE Analytical • PE Applied Biosystems

Phase Separations

http://www.phasesep.co.uk/phasesep/

Founded in 1965, Phase Sep is one of the world's leading experts in the field of chromatography columns, supplies an accessories. We are structured to be your large-scale, single-source supplier. Our full line of chromatography products includes the foremost, high-quality

brand names in the science-not the clones and generic versions. Furthermore, we combine this product quality and breadth with 30-plus years of experience in chromatography, enabling us to provide full technical support for all the products we supply.

Links

Company Profile • Catalogue • Special Offers • Technical Support

Phase-Transfer Catalysis Communications Inc.

http://www.acorncomm.com/ptc/

Phase-Transfer Catalysis reduces the cost of manufacture of organic chemicals. PTC increases profits by providing PTC technology to enhance the productivity, quality, safety and environmental performance of manufacturing processes for the production of organic chemicals and polymers.

Links

Mission Statement • Benefits of Phase-Transfer Catalysis • Request for Consulting and Training Information • Criteria for PTC Retrofit • In House Course: Practical Phase-Transfer Catalysis • Increasing Plant Profits • Subscribe to Phase-Transfer Catalysis Communications • WANTED: PTC Course Coordinators - WorldWide • Track Record • What is Phase-Transfer Catalysis? • About our FREE Journal

PIXE Analytical Laboratories

http://www.supernet.net/~pixe/pixe.html

We are an analytical service laboratory specializing in Proton Induced X-Ray Emission Spectroscopy (PIXE). Utilizing this technique we offer simultaneous, non-destructive, multi-element analysis in a variety of sample matrices for the elements from Sodium through Uranium, (excluding the Noble gases and the radioactive actinides). PAL offers analysis of liquids, solids, aerosols and thin film samples with applications ranging from routine quality assurance and quality control for industrial processes and raw materials to environmental monitoring and industrial hygiene, as well as specialized R&D.

Links
Clients • Browsers and the Just Plain Curious • PIXE Users Group • etc. etc.

Polymer Testing of St. Louis

http://www.polymertesting.com/

Polymer Testing of St. Louis, Inc. offers over 1,000 plastics and coatings test procedures. We specialize in: Formulation; Deformulation; Research and development; Failure analysis; International FDA compliance certification; Routine and non-routine testing; Methods development; Data interpretation; Expert legal testimony. We offer three levels of competitive product evaluation. they include: Identify main polymeric components; Perform partial deformulations with identification of source for major formulation components; Provide quantitative reverse engineering including generation of complete mass balance sheets, locating sources for raw materials, setting production parameters and development of QC programs

Links
About Polymer Testing • Service Price Lists • Our Customers • Contacting Us • For More Information

Polysciences Inc.

http://www.polysciences.com/

Polysciences was founded by Dr. B. David Halpern in 1961 with the intention of developing a specialty chemical supply business. The first market addressed was the nascent electron microscopy sample preparation supply market. At the time, high purity reagent chemicals were not easily obtained, and Polysciences became a critical supplier to the new electron microscopists established at universities around the world. From the very beginning, (the first sale of the company was to England) Polysciences has had an international focus. Now the company operates Polysciences GmbH in Eppelheim, Germany, and has distributors virtually for all locations on earth.

Links
Polysciences, Inc. Founded 1961 • Latest Developments • Polymers & Monomers • Microscopy & Histology • Particles & Diagnostic Reagents • Biochemicals • Custom Synthesis

Precision Weighing Balances

http://www.balances.com/

Precision Weighing Balances sells quality brand balances and scales bearing: Acculab®, Calibron™, Gem 7™, LAPD, Ohaus®, Siltec and Tanita brands. If you do not see the particular model of scale or balance listed on this web site simply E-mail us and we will supply you with a super price.

Links
Special of the Week • Analytical Balances • Moisture Balances • Precision Toploader Balances • Portable Balances • Pocket Scales • Mechanical Balances • Industrial Bench Scales • Accessories & Weighing Boats • Classified Listing of New & Used Scales • etc. etc.

Process Associates of America

http://www.processassociates.com/index.htm

Process Associates of America is a confederation of top, US based, engineering, management and computer applications consultants. Our 23 affiliated engineering consultants possess technical capabilities that span all the technologies encountered in today's modern refineries and petrochemical plants. Four management and TQM experts plus eleven computer applications consultants specializing in numerical methods, computer languages & systems programming, and electronic publishing roundup our staffing as of January 1996. All of our associates are veterans of the hydrocarbon processing industry or academic and research institutions. Our average experience level is, currently, 27 years with no associates with less than 21 years of experience.

Links
Company Information • Products & Services • Client Access & Support • Associates Access & Support • Process Tools • Technical Papers • Job Opportunities • What's New • Technology Alert • Shameless Promotion of the Month • Refining, Petrochemical & Chemical WWW Sites • Chemical Engineering WWW Virtual Library

Process Vacuum Services Incorporated

http://gnosis.computime.bc.ca/pvs/

Process Vacuum Services Inc. is a newly established company built upon 40 years of combined vacuum equipment experience, primarily in the Silicon Valley. Our new 18,000 square foot facility is equipped with state-of-the-art equipment, allowing us to have the most efficient pump rebuilding line in the country.

Links
Product's • Service • Corporate

Proflow

http://www.proflow.com/

Proflow is a fast-response direct-ordering catalogue service designed to supply high-quality Fisher-Rosemount flow measurement, monitoring and control products in lower-volumes for laboratories, universities, research labs, pilot plants and many other smaller process applications. If you're accessing from outside the UK, please read our Non-UK visitor's page first.

Links
Contents • Products • Hotline • About • Non UK • Register

Raychem Corporation

http://www.raychem.com/

Founded in 1957. Current annual sales: $1.7 billion. Headquarters in Menlo Park, California. Manufacturing, Sales, or R&D facilities in more than 40 countries. Customers in more than 85 countries. Raychem invents, makes, and sells thousands of innovative products based on materials science technology. Drawing on years of experience in product design, process engineering, and customer technical support, Raychem has developed a wide range of solutions for telecommunications, electronics, and industrial applications. Raychem has six divisions: Chemelex, Electrical Products, Electronics, PolySwitch, Telecom, Elo TouchSystems, a wholly owned subsidiary. Approximately 8,500 employees, about half of whom are in the United States, the remainder in more than 40 other countries.

Links
About Raychem • Products • Technologies • News

Remspec Corporation

http://www.remspec.com/

Remspec manufactures and supplies reaction monitoring and rapid analysis systems and probes using fiber optic infrared (FTIR) spectroscopy.

Links
Frequently asked questions about Mid-IR fiber optics • Examples of Fiber-Optic IR Spectroscopy • About Remspec's Systems • About Remspec Corporation • Request Information • Catalog • Get Remspec's PGP Key

Renishaw Raman Spectroscopy

http://ourworld.compuserve.com/ homepages/RenRaman/homepage.htm

Renishaw is widely known as the leading manufacturer of a new generation of Raman microscopes and

spectrometers. This page describes Renishaw's Raman products as well as giving many useful sources of information on Raman spectroscopy.

Links
Renishaw Raman publications • information on applications • A biography of C.V.Raman • A New Type of Secondary Radiation • Raman Scattering Theory • Society for Applied Spectroscopy • Chemistry Index • Labmart Online • etc.

Research Triangle Institute

http://www.rti.org/

Research Triangle Institute making a difference with experience and expertise. Research Triangle Institute excels in research tailored to client need. As an independent research institute, RTI provides research, development and technical services within the US and abroad to both government and private industry. With scientific expertise dedicated to client problem resolution, RTI delivers results that make a difference in the real world.

Links
Research Areas • Publications • Discoveries • About RTI • Employment Opportunities At Rti • Search This Site • Sudaan - Software for Analysis of Correlated Data

Rheodyne

http://www.rheodyne.com/

Rheodyne is the leading manufacturer of high pressure liquid chromatography sample injection valves, fluid switching valves, and valve accessories for use by analytical chemists and manufactures of scientific instruments. Additionally, Rheodyne manufactures low pressure valves for similar applications.

Links
What's New • Contact

Roadway Express Online

http://www.roadway.com/

Roadway Express is now offering faster business-to-business transit times for LTL freight in 12 origin markets. How fast? We can reach up to 70% of the US population with 1-2 day service.

Links
President • Cyber Service Center • Who We Are • Where We Serve • What's Hot • Current News • RexWorld

SAP AG

http://www.sap.com/

Founded in 1972, SAP (Systems, Applications and Products in Data Processing) in Walldorf, Germany, is the leading global provider of client/server business application solutions. Commanding a 31% share of the worldwide client/server enterprise application software market (source: IDC), SAP is the number one vendor of standard business application software and is the fifth largest independent software supplier in the world. Today, more than 6,000 companies in over 50 countries have chosen SAP.

Links
Events • Mall • R/3 system • R/2 System • Business Framework • History • Road Map • Search • Contact • Order • SAP Home Link Program • etc.

Sampling Systems by PMMI

http://mfginfo.mfginfo.com/mfg/sampling/

Sampling Systems by PMMI, Inc. designs and manufactures liquid and gas sampling equipment to help you comply with EPA, OSHA, and NESHAP regulations. Volatile Organic Chemicals, VOC's, can now be sampled with safety while obtaining the most representative sample possible.

No Links

Schrodinger, Inc.

http://www.psgvb.com/

Schrodinger is a software company committed to the development of highly refined and efficient software to solve electronic structure and computational chemistry problems. During the past several years, Schrodinger has developed a new approach to solving ab initio electronic structure equations which involves the use of pseudospectral methods. These new algorithms are now available in the program.

Links
Why use PS-GVB for computational chemistry? • main features • platforms • Pseudospectral Hartree-Fock • Generalized Valence Bond Calculations. • Density Functional Theory • Accurate Molecular Modeling in Solution • Graphical User Interface • SPARTAN • New Features in PS-GVB • Publications • Parallelization of PS-GVB for the IBM SP • Job Openings • Sales information

Scientific Instrument Services

http://www.sisweb.com/

Supplies and Services for Mass Spectrometers, Gas Chromatographs, Liquid Chromatographs and related Scientific Instruments

Links
Mail List Update • What's New • Products • Services • Company Profile • Ordering Information • International Dealers • Catalog Request • Short Path Thermal Desorption • GC Cryo-Trap • Micro Cryo-Trap • SIMION 3D • Mass Spec Software • Scientific Software • Pocket Reference Handbook • etc.

SEI Laboratory Glassware

http://pages.prodigy.com/labglass/

SEI, the Internet Scientific Equipment & Laboratory Glassware Supplier

Links
Table of Contents • Order Form

Sigma Chemical Company

http://www.sigma.sial.com/sigma/sigma.html

Sigma has been providing high purity research chemicals and other specialty products for the laboratory since 1948. We have grown steadily by offering a very wide selection of quality products, prompt delivery, and excellent customer service.

Links
What's New at Sigma • Customer Information • Product Information • Customer Services • Topics of Interest • Sigma-Aldrich International Offices

SiliconGraphics Inc.

http://www.sgi.com/

Silicon Graphics, Inc. (NYSE: SGI) is a leading supplier of high-performance interactive computing systems. The company offers the broadest range of products in the industry--from low-end desktop workstations to servers and high-end Cray® supercomputers. Silicon Graphics also markets MIPS® microprocessor designs, Alias|Wavefront TM entertainment and design software and other software products. The company's key markets include manufacturing, government, science and industries, telecommunications and entertainment sectors. Silicon Graphics and its subsidiaries have offices throughout the world and headquarters in Mountain View, California.

Links
Index • Find • What's New • Subscribe • Company Info • Products & Solutions • Sales & Support

Simsci Inc.

http://www.simsci.com/

Simulation Sciences Inc. pioneered the use of simulation software for the process industries, providing integrated software solutions to the world's leading companies in the oil and gas, chemical, petrochemical, and engineering and construction industries. SIMSCI has developed programs to effectively model both steady state and dynamic operations as well as batch processes. Core applications include design and operational analysis; online modeling, control, and optimization; and plant and enterprise-wide economic models. These programs help companies develop better process designs, predict plant performance more accurately, and increase plant safety and efficiency.

Links
What's New • Join Our Team • Company Profile • Products • Technical Support • Search

SoftShell Online - Software

http://www.softshell.com/

SoftShell International, Ltd. is a developer, manufacturer, and distributor of software products that serve the needs of chemistry professionals. SoftShell was started in 1986 by Ph.D. chemist Craig Shelley in the basement of his home in Rochester, N.Y. At the time, Dr. Shelley worked for Eastman Kodak as a programmer of Laboratory Information Management Systems. Recognizing the popularity of Macintosh computers among scientists, Dr. Shelley wrote ChemIntosh, a simple yet powerful chemistry drawing program. Sales of ChemIntosh were substantial enough that by 1988, Dr. Shelley had quit his job and relocated his business to Grand Junction, CO. Anticipating the growth of Microsoft Windows as early as 1989, SoftShell released ChemWindow, a sister product to ChemIntosh that also helps scientists to draw chemical structures. Today, these two products lead SoftShell's line of innovative chemistry software packages. In recent years, SoftShell has opened an office in France, shipped many new products and upgrades, and moved its home office to a 27,000 sq.ft. building in Grand Junction, Colorado. SoftShell products are tested by hundreds of beta testers and used by thou-

sands of professionals, educators and students throughout the world. SoftShell products are published in English, French, and German.

Links
The Index To SoftShell Online • ChemWindow 4.0 Now Available • ChromKeeper Simplifies Chromatography Publishing • Free Chemfont Creates Chemical Equations

Software 2000

http://www.s2k.com/

Software 2000 is a leading provider of client/server Financial, Human Resources/Payroll, Materials Management, and Process Manufacturing business solutions. Founded in 1981, the company has more than 1,300 customers around the world. These organizations represent a variety of industries, including manufacturing, healthcare, hospitality, entertainment, transportation, utilities, and insurance.

Links
About Us • Products • Newsflash • Investor Info • Customer Center • Table of Contents • What's New

Southwest Research Institute

http://129.162.25.66/indexpix.htm

Southwest Research Institute (SwRI) is the realization of a Texas wildcatter's dream. It was founded in 1947 by Thomas Baker Slick Jr., an oilman-rancher-philanthropist. SwRI is an independent, nonprofit, applied research and development organization that serves industry, government, and the public through science and technology. Slick's vision of an internationally known scientific research center in San Antonio took root with his donation of a ranchland site west of the city. He challenged a group of pioneer scientists and engineers from around the nation to move to the new center to seek revolutionary advancements in many areas by developing and applying technology. Today's staff consists of more than 2,500 scientists, engineers, technicians and support personnel who conduct about 1,500 nationally and internationally sponsored projects each year. Gross revenues in 1995 exceeded $243 million. SwRI operates from almost two million square feet of laboratory and office space in facilities located on 1,200 acres -- part of the original ranchland donated in 1947.

Links
About SwRI • News and Job Opportunities • What's New • Organization • Doing Business with SwRI • Publications • Search Site by Keyword

Spectral Data Services, Inc.

http://www.sdsnmr.com/

Spectral Data Services, Inc. was founded in 1985, in order to provide rapid, first class NMR data acquisition capabilities and data analysis to industrial, university, and governmental clients who either do not have modern Fourier transform NMR spectrometers, or who are plagued by extremely long in-house turnaround times, or who require strict adherence to Federal regulations. We have capabilities for all modern 1D and 2D experiments, as well as solid-state, liquid-state, and gas phase(e.g. Xe-129) experiments.

Links
About Us • Our Background and Philosophy • Typical Projects • GLP Compliance • See Us At These Meetings • Who makes SDS work? • Our Services • Liquids NMR • Solids NMR • Sample Submission • Frequently Asked Questions • Price Schedule

Spectral Research Techologies Co.

http://www.tenn.com/srt/srt.html

Spectral Research Technologies company provides a broad range of spectral modeling tools for quantitative analysis of UV-VIS atomic radiation and determination of species densities, or concentrations, and static temperature. Our current model is undergoing validation against high temperature and standard pressure using data from NASA Stennis Space Center and NASA Marshall Technology Test Bed. The NASA Ames Center Artificial Intelligence group has provided expertise in performing data analysis, fitting, parameterization, and statistical analysis of spectral data. The University of Alabama is presently training a Neural Network to provide high speed inversion and prediction of temperature and species number densities from calibrated spectral data.

Links
A nice Periodic Table • Here's another one! • Atomic resonance lines

Spectrocell

http://www.netaxs.com/~gerryms/ spctrcll.html

Spectrocell Inc., is an outgrowth of Precision Glass Products Company, a pioneer in the manufacturing of absorption cells for spectrophotometry, colorimetry, and fluorimetry. Operation has been continuous since 1955. Today, Spectrocell is the only facility in the United States dedicated to the manufacturing of cells and cuvettes. This facility provides for the needs of customers large and small, individual users as well as large volume production for OEMs. Spectrocell also has the capability to manufacture custom designs for research or prototypes. Spectrocell offers a wide choice of cells and cuvettes to meet nearly any imaginable need of the analytical spectroscopist, in the visible, UV, FUV, and NIR ranges. Both standard and special custom designed cells and cuvettes are available.

Links
About Spectrocell • Product and Pricing Information • The Spectrocell Catalog • Care of Spectrophotometer Cells • Spectrocell Feedback Page • Spectro-Links

SRI International

http://www.sri.com/

SRI International, formerly known as the Stanford Research Institute, is an independent, nonprofit corporation chartered by the State of California, performing a broad spectrum of problem-oriented research under contract to government, business, and industry. SRI serves clients in all parts of the United States and throughout the world. SRI was founded in 1946 by a group of West Coast business leaders to provide a center where diversified scientific research could be performed. Headquarters and principal laboratories are in Menlo Park, California. Regional offices are located in Boston, MA;

Princeton, NJ; Washington, D.C.; Westport, CT; Tokyo; Seoul; Zurich; as well as Cambridge, Croydon, and London, England. Field offices are established as needed to facilitate on-site technical assistance and engineering support as warranted by individual research programs. Because SRI is an applied research organization, all activities, except those undertaken to develop internal skills or to perform a public service, are conducted under specific contract with clients. Typically, SRI's programs are distinguished from those conducted by universities by being less theoretical and more directly oriented to the immediate problems of a client. At the same time, professional competence and innovativeness are maintained at high levels.

Links
About SRI • Organization • What's New • Contact Info • Questions • Search

Sunkyong Engineering & Construction Limited

http://cosmos.skec.co.kr/

SKEC is a customer-oriented EC (Engineering & Construction) company, and it does its best to satisfy customers by its perfect completion of ordered projects. SKEC's aim is to engineer and construct plant projects cost-effectively with better quality, on time and within budget to satisfy its clients. SKEC has all-round capability to execute every process of plant project. If each construction process of plant project is respectively executed, its quality, cost and schedule would not be guaranteed. SKEC has provided a full range of services from feasibility and conceptual study, basic & specific process design, procurement, construction, construction management, start-up, operation to maintenance. Clients can access any or all of these services by Turn-Key concept.

Links
Overview • Civil • Housing • Building • Overseas • Plant • R&D • System • Facility Operation • Sunkyong Group • SKEC News

Tetra Tech Research and Development

http://www.tetratech.com/

Tetra Tech is a multidisciplinary environmental engineering firm, providing engineering and consulting services to solve complex environmental problems. Tetra Tech's specialties include surface and groundwater investigations, environmental assessments, remedial investigations/feasibility studies for hazardous waste sites, and model development. Tetra Tech's clients include the U.S. Department of Defense, the U.S. Department of Energy, the U.S. Environmental Protection Agency, the Electric Power Research Institute, private corporations, and state and local government agencies.

Links
Offices • Press Releases • Modeling • Risk Assessment • Remediation • Links

UMETRI

http://www.it-center.se/umetri/

Umetri was established 1987 to provide software products and services to scientists and engineers to help investigate and optimize complex products and processes. The products are based on the tools of modelling, experimental design and multivariate analysis. Umetri has extensive collaboration with the chemometrics group at Umeå University, and is in the forefront of the methodology of modelling, design and analysis. A presentation of Umetri's software for and courses in statistical experimental design and multivariate data analysis. Demo versions of the programs are available.

Links
About Umetri • Statistical Experimental Design • Modde • Courses • Download Software • International Cooperating Companies • Multivariate Analysis • Simca • Consulting

Universal Process Equipment

http://www.upe.com/

The world's largest surplus machinery/process equipment dealer, over 35,000 pieces of equipment in inventory. We have satellite yards worldwide and offices in the USA, UK, Germany, Poland, China, Russia, Mexico and the Czech Republic.

Links
Equipment Index • Hot New Items • About the Universal group • Request a Brochure • Contact UPE • Boilers • Centrifuges • Chillers • Columns • Dryers • Dust Collectors • etc. etc.

Varian Associates

http://www.varian.com/

Varian is a billion-dollar, worldwide, high-technology company. . . but that wasn't always the case. In 1948, with the world still recovering from World War II, a small group of enthusiastic men and women, led by Russell and Sigurd Varian, pooled their financial resources and intellectual talents to form a research laboratory to find practical, commercial applications for research being conducted at Stanford University's physics department. Today, Varian is a diversified, international electronics company that designs, manufactures, and markets high-technology systems and components for applications in worldwide markets. Major product lines include radiation therapy and planning equipment for cancer treatment; X-ray tubes for diagnostic imaging, wafer fabrication equipment for the semiconductor industry, and analytical instruments and vacuum equipment for science and industry. The company now has more than 80 sales offices around the world, and manufacturing sites at nine locations in the U.S. and in eight other countries.

Links
Products • Services • About Varian • News • Jobs • Index • Search • What's New • Varian's board declares dividend; adds Stanford computer science expert • Varian acquires Dynatech Precision Sampling Corp.

Viscona Ltd.

http://www.scotborders.co.uk/horizons/viscona.html

Viscona work on the production of stabilized chlorine dioxide together with associated R&D activities. This is a product with a wide variety of uses within the water treatment industry and also as an odor control agent. The uniqueness of the project is in the stability achieved for chlorine dioxide. The manufacture of this product is un-

dertaken in factory premises within the rural setting of the Scottish Borders. Anthium Dioxcide is an aqueous solution containing 5% chlorine dioxide which is stabilised in solution by a patented system of buffers.

Links
Long text without links

VWR Scientific Products

http://www.vwrsp.com

This is the laboratory professional's online guide to a world of information on VWR. Browse our Market Focus area to learn more about how VWR can help you increase lab productivity. Access our Online Catalog to check out the vast selection of lab supplies, equipment and chemicals. Learn more about VWR's recent acquisition of Baxter Scientific Products and our future goals in the President's Forum.

Links
VWR Releases First VWRbrand Catalog • VWR Introduces The Premier Issue Of Its Lab Animal Research Newsletter • What's New • Market

UE Systems - Ultrasound

http://www.uesystems.com/

Specializing in the technology of Airborne Ultrasound, UE SYSTEMS INC. produces highly effective and reliable instrumentation. Applications include monitoring mechanical component defects, detecting system leaks and locating potential problems in high voltage electrical equipment.

Links
Technology Overview • Applications •
What's New • Products

Waterhouse Chemical

http://www.explore-br.com/115014/
explore.htm

All Waterhouse consultants have over
ten years field experience in specialty
chemicals and the knowledge to rec-
ommend improvements in system operations and monitoring. Our manufacturing and shipping capabilities include
North America, South America,
Europe, and the Pacific Rim.

Links
Buy Chemicals • Water Treatment •
Corrosion Inhibitors • Scale Inhibitors •
Biocides • Antifoams • Chemicals -
Wholesale • Chemical Cleaning - In-
dustrial • Corrosion Control • Water
Softening & Conditioning Equip,
Service & Supplies • Water Pollution
Control • Water Consultants

Waters Corporation - HPLC

http://www.waters.com/

Waters is the only analytical instrument
and chromatography chemistries
manufacturer devoted exclusively to
High Performance Liquid Chromatography (HPLC) technology.

Links
Corporate Info • Catalogs • Seminars
etc. • Regulatory Compliance Seminars
• Millennium Users Group • Internet
Update List • search • Waters office

Whatman

http://www.whatman.com

Whatman is an international separations technology business with a unique
range of core technologies-including
fiber engineering, membrane fabrication and substrate chemistry. We apply
these core technologies to create products that meet the filtration needs of
customers in the analytical, healthcare
and industrial market sectors. We encourage you to discover more about us
and our products, and to keep up-to-
date on applications and technology
through our What's New, Lab Forum,
and Library pages.

Links
Explore Our World • Whatman World •
About Us • Products • What's New •
Lab Forum • Library

Windowchem Software

http://www.windowchem.com/

Number One Source For Windows-
Based Chemistry/Laboratory Software

Links
Software Categories • How to place and
order • Specials • How to become a
WindowChem Author • About WindowChem Software

Zeolyst

http://www.zeolyst.com

Zeolyst International is a global joint
venture of PQ Corporation and CRI
Zeolites, Inc. focusing on the development and sale of zeolite catalysts and
zeolite powders for catalyst applications. The mission of Zeolyst Interna-

tional is to provide zeolite products and catalyst-related services that will increase the profitability of our customers' operations more than any other supplier of zeolite products.

Links
Guided Tour • What is Zeolyst International? • Survey • Products

Zipperling Kessler & Co.

http://www.zipperling.de

Zipperling sold its compounding and masterbatch business to Clariant and will now exclusively focus on research, development and market introduction of organic metals with its subsidiary Ormecon Chemie.

Links
Welcome to Ormecon • Welcome to Zipperling • Masterbatch • Compounds • Organic Metals • Research • CORRPASSIV • ORMECON • Corrosion Protection • Polyaniline • Products • News • Environment • Query

Chemical Associations
and Societies

These web sites and links are for those associations and societies designed for members of the worldwide organic and petrochemical industry.

Air & Waste Management Association

http://www.awma.org

Vision...To be the premier international environmental organization promoting global environmental responsibility. Mission...To assist in the professional development and critical environmental decision making of our members to benefit society. Purpose.....To enhance environmental knowledge and provide quality information on which to base environmental decisions.

Links
Membership • Publications • Meetings • Section/Chapter • Employment • Links • News • Staff • Public Outreach • Education • International • Board Info • Survey • Certification • Consultants Guide

American Association for the Advancement of Science

http://www.aaas.org/aaas/aaasinfo.html

The American Association for the Advancement of Science (AAAS, pronounced "Triple-A-S") is a nonprofit professional society dedicated to the advancement of scientific and technological excellence across all disciplines, and to the public's understanding of science and technology. AAAS is among the oldest societies in America, having been founded in Philadelphia in 1848. Many of today's most prestigious and influential scientific societies have their historical origins in AAAS.

Links
Science • Science's Career Opportunities • Meetings and Announcements Advertisements • Science Electronic Marketplace • Join AAAS • Science's Next Wave • Open Forum: The Situation of Postdocs • News • EurekAlert

American Chemical Society

http://www.acs.org/

The American Chemical Society was founded in 1876 and is a not-for-profit organization. It is the world's largest scientific society and has a membership of over 151,000 chemists and chemical engineers. The American Chemical Society was chartered by a 1937 Act of the U.S. Congress. The Society is recognized as a world leader in fostering scientific education and research, and promoting public understanding of science.

Links

Search the ACS Web • What's New • Event Calendars • ACS at a Glance • Customer Service Directory • Chemical Abstracts Service Division • Education Division • Membership Division • Pub-Resources (Grants and Awards) • Technical Divisions • Local Sections

American Institute of Chemical Engineers

http://www.che.ufl.edu/aiche/welcome/

Welcome to the American Institute of Chemical Engineers (AIChE) Web - An interactive information network to advance the theory and practice of the profession and support excellence in education.

Links

Welcome to AIChE • Mission Statement • History • Headquarters Operations • How to Contact the AIChE • Announcements • AIChE HQ Announces New Executive Director • Meeting Programs • 1996 Annual Meeting • 1997 Spring Meeting • Call For Proposals To Present • Submit Proposals To Present A Paper • Programs and Activities • Meetings

American Society for Metals International - ASM

http://www.asm-intl.org/

ASM International is a society whose mission is to gather, process and disseminate technical information. ASM fosters the understanding and application of engineered materials and their research, design, reliable manufacture, use and economic and social benefits. This is accomplished via a unique

lications Division • Office of Government Relations and Science Policy (GRASP) • Office of Industry Relations • Office of Public Outreach • ACS Software • National Meeting in Orlando, Florida • Minority Affairs • global information sharing network of interaction among members in forums and meetings, education programs, and through publications and electronic media.

Links

Materials Week '96 • The ASM Book Store • ASM's CD-ROM Resources • About ASM International • Membership, Society & Chapter Activities • ASM Press Releases

American Society for Quality Control

http://www.asqc.org/

ASQC is the leading quality improvement organization in the United States, with more than 130,000 individual and 1,000 sustaining members worldwide. A not-for-profit professional association headquartered in Milwaukee, WI, ASQC carries out a variety of professional, educational, and informational programs. ASQC's vision is to be the world's recognized champion and leading authority on all issues related to quality. ASQC was founded in 1946 with the merger of several local quality societies. These groups were formed to share information about statistical quality control after classes on that subject were held during World War II to improve and maintain the quality of defense materials.

Links

About ASQC • Quality News • Membership Services • Ten Reasons for

Joining • Publications • Education • Other Programs and Services • Society Alliances and Collaborations • Other Quality Related Resources • What's New in this Home Page • Feedback Form • Survey • Contact ASQC

American Society of Safety Engineers - ASSE

http://www.asse.org/

ASSE has 139 chapters nationwide and 54 student sections within 13 regions (decreasing to eight regions in 1997). Chapters offer localized membership services, networking and professional development opportunities through seminars, conferences, meetings and newsletters. Through its ten divisions, ASSE offers professional development opportunities and technical assistance in various career paths. These divisions are: construction, consultants, engineering, environmental, healthcare, management, public sector, risk management/insurance and transportation.

Links
Main Menu • What's new at the ASSE org site! • About the ASSE • Overview • History • Safety Professional • ASSE Membership Information • Look here for Chapter and Division Pages • Educational Offerings • Guest Book

American Society for Testing and Materials - ASTM

http://www.astm.org/

ASTM has developed and published 10,000 technical standards, which are used by industries worldwide. Members develop the standards within the ASTM consensus process. Behind every volume of the Annual Book of

ASTM Standards stands a rigorous due process system of checks and balances that has ensured the integrity of ASTM standards for over 95 years. This system is known as the voluntary consensus system, and it is practiced by over 35,000 members on our 132 standards-writing committees.

Links
Search for Standards • Products & Services • Technical Committees • What's New • Contact ASTM • Technical publications

Analytical Laboratory Managers Association

http://www.siu.edu/departments/ shops/almahome.html

The objective of this Association is to promote the dissemination of information about the management of analytical services and instrumentation laboratories. Managing an analytical chemistry laboratory requires a unique blend of technical and managerial skills. Most laboratory managers, by virtue of their education and experience, are thoroughly capable of handling the technical aspects of their jobs, but often the managerial skills are obtained on the job in a haphazard manner. The literature on management and educational opportunities is geared primarily to manufacturing and typical service operations, neither of which matches the operation of an analytical laboratory. Thus, a small group of university laboratory managers banded together in 1980 to share experiences in the practical problems of operating a university analytical instrumentation laboratory. ALMA fosters the interchange of ideas among managers from similar institutions and companies. The unique strength of ALMA lies in providing a forum for you to interact with managers who have similar problems and who are willing to share solutions and ideas that have worked in their laboratories.

Links
The 1996 ALMA Conference • ALMA Short Courses • The ALMA E-Mail Listserver • Managing the Modern Laboratory (new journal • Science & Technology Policy Page • Other Sites of Interest • Employment Opportunities

Association of the Chemical Profession of Ontario (Association des chimistes professionnels de l'Ontario)

http://www.acpo.on.ca/index-a.htm

The objects of the Association shall be: To make the profession of increasing service to industry and the public; To maintain high standards of competence, integrity and ethics within the profession; To develop further an appreciation of the profession among other professions, industries and the public; To improve the conditions under which members of the profession are working within the province; To promote among students a recognition of the importance of the study of chemistry and chemical engineering; To promote and increase the knowledge, skill, and proficiency of its members in all things relating to chemistry and chemical engineering; To improve the standards of excellence in research, investigation, education, and publicity as they pertain to the profession; To do any other thing that the Council reasonably considers will further its objects.

Links
President's Message • Change of Address • Objects of the Association • Professional Affairs • Members of Council • Current Issue • Past Issues • Advertising Rates • Benefits of Membership • Fee Schedule for 1996 • Links to Other Chemistry Associations and Societies

Association of Water Technologies - AWT

http://www.awt.org/

Association of Water Technologies is a non-profit trade organization representing hundreds of regional water treatment companies throughout the USA and internationally. These full-service companies specialize in the application of chemical water treatments for industrial and commercial cooling and heating systems. The Association was founded in 1985 by a small group of entrepreneurs who were concerned about the rising cost of product liability insurance for their industry. AWT was formed as a means for distinguishing the water treatment industry, which was necessary in order to provide a basis for an industry-wide insurance program. Over the past 10 years the Association has grown in both size and scope, currently representing nearly 450 companies.

Links
About AWT • Industry Events • The Mentor • The Analyst • Full Members Only • Membership • Related Links • Test Our • Web Based News Groups

Brazilian Chemical Society - Sociedade Brasileira de Química

http://www.sbq.org.br/

da Sociedade Brasileira de Química. Este Servidor está localizado na Fundação de Amparo à Pesquisa do Estado de São Paulo, FAPESP, e mantém informações sobre as atividades científicas da Sociedade, e Associados.

Links
Sobre • Publicações da SBQ • Eventos • Sítios WWW • Divisões • Informações • Repositório de Programas • Journal of the Brazilian Chemical Society Online • Procura de dados e documentos

Canadian Society for Chemical Engineering

http://fox.nstn.ca/~cic_adm/csche.html

The Canadian Society for Chemical Engineering, one of three Constituent Societies of The Chemical Institute of Canada is the national technical association of chemical engineers. As the preeminent technical Society for chemical engineers in Canada, the CSChE provides its members with services that enhance their professional careers, contributes to the practice of chemical engineering and represents the profession to the public. The Society publishes The Canadian Journal of Chemical Engineering, an internationally recognized research journal. The Society publishes the Directory of Chemical Engineering Research in Canada every two years.

Links
Benefits of Membership • Membership Requirements • Fee schedule • Application Form

Canadian Society for Chemical Technology

http://fox.nstn.ca/~cic_adm/sctc.html

The Canadian Society for Chemical Technology is the national technical association of chemical and biochemical technicians and technologists. The Society has approximately 400 members across Canada who work in industry, government or academia. The purpose of the Society is the advancement of chemical technology, the maintenance and improvement of standards of practitioners and educators and the continual evaluation of chemical technology in Canada.

Links
Benefits of Membership • Membership Requirements • Fee schedule • Application Form • Certification Information and Requirements

Canadian Society for Chemistry

http://fox.nstn.ca/~cic_adm/scc.html

The Canadian Society for Chemistry, one of three Constituent Societies of The Chemical Institute of Canada, is the national scientific and educational society of chemists. The purpose of the CSC is to promote the practice and application of Chemistry in Canada. The Society organizes National Chemistry Week with assistance from the CSChE and the CSCT and Local Sections across Canada. The Society Officers meet with government officials and elected representatives in Ottawa each February to discuss issues of importance to the members. The Society has Student Chapters on many university campuses and organizes four Regional Student Conferences each year. The Awards of the Society recognize major achievements in chemical research and education. Scholarships reward academic excellence and student chapter participation. The CSC, together with the Steacie Institute of the National Research Council, sponsors the Canadian National Committee for IUPAC.

Links
Accreditation • Benefits of Membership • Membership Requirements • Fee schedule • Application Form

Chemical Institute of Canada - L'Institut de chimie du Canada

http://fox.nstn.ca/~cic_adm/cictop.html

The Chemical Institute of Canada is an umbrella organization for three Constituent Societies: the Canadian Society for Chemistry, the Canadian Society for Chemical Engineering and the Canadian Society for Chemical Technology. The purpose of the Institute is to promote common scientific and technical interests and to provide service to all its members. Individual chemists, chemical engineers and chemical technologists who join one of the Constituent Societies are automatically members of the CIC. The Institute has about 5700 members employed by industry, government and academia across Canada and maintains a Head Office in Ottawa to coordinate its activities.

Links
General Information • Local Sections • Subject Divisions • Students • Awards and Fellowships • Employment Services • National Chemistry Week • Publications

Chemical Industry Institute of Technology - CIIT

http://www.ciit.org/

CIIT is located in Research Triangle Park, North Carolina. Founded in 1974, CIIT is a not-for-profit toxicology research institute dedicated to providing an improved scientific basis for understanding and assessing the potential adverse effects of chemicals, pharmaceuticals, and consumer products on human health. CIIT is supported by 36 industrial organizations.

Links
Goals and Research Objectives • Staff and Facility • Technology Transfer • The Research Program • Supporting Companies • Educational Programs • CIIT Activities • CIIT 1995 Annual Report • CIIT Impact • CIIT Insights • CIIT Staff Publications • Business Impact From CIIT

Chemical Manufacturers Association

http://www.cmahq.com/

The Chemical Manufacturers Association was founded in 1872 and is one of the oldest trade associations in North America. CMA sponsors Responsible Care®, the industry's commitment to the public to continuously improve its health, safety and environmental performance. It also serves as the focal point for the chemical industry's collective action on legislative, regulatory and legal matters at the international, national and state levels. CMA's strength lies in its membership. The more than 200 members and partners of CMA have a productive capacity of 90% of U.S. basic industrial chemicals. More than 2,000 scientists and engineers, health, safety and environmental managers from CMA's member companies participate in CMA committees and task groups. Thousands more participate in activities to implement industry programs.

Links
About CMA • Membership • Responsible Care® • News And Issues • Protecting Our World • What's In It For You

Danish Chemical Society

http://frederik.ruc.dk/dis/chem/ kemfor/kemfor.htm

The Danish Chemical Society is a forum for Danish Chemists and other with an interest in Chemistry. The Danish Chemical Society participate in international cooperation as co-publisher of the scientific journal Acta Chemica Scandinavica and through the organizations Federation of European Chemical Societies (FECS) and International Union of Pure and Applied Chemistry (IUPAC). Members receive the monthly journal Dansk Kemi and a substantial discount on personal subscription to Acta Chemica Scandinavica.

Links
Danish Chemical Society • Rejsestipendier • ECCC • FECS • IUPAC • Main Meetings • History • Analytical •

Molecular Spectroscopy • Inorganic • Organic • Environmental • Theoretical • Chemistry Meetings • Department of Chemistry • Risø National Laboratory • Dep. of Applied Chemistry and Engineering • Roskilde University Library

The Electrochemical Society

http://www.electrochem.org/

The Society was founded in 1902 to advance solid-state and electrochemical science and technology. The Electrochemical Society is an international nonprofit, educational, organization concerned with a broad range of phenomena relating to electrochemical and solid state science and technology. The Society has more than 7,000 scientists and engineers in over 65 countries worldwide who hold individual membership, as well as roughly 100 corporations and laboratories who hold contributing membership. What makes the ECS unique is the extraordinary synergy created by the interaction of Society members and their work, both in the solid state sciences and in the more traditional areas of electrochemistry. The Society has sought to bridge the gap between academia, research and engineering, bringing together scientists from around the world for the exchange of technical information. This unique blend provides an unparalleled forum for the integration of these areas of science and technology.

Links
New and updated features on our Web Site • Answers to frequently asked questions • General information about The Electrochemical Society, Inc. • Individual Membership benefits and Membership Application • Contributing Member listing, benefits and applica-

tion • Descriptions of technical Divisions and Groups • Descriptions of benefits and awards specifically for Student Members • Searchable Tables of Contents and information on the JOURNAL, Interface Magazine, Proceedings Volumes, Meeting Abstract Volumes, and Monograph Volumes • Information on future meetings • Call for Papers, Programs • Instructions for submitting Meeting Abstracts electronically • Descriptions and recipients of Society Awards • A listing of the Committees of the Society • A listing of the Local Sections of the Society • A listing of upcoming Society Short Courses

European Chemical Industry Council

http://www.innet.net/cefic/

CEFIC, the European Chemical Industry Council, is both the forum and the voice of the European chemical industry. It represents an industry which employs more than two million people and accounts for approximately 30% of world chemical production. CEFIC is the Brussels-based organization made up of the national chemical industry. The purpose of this web site is to introduce you to the organization of CEFIC and to explain as simply as possible, the complex network of its relationships - committees, departments and affiliates.

Links
About CEFIC • Upcoming Events • Press Releases • CEFIC Position Paper • Responsible Care • Search the Site • What's New ?

European Colloid and Interface Society

http://mat.ethz.ch/ecis/

ECIS is a voluntary, non-profit organization of scientists. Its objective is to advance colloid and interface science and to promote cooperation between European scientists. Particular emphasis is given to the support of young scientists. ECIS seeks to cooperate with existing national Societies in European countries as well as with other international organizations. ECIS seeks to achieve its objectives by: Collecting and disseminating information on the activities of the national and international Societies; Organizing each year a conference in a European country in the field of colloid science; Establishing working parties to survey and report on specific aspects of areas of colloid and interface science in a European context

Links
What's New • Conferences • Employment Services • How to Join

Federación Empresarial de la IndustriaQuímica Española (Spanish Chemical Society)

http://www.innet.net/cefic/spain2.htm/

¡Bienvenido a la página principal de la Federación Empresarial de la Industria Química Española (FEIQUE) en Internet! FEIQUE es la organización empresarial que representa los intereses del Sector Químico. Debe indicarse que esta página no es más que una declaración de intenciones, con propósitos promocionales y que FEIQUE desarrollará con amplitud los diversos puntos que a continuación se señalan, y otros, así como promocionará la incorporación de sus Asociaciones y la de sus Compañías miembro.

Links

Mensaje Del Presidente • Es Feique • El Consejo Europeo De La Industria • Asociaciones Miembros De Feique • Grupos De Empresas Miembros De Feique • Empresas Miembros De Feique • Miembros Adheridos • Otras Organizaciones Relacionadas Con El Sector Quimico

French Group of Process Engineering

http://www.ensic.u-nancy.fr/ GFGP/GFGPgb.html

The goals of the French Group of Process Engineering are : 1. promoting process engineering in industry, education system at different level, from college to university, in research and in public in general; 2. improving the exchange of knowledge, methods and experience required to set-up, develop and optimize industrial processes in the field of process industries; 3. assembling industrialists who are involved in process industries like chemical industry, material industry, agro-food industry, energy and environment; 4. being a link between the users, specialists or experts in process engineering, Public Bodies and Administration, French Ministries or national research organization; 5. setting-up co-operation with organization involved in France and abroad, such as the European Federation of Chemical Engineering 6. publishing scientific works and organizing symposia, congresses, international conferences; 7. giving a general overview of process engineering (state

of art, analysis, needs) and initiating required research or actions

Links

History of GFGP • Goals of the institution • Organization, local sections • Contacts with companies • Contacts with universities • Information on European research programmes • National regular publications • Scientific topical symposium

Industrial Research Institute

http://www.iriinc.org/

The Industrial Research Institute (IRI) is a non-profit organization of over 260 leading industrial companies. These companies -- representing such industries as aerospace, automotive, chemical, computer, and electronics -- carry out over 80 percent of the industrial research effort in the United States, employ some 500,000 scientists and engineers, and account for at least 30 percent of its gross national product.

Links

IRI • Networks • IRI News • RTM • What's New • PDP • Publications • Audio Tapes • Committees • TVP • Position Statements

The Institution of Chemical Engineers

http://icheme.chemeng.ed.ac.uk/

The Institution of Chemical Engineers is an international body of chemical and process engineers based in Rugby, UK. The Institution of Chemical Engineers (IChemE) was founded in 1922 as a qualifying and professional body for chemical engineers. These original roles, and the accompanying one of a learned society, have continuously expanded and today IChemE has a membership of over 20,000. Of a total membership in excess of 20,000, over 25% are based outside the UK. IChemE membership supports chemical engineers in over 80 countries. Membership offers new opportunities and exciting possibilities for all those involved, working or qualified in chemical engineering. There are seven grades of membership depending on your age, qualifications and experience. Those in the Corporate grades of Member and Fellow are recognized as Chartered Chemical Engineers.

Links

General information on IChemE • Membership • Professional Development Information • Journals and Bulletins page • Diary Dates • Branches • Subject Groups • Book Catalogue • Library and Information Services • Safety and Environmental Training Packages • Health and Safety Activities Box • Courses and Training • Other Information

Instituto Mexicano de Ingenieros Quimicos A.C. (Mexican Institute of Chemical Engineers)

http://www.ur.mx/imiq/imiq.htm

El IMIQ como grupo profesional, se encuentra renovado en su propósito fundamental; ahora se propone ser más participativo en la busqueda de soluciones para resolver los principales problemas que aquejan al gremio, a la industria y en última instancia a nuestro país. El objetivo de este reportaje consiste en informar a todos nuestros colegas, a los sectores industriales, a la comunidad académica y al

gremio en general que el IMIQ ha tomado Un nuevo "Rumbo Estrategico" a través de un plan bien definido, el cual ya fue aprobado por los Consejos del IMIQ y en el que sólo falta la participación de todos sus miembros, directivas y autoridades del IMIQ para que se desarrolle con plenitud. En primer lugar queremos informar que se realizó una reunión de planeación en la Ciudad de Monterrey N.L. en la Universidad egiomontana los días 17 y 18 de febrero de 1995 gracias al ofrecimiento del Dr. Pablo Adolfo Longoria Trevino, Rector de Ia citada universidad, miembro de la presente directiva y anfitrión de la reunión.

Links

Libro de visitantes • Aquí puede ver el libro de visitas • Información sobre Monterrey • Universidad Regiomontana • American Institute of Chemical Engineers • Instituto Mexicano de Ingenieros Químicos • Historia de la Ingeniería Química • Evolución de la Ingeniería Química • Chemical Engineering Sites all over the World

International Association for Stability and Handling of Liquid Fuels

http://chemdiv-www.nrl.navy.mil/iash/iashmain.htm

The International Association for Stability and Handling of Liquid Fuels, IASH, was founded in 1986. The purposes of IASH are to promote research and experimentation on the scientific and operational factors that affect the stability and handling of liquid fuels during their manufacture and blending, transportation, storage, and use; and to provide a forum for the exchange of related ideas and information. Liquid fuels include crude oil and its refined products; fuels derived or processed from oil shale, tar sands, coal, and natural gas; and alternative fuels containing oxygenated components. To accomplish its purposes and to promote a better understanding of the problems associated with the stability and handling of liquid fuels, IASH publishes a biannual newsletter, and sponsors triennial international conferences and publishes their proceedings. IASH is an international, non-governmental, interdisciplinary, volunteer association. Membership is open to all individuals and organizations subscribing to its purposes.

Links
Summary of the 5th International Conference • Notices of Upcoming Society Activities • IASH Officers

International Centre for Heat and Mass Transfer - ICHMT

http://www.metu.edu.tr:80/~wwwichmt/

The International Centre for Heat and Mass Transfer (ICHMT) is an international, professional, non-governmental, non-profit organization. The general objective of the Centre is to promote and to foster international cooperation in the science of heat and mass transfer and its applications. Its secretariat is located at the Mechanical Engineering Department of Middle East Technical University (METU), and is supported by both METU and Scientific and Technical Research Council of Turkey (TÜBİTAK). The first meeting of the International Centre for Heat and Mass Transfer (ICHMT) was held in Herceg Novi, Yugoslavia, on September 16, 1968, during the International Seminar

on Heat and Mass Transfer in Turbulent Boundary Layers, organized by the Boris Kidric Institute of Nuclear Sciences in Belgrade. This meeting was the culmination of activities initiated by a group of leading scientists in the field from different countries. These activities resulted from a long felt need to create an international organization in the fast growing field of heat and mass transfer.

Links
What is ICHMT? • Executive Committee • Secretariat • Scientific Council • Statutes • Member Institutions • Bylaws • Past ICHMT Meetings and Publications

International Society of Heterocyclic Chemists

http://euch6f.chem.emory.edu/ishc.html

This is the Home Page for the International Society of Heterocyclic Chemistry and the Royal Society of Chemistry Perkin Division Heterocyclic Group. The ISHC now has a joint World Wide Web home page with the Royal Society Heterocyclic Group; the URL is listed under our letterhead. Newsletters, meeting registration forms and other information will be available in this way - please use this service if you are a Net "surfer". E-mail is a good way to contact your President as well as the 1997 Congress Chairperson. The ISHC is Financially Dependent on our Membership. Please help us sustain our vibrancy by joining the Society in 1996.

Links
International Society of Heterocyclic Chemistry • Royal Society of Chemistry Perkin Division Heterocyclic

Group • Electronic Conference on Heterocyclic Chemistry

International Union of Pure and Applied Chemistry - IUPAC

http://chemistry.rsc.org/rsc/iupac.htm

IUPAC is a voluntary non-
governmental, non-profit organization
that unites chemists from all over the
world. The object of the Union is the
advancement of both pure and applied
chemistry. IUPAC grew out of the
international recognition of a need for
standardization in chemistry, it being
accepted that standardization of
weights, measures, names and symbols
is essential to the well-being and continued success of the scientific enterprise. Indeed, it is essential for the
smooth development and growth of
international trade and commerce. It
was this desire for international cooperation amongst chemists, and to facilitate the work of the international, but
fragmented, chemistry community
chemistry that was one of the earliest
characteristics of the Union. Indeed,
even before the creation of IUPAC
(1919), the body out of which the Union developed, International Association of Chemical Societies (IACS), had
met in Paris in 1911 and produced a set
of proposals for the work that the new
Association should address. These included: Nomenclature of inorganic and
organic chemistry; Standardization of
atomic weights; Standardization of
physical constants; Editing tables of
properties of matter; Establishing a
commission for the review of work;
Standardization of the formats of publications; Measures required to prevent
repetition of the same papers.

Links
What is IUPAC? • News from IUPAC •
Organization of IUPAC • Scientists in
IUPAC • Programs in IUPAC • Confer-
ence Calendar • IUPAC publications •
White Book on Chlorine • Discussion
Paper on Chemical MIME Standards •
IUPAC Seeks An Executive Director /
Executive Secretary • Thieme-IUPAC
Prize in Synthetic Organic Chemistry
1996

Italian Chemical Society

http://www.xmission.com/
~gastown/chemistry/sci.htm

The Italian Chemical Society is a very
large cultural association with over
6,000 members. The branches of the
society cover all the aspects of the
chemical science and technology.
Among the members are university and
high school professors, researchers
from government and industrial laboratories, and many others having diversified interests in the various fields of
Chemistry. The finality of the Society
is that of encouraging and promoting
cultural and scientific interactions between the members and generally, to
represent and support the national
chemical community. To reach this
goal, the Society is structured in
disciplinary divisions and regional sessions.

Links
SCI Divisions • Official Gazette • News
and Information

Korean Chemical Society

http://www.kcsnet.or.kr

The Korean Chemical Society was founded by the 53 chemical scientists on July 7, 1946. In 1971 the Society held an international convention to celebrate its 25th anniversary. The Society is currently planning grand ceremonial activities including several international conventions from 1995 to 1997 to commemorate its 50th anniversary in 1996. Now the Society is one of the largest and most active professional societies in Korea, with over 4,500 regular and student members. It publishes 4 scientific journals and 1 news magazine.

Links
What's New • KCS • 50th • ChemInfo • Publications • KCSnet BBS • Science • Education • Meetings & Announcement • The Korea Science and Engineering Foundation

National Association of Chemicals in Spain -- ANQUE

http://www.gui.uva.es/
~polyfemo/index.html

La ANQUE es la A sociacin Nacional de Quimicos de Espane;a, cuyo fin es hacer valer los derechos de los profesionales del sector. Edita conjuntamente con el Consejo General de Colegios Oficiales una revista, llamada Química e Industria.

Links
Publications #82-94 • ENUSA • Visita A UCB Films (Cellophane Española S.

New Swiss Chemical Society

http://sgich1.unifr.ch/nscs/nscs.html

The New Swiss Chemical Society represents chemistry in the broadest sense in Switzerland and in international organizations. It notably engages in: Information, discussion and education in all fields of pure and applied chemistry including economical, ecological and social perspectives. For this purpose it organizes and supports scientific meetings, workshops and other activities that serve the chemical community in Switzerland. Activities that promote the interests of chemists in Switzerland and in international professional organizations. Publications like Helvetica Chimica Acta and Chimia.

Links
NSCS history • Organization • Sections of the NSCS • Statistics • Activities • Awards • Become a member • Students and young researchers area • Swiss Chemical Society conferences • Information for NSCS's members

The North American Catalysis Society

http://www.dupont.com/nacs/

The North American Catalysis Society was founded in 1956 to promote and encourage the growth and development of the science of catalysis and those scientific disciplines ancillary thereto; to provide educational services to members and other interested individuals; to organize and participate in professional meetings of scientists; to report, discuss and exchange information and viewpoints in the field of catalysis; to serve as a central exchange for the several catalysis clubs concerning information on their activities; and to provide liaison with foreign catalysis societies, with the International Congress on Catalysis, and with other scientific organizations and individuals, no pecuniary gain or profit to members, incidental or otherwise, being contemplated.

Links

Canadian Society Honors John Moffat and Mark Davis • The Catalysis Society of New York 1996-1997 Program • Catalysis Club of Philadelphia Message and 1996-1997 Information • 1996-1997 Local Clubs and Societies Directory • Heinz Heinemann's 40th Anniversary Lecture at the 11th ICC • President Gonzalez's Annual Letter • Summary of the 11th International Congress on Catalysis • Proceedings of 11th International Congress on Catalysis available • History of the Catalysis Division of the Chemical Institute of Canada • Herman Pines 1902-1996 • Complete Information and Program for the 11th International Congress on Catalysis • Kokotailo Named Ciapetta Lecturer • Visability of Catalysis - Update by John Armor • March 1996 Newsletter • Officers and Representatives • Local Clubs/Societies • Newsletters • Meetings • Awards

Royal Australian Chemical Institute

http://131.236.60.11/RACI/

The Royal Australian Chemical Institute, founded in January 1917, is both the qualifying body in Australia for professional chemists and a learned society promoting the science and practice of chemistry in all its branches. The Institute has 9,800 members and was granted a Royal Charter in 1932.

It is concerned with the teaching and practice of chemistry and with the application of chemistry in industry, academia and government authorities. Thus, it represents and caters for the professional needs of all chemists, providing various activities and services that encompass the profession of chemistry in Australia.

Links

About the RACI • Branches • Divisions • Meetings and Conferences • National Secretariat • Chemistry in Australia • Search the RACI and OzChemNet Web pages

The Royal Flemish Chemical Society - Jong KVCV

http://sch-www.uia.ac.be/u/thys/kvcv/kvcv_eng.html

In 1939 a small group of chemists gathered to form the Flemish Chemical Society. The main goal of this association was to group all Flemish chemists. Since 1939, KVCV has indeed become the representative of all chemists in Flanders irrespective of their specialization, in education (professors, teachers and students), research and industry. In order to better keep in touch with the members, KVCV is organized in different sections. These sections group people with the same specialization, of the same geological region or with the same background. Specialization : Analytical Chemistry, Biotechnology, Chromatography, Physical Chemistry, Chemical History, Computational Chemistry, Medical Chemistry, Environmental Chemistry, Organic Chemistry, Polymer Chemistry, Thermal Chemistry and Food Chemistry.

Links
Info (Dutch) • Calendar • Contacts

The Royal Society of Chemistry

http://chemistry.rsc.org/rsc/

If you are interested in science then you're in the right place. Visit these pages regularly to keep up to date with the latest chemistry news and best links to other science sites on the Web. You don't need to wear a white coat, you don't need to be a member, you don't even need to be a chemist - come and discover what we can offer.

Links
About The Royal Society of Chemistry • Who to contact • Information for members • Online and CD-ROM products • Books • Journals • Publications catalogue • Scientific activities • Meetings • Conference diary • Library and Information Centre • Chemistry by specialty • Index of RSC web pages • Employment services, careers advice • Jobs

The Royal Swedish Academy of Sciences

http://www.kva.se/

The Royal Swedish Academy of Sciences is an independent, non-governmental organization that was founded in 1739. The major aims of the Academy are to promote research in mathematics and the natural sciences. These aims are achieved by stimulating national and international scientific cooperation, through seven scientific institutes; by publishing scientific journals; by distributing scientific information and by promoting contacts between scientists and society. Prizes and grants are awarded annually from funds held in trust by the Academy. The Nobel Prizes in Physics and Chemistry have been awarded by the Academy since 1901 and the Prize in Economic Sciences in memory of Alfred Nobel since 1968.

Links
About the Academy • News • Activities • Prizes • Text in Swedish

Société Française de Chimie (French Chemical Society)

http://www.sfc.fr/

S'agissant des compétences, la SFC est composée de 8 divisions scientifiques ainsi que de 13 groupes thématiques. Sur le plan géographique, elle est répartie en 18 sections régionales et clubs de jeunes sociétaires. Les membres de la Société Française de Chimie bénéficient de réductions très importantes sur l'abonnement à ces revues. Publications: L'Actualité Chimique; Analusis; Bulletin de la Société Chimique de France; Journal de Chimie Physique; Journal of Chemical Research

Links
Organigramme • Nouveautes • Activites • Clubs • Manifestations • Publications • Formation • Adresses • Emploi • Exposition • Forum

Society of Chemical Engineers, Japan

http://wwwsoc.nacsis.ac.jp/~scej/index.html

The Society of Chemical Engineers, Japan (SCEJ) is a major academic group in Japan, having about 8000 members, 1300 student members and 670 company members. The society works on the "Chemical Engineering", which covers many academic fields related to chemical industry. The society provides bimonthly journals, Kagaku-Kogaku Ronbunshu (in Japanese) and Journal of Chemical Engineering of Japan (in English). Members also receive monthly issues of Kagaku-Kogaku, SCEJ's flagship publication. SCEJ provides many other publications including Recent advances in Chemical Engineering, Symposium Series and so on. SCEJ has annual meetings twice a year. Local or specific meetings are also held in each regional and technical division.

Links
About the SCEJ • Events on SCEJ • SCEJ publications • Technical Societies • Regional Activities • Related Departments in Japan

Society for Applied Spectroscopy

http://esther.la.asu.edu:80/sas/

This home page is organized to disseminate information regarding the Society, its journal, and related spectroscopy events. Follow the links below to specific topics. The scope of this Society is to undertake and promote activities which shall accomplish the objective. The term spectroscopy as used here means the science and art of absorption, emission, Raman, mass, and related forms of spectral study for determining the composition and structure of matter. To accomplish the objective, this Society and/or Local Sections may conduct conferences or symposia on scientific subjects and may, in addition to the Journal, publish or give financial support to the publication of other scientifically useful information pertaining to spectroscopy.

Links
The Society • The Journal • The Newsletter • Spectroscopy Conferences/Events • Products and Services • SAS Short Courses • Submission/Subscriptions/Membership • Other Spectroscopy Related Sites

Society of Chemical Industry

http://sci.mond.org/

The Society is an international association of about 6000 members aimed at furthering applied chemistry. Its principal activities are to hold meetings organized by its members through its 38 subject and regional groups, to publish journals and books, and to give awards to individuals. SCI is involved in the activities of the European Federation of Biotechnology (EFB), the European Federation of Food Science and Technology (EFFoST), and Chemical Industry and the Young (CIY). The Society publishes several journals and books, and the fortnightly magazine Chemistry and Industry. There are 38 subject and regional groups in the Society. Each has a lively diary of meetings and events.

Links

Who We Are • Society News • How to Join • Groups • Publications • Meetings • Chemistry & Industry • European Federation of Biotechnology (EFB) • European Federation of Food Science and Technology (EFFoST) • Chemical Industry and the Young • SCI International Medal

Society of Environmental Toxicology and Chemistry

http://www.setac.org/

The Society of Environmental Toxicology and Chemistry (SETAC) is an independent, non-profit professional society that provides a forum for individuals and institutions engaged in the Study of environmental issues, Management and regulation of natural resources, Environmental education, and Environmental research and development. Environmental toxicology and chemistry embrace these fields of study: Analytical chemistry; Anatomy; Atmospheric sciences and engineering; Biology; Classical toxicology; Ecology; Economics; Environmental chemistry; Genetics; Microbiology; Organic chemistry; Physiology; Soil sciences and engineering; Water sciences and engineering.

Links

Membership Information • SETAC Foundation for Environmental Education • Society Activities • Awards & Fellowships • Meetings • Life-Cycle Assessment • Publications • Ecological Risk Assessment • Society History and Governance • Contaminated Soils

Society of Plastics Engineers

http://www.bbsnet.com/SPE/

As part of your annual membership dues, you are entitled to membership in one local Section (chapter) and one Technical Division. Local Section activities enable you to meet other plastics professionals, gather and renew acquaintances at monthly meetings and keep abreast of current industry happenings via newsletter. Your area of technical interest guides your choice of SPE Divisions. SPE's 20 Divisions sponsor technical conferences, secure authors and papers for presentations, provide members with the latest in technical information, and publish newsletters. Additional Division memberships are only $4 each.

DIVISIONS LIST: Advanced Polymer Composites; Automotive; Blow Molding; Color and Appearance; Decorating and Assembly; Electrical and Electronic; Engineering Properties and Structure; Extrusion Injection Molding; Marketing and Management; Medical Plastics; Mold Making and Mold Design; Plastics Analysis; Plastics Recycling; Polymers Modifiers and Additives; Product Design and Development; Thermoforming; Thermoplastic Materials and Foams (Nonvinyl); Thermoset; Vinyl Plastics

Links

Membership • Awards • Conferences • Continuing Education • Technical Journals • Electronic Online Services • Sections

Society of the Plastics Industry

http://www.socplas.org/

SPI is the principal trade association for the U.S. plastics industry. Our 2,000 members represent every segment of the plastics industry, including processors, materials suppliers, machinery manufacturers, moldmakers, distributors and other industry-related groups and individuals. SPI reflects the diversity of the industry it serves. In addition to its core services -- Government and Technical Affairs, Communications, Trade Shows, Membership and Administration -- SPI has nearly three dozen divisions, committees and special purpose groups that offer programs specifically geared to the interests of particular industry segments. SPI's regional offices, along with state and local chapters, address the industry's needs on a localized basis. SPI represents the industry before government bodies, the public, and other industry groups with which the plastics industry has marketplace relationships. SPI fulfills its leadership role by providing forums that enable diverse interests within the industry to set policy and develop common goals and objectives, as well as programs to carry them out.

Links
About SPI • Member Benefits • Trade Shows • Literature • General Plastics Information • Government Affairs

Synthetic Organic Chemical Manufacturers Association

http://www.socma.com/

SOCMA, the Synthetic Organic Chemical Manufacturers Association, is a dynamic, member driven trade association representing the legislative, regulatory and commercial interests of its more than 260 member companies from the chemical industry. SOCMA's reputation for achievement is built upon 75 years of unmatched expertise in identifying and taking action on important issues related to batch manufacturing operations and the spectrum of commerce associated with them. This expertise is the foundation from which SOCMA develops "needs focused" products and services that are highly valued by member companies because they enable them to improve their performance, effectively manage environmental, health, safety and trade regulations, successfully voice concerns to government, as well as create opportunities to profit commercially.

Links
About SOCMA & AMC • Services • Current Events • Conventions • Advocacy Network • SOCMA Solutions • Product Catalog

Technical Association of the Pulp and Paper Industry

http://www.tappi.org/

Welcome to TAPPI - The Technical Association of the Pulp and Paper Industry (TAPPI) is the world's largest paper and related industry association. TAPPI is a professional membership association sponsoring educational programmes, conferences, publications, and products that serve the thousands of scientists, engineers, and businesses in the industry. TAPPI conducts conferences, exhibits, and seminars throughout the world on topics related to the industry and publishes Tappi Journal, a leading publication.

Links
Announcements • Membership • Inside
TAPPI • Events • TAPPI Foundation •
Education • Awards • Divisions,
Committees, Sections • Services • Pub-
lications

Texas Chemical Council

http://www.txchemcouncil.org/
~txchem/index.html

Texas Chemical Council (TCC) is a
statewide trade association of businesses operating chemical manufacturing facilities in Texas. Currently, 101
member companies produce vital products for our way of life, fulfill educational and quality-of-life needs, and
provide employment and career opportunities for more than 70,000 Texans at
more than 200 separate facilities across
the state. Their combined economic
activity sustains about 450,000 jobs for
Texans. Organized in 1953, TCC was
the country's first state trade association
which represented the chemical industry's common interests at the state level.
Each TCC member company appoints a
top executive to serve as a liaison with
TCC. The business and affairs of the
Council are managed by a Board of
Directors whose members are chosen
from among these member-company
representatives.

Links
About the Texas Chemical Industry •
Environmental Information • Safety
Information • Economic Information •
About Texas Chemical Council •
Statement of Position • Membership
List • Key Staff • Related WWW Sites

UK Computational Chemistry Working Party

http://www.ccwp.ac.uk/ccwp/

The Working Party draws its membership from the staff of Chemistry Departments of UK Universities who are
using computational techniques for
their research. Its main function is to
collectively maintain computational
chemistry software for the UK academic community.

Links
Nicholas C. Handy, Cambridge Uni-
versity • Julie Altmann, ULCC • Mem-
bership list • Computer Programs sup-
ported by the Working Party at ULCC •
Forthcoming conferences and meetings
• Typical publications by members •
Joining the Working Party

Verein Deutscher Ingenieure (Association of German Engineers)

http://www.vdi.de/

Mit 127.000 persönlichen Mitgliedern,
darunter mehr als ein Drittel Studenten
und Jungingenieure unter 33 Jahren, ist
der VDI der größte technisch-
wissenschaftliche Verein Europas. Der
VDI ist in Deutschland eine führende
Institution für die Weiterbildung und
den Erfahrungsaustausch technischer
Fach- und Führungskräfte: Er fördert
den Transfer von Technikwissen - als
Dienstleistung für alle in Beruf und
Studium stehenden Ingenieure und
Naturwissenschaftler, für die Un-
ternehmen, den Staat und die Öffentlichkeit. Der VDI vertritt die berufs-
und gesellschaftspolitischen Interessen
der Ingenieurinnen und Ingenieure
sowie der Ingenieurstudenten. Der VDI

ist gemeinnützig und unabhängig von wirtschaftlichen und parteipolitischen Interessen.

Links

Mitwirkung und Mitgliedschaft im VDI • Der VDI im Überblick • VDI-Publikationen • VDI-Veranstaltungen • VDI-Dienstleistungen • Studenten und Jungingenieure

World Association of Theoretically Oriented Chemists

http://www.ch.ic.ac.uk/watoc.html

WATOC was founded in 1982 as the World Association of Theoretical Organic Chemists in order to encourage the development and application of theoretical methods generally. The most conspicuous activities have been the WATOC World Congresses, but WATOC has sponsored or co-sponsored numerous smaller conferences on more specialized topics, and serves to facilitate contacts and to disseminate information. From the beginning, WATOC never was restricted to organic chemistry. Consequently, Prof. Gernot Frenking, the WATOC World Coordinator, suggested that "World Association of Theoretical Oriented Chemists" would be a more appropriate name, and this was adopted by the Officers and Governing Board. Besides these, WATOC is organized by having Regional Representatives, and National Representatives for larger countries.

Links

About WATOC and its membership • Information about WATOC Officers • WATOC-99 in London, England • WATOC-96 In Jerusalem, Israel • Electronic Posters • Final Program for Speakers •

Government Sites

These sites describe the various government agencies throughtout the world that govern and assist the chemicals industry.

Africa

MBendi - African Chemical Industry

http://mbendi.co.za/indy/chem/chemaf.htm

There are three regions in Africa which have stronger chemical industries than the rest of the continent. These are the North African region, West Africa and Southern Africa. The development of chemical industries in these regions has been facilitated by access to larger markets and by the presence of feedstocks such as natural gas coupled with good downstream oil refining or cracking infrastructure. In North Africa, there are strong chemicals industries in Algeria, Egypt, Libya, Morocco and Tunisia. In the West African area, Nigeria is the main producer and user of chemicals. In the south, the prime market and producer is South Africa. This country differs from the others in that its chemical industry is largely based on coal which is used as feedstock for its extensive synthetic fuels industry. The chemical markets in Africa are largely targeted at meeting local needs for chemical feedstocks and intermediates rather than being export orientated.

Links
Companies • Conferences • Countries • Industries • Organisations • Personali

ties • Products • Stock Exchanges • Mbendi Home Page • Overview of African Chemical Industry • Chemical Companies Review • Chemical Companies List • Other Industries of Africa • Oil refining • Algeria • Egypt • Libya • Morocco • Tunisia • Nigeria • South Africa • Synthetic fuels • Carbon tar products • Rogoff Fine Chemicals

Asia-Japan

JICST : JST, Information Center for Science and Technology

http://www.jicst.go.jp

Announcement: :JICST and JRDC will be merged into "Japan Science and Technology Corporation (JST)" on October 1st. This information center from Japan provides access to worldwide scientific and technical information. The organization gathers, processes, and disseminates this information from not only Japan but also from around the world.

Links
JST Service • JST publications • Information for Science and Technology • Japanese Information related to Science and Technology

Institute of Physical and Chemical Research (RIKEN)

http://www.riken.go.jp

RIKEN is an abbreviation of the Japanese name of this organization: Rikagaku Kenkyusyo. It was the first private scientific foundation in Japan.

Links

History • Organization • Campus Information • Access Guide to RIKEN • Institute Laboratories • Research Support Sector • Basic Science Research and Others • International Cooperation • Special Postdoctoral Researcher • Frontier Research Program • Special Laboratories • List of Publication • Frontier Research System • Special Postdoctoral Research Program • Chief Scientist • Research/Technical Staff • Administration Staff • Special Postdoctoral Researchers • Event Information • Press Releases • RIKEN NEWS • RIKEN Review • Newsletter from Frontier Research Program

National Institute of Materials and Chemical Research (NIMC)

http://www.aist.go.jp/NIMC/

Welcome to NIMC Home Page. Japanese version is also available.

Links

Message from the Director-General • Research Subjects • History • Recent Major Research Results • Organization • Publication • Overview • Cooperation • Guide Map • Bulletin Board • NIMC Staff's Pages • WWW Servers Link

Australia

Royal Australian Chemical Institute

http://apamac.ch.adfa.oz.au/RACI

The Royal Australian Chemical Institute, founded in January 1917, is both the qualifying body in Australia for professional chemists and a learned society promoting the science and practice of chemistry in all its branches. The Institute has 9,800 members and was granted a Royal Charter in 1932. It is concerned with the teaching and practice of chemistry and with the application of chemistry in industry, academia and government authorities. Thus, it represents and caters for the professional needs of all chemists, providing various activities and services that encompass the profession of chemistry in Australia.

Links

Royal Australian Chemical Institute • About the RACI • Branches • Divisions • Meetings and Conferences • National Secretariat • Chemistry in Australia • Other Professional Societies • Search the RACI and OzChemNet Web pages

Europe-ECC

Community of Research & Development Information Services (ECC)

http://www.cordis.lu

This is the central source of scientific information and research results within the European Union.

Links

Irish Presidency Homepage - RTD Information Service • English • Francais • Deutsch • Publications • European Union R&D • Fourth RTD Framework Programme • Fifth Framework Focus • Research Themes • Document Library • Programme Home Pages • Green Paper on Innovation • Submit your research results online! • Innovation Homepage • R & D Events around Europe • European Commission

Europe-Romania

Companies Offered for Privatization - Chemical and Petrochemical

http://www.embassy.org/romania/economic/econ5a6.html

Economic, business, and production information relating to Romanian chemical and petrochemical companies offered for privatization are provided at this site.

Links

Romanian Embassy Trade and Economic Section

Canada

Canadian Centre for Occupational Health and Safety

http://www.ccohs.ca

Welcome to the Canadian Centre for Occupational Health and Safety Server! The Canadian Centre for Occupational Health and Safety (CCOHS) promotes a safe and healthy working environment

by providing information and advice about occupational health and safety. CCOHS provides a comprehensive computerized information service, CCINFO, delivered through compact disc (CD-ROM), an online system, CCINFOline, and diskette products. CCINFO assists thousands of users in some fifty countries in meeting their information needs.

Links

Information about CCOHS Products and Services • Demonstrations of CCOHS CD-ROM Products • Courses Available from CCOHS • Connect to CCINFOline (Requires a user name and password) • Health & Safety Canada Mailing List • CCOHS News Releases • Quick Access to the Most Popular Pages on This Server • Other Health and Safety-related Information on the Internet • Internet Search Tools, Software and Information • Collaborative Projects (in Canada and Worldwide)

United States

Argonne National Laboratory

http://www.anl.gov

Welcome to Argonne National Laboratory's home page, the gateway to Argonne's electronic information resources. One of the nation's largest federally funded scientific laboratories, Argonne is operated by the University of Chicago as part of the U.S. Department of Energy's national laboratory system.

Links

Argonne National Laboratory • University of Chicago • U.S. Department of

Energy • Argonne Calendar • Argonne Combined Appeal • Employee Directory • Other Web Information Resources • Help • What's New

Brookhaven National Laboratory - Chemistry Dept.

http://www.chm.bnl.gov/
chemistry.html

The research programs in the Chemistry Department share a single goal: the fundamental understanding of the properties of nuclei, atoms and molecules. The broad range of research includes nuclear and radiation chemistry, radiotracer development and studies in the eurosciences, homogeneous and heterogeneous catalysis, state-to-state chemistry, and thermal and photo-induced charge-transfer processes. Detailed structural and spectroscopic information on solids, liquids and gases and the dynamics of physical and chemical change are made possible by the special facilities, apparatus and techniques available at Brookhaven. A few examples of current research programs are outlined.

Links
Laser Chemistry • Gas-Phase Molecular Dynamics • Photoinduced Molecular Dynamics • Photo- and Radiation Chemistry • Catalysis - Reactivity and Structure • Neutron and X-Ray Diffraction Studies • Solar Neutrinos • Nuclear Chemistry - Relativistic Heavy Ions • Brookhaven Center for Imaging and Neurosciences • Research in the Neurosciences with Short-Lived Positron Emitters • High Field Magnetic Resonance Imaging • in vivo Microdialysis • The BNL Glass Shop • Chemistry Department Telephone List • Chemistry Department Seminars • Re-

lated Work in Other Departments • The Protein Data Bank • laser absorption spectroscopy • theoretical studies employing quantal wavepacket propagation to describe the dynamics of molecules in laser fields • Photo- and Radiation Chemistry program • Catalysis Program • HFBR crystallography • X7B; The Chemistry Beam Line at the NSLS • PDB Browser

Brookhaven National Laboratory - National Nuclear Data Center

http://www.nndc.bnl.gov

The National Nuclear Data Center (NNDC) is funded by the U.S. Department of Energy to provide information services in the fields of low and medium energy nuclear physics to users in the United States and Canada. In particular, the Center can provide information on neutron, charged-particle, and photonuclear reactions, nuclear structure, and decay data. The information available to the users of NNDC services is the product of the combined efforts of the NNDC and cooperating data centers and other interested groups, both in the United States and worldwide.

Links
Nuclear Structure • Decay Data • Nuclear Reaction Data • NNDC Brochure • ENSDF • Atomic Masses • IRDF • Newsletters • Manuals • Nuclear Wallet Cards • Nuclear Data Access • MIRD • Thermal neutron capture • Nuclear Data and References CD-ROM • Reports • NNDC Online • Other Web sites of interest • Conferences • Table of Nuclides at the Korea Atomic Energy Research Institute (To K.A.E.R.I) • International and U.S. Nuclear Data

Centers • Cross Section Evaluation Working Group • International Nuclear Structure and Decay Data Network • Nuclear Data Centres

CBIAC -- The Chemical Warfare/Chemical and Biological Defense Information Analysis Center

http://www.cbiac.apgea.army.mil.

Documents found at this site include information on material selection, detection, weapons types, delivery systems, and chemical and physical properties of chemical and biological weapons.

Links--many

Census Bureau -- Inorganic Chemicals (Quarterly)

http://www.census.gov/cgi-bin/ print_hit_bold.pl/pub/econ/ www/ip5200b.html?energy+and+ consumption#first_hit

The purpose of this quarterly bulletin is to provide detailed data on production and end-of-quarter stocks of selected inorganic chemical products. The United States Code, Title 13, authorizes this survey and provides for voluntary responses. It covers all companies that manufacture selected inorganic chemicals in the United States (most but not all SIC 2812, 2816, and 2819). In 1993 shipments of organic chemicals totaled nearly $18 billion. Data are collected for over 50 types of inorganic chemicals. Product data at the 7-digit SIC level include total quantity of production and end-of quarter stocks.

Links
Related Programs • Search • Inorganic Chemicals (Annual) • Fertilizer Materials (Annual) • Industrial Gases (Annual) • Census of Manufactures • Annual Survey of Manufactures • County Business Patterns • Export Statistics • Import Statistics • Industrial Products • U.S. Economy • Economy Overview

Department of Commerce Information Services

http://www.doc.gov

Established on February 14, 1903, to promote American businesses and trade, the U.S. Department of Commerce is the most versatile agency in government. Its broad range of responsibilities include expanding U.S. exports, developing innovative technologies, gathering and disseminating statistical data, measuring economic growth, granting patents, promoting minority entrepreneurship, predicting the weather and monitoring stewardship. As diverse as Commerce's services are, there is an overarching mandate that unifies them: to work with the business community to foster economic growth and the creation of new American jobs.

Links
What's New • Information from the Office of Secretary • ,U.S. Department of Commerce Agencies • Department of Commerce Online Information Services • STAT-USA • Budget of the United States Government, Fiscal Year 1997 • Connect to the White House WWW

Defense Technical Information Center - Information Science and Technology

http://www.dtic.mil/dtic/
dtic-e/dticehp.html

Welcome to DTIC-E, the Directorate of Information Science and Technology. This group supports the Department of Defense and its web site discusses R&D projects of interest to the U.S. defense system.

Links
Mission • Projects • Staff • News • Other Home Pages of Interest • Technical Reports

Department of Energy Reports Bibliographic Database

http://www.doe.gov/dra/dra.html

The Department of Energy Reports Bibliographic Database contains citations for Department of Energy (DOE) sponsored scientific and technical reports covering the period of January 1, 1994 to present. Current Department citations are added weekly as new reports are made available. Patrons searching the DOE database will be directed to the National Technical Information Service (NTIS) for purchasing information, or to the Government Printing Office (GPO). DOE or DOE Contractors may also purchase reports from DOE's Office of Scientific and Technical Information.

Links
Search The DOE Reports Bibliographic • Database • Database Search Help • Document Ordering and Retrieval Information

Department of Energy - OpenNet

http://www.doe.gov/html/osti/opennet/opennet1.html

Welcome to the Department of Energy's OpenNet database. This searchable database contains documents which have been declassified and made publicly available after October 1, 1994.

Links
Scope Note: Information about what's in the database • Search the OpenNet database • DOE Openness Initiative: Access the full text of documents announced to the public by Energy Secretary Hazel R. O'Leary • Access other DOE Openness Initiative Information Resources

The US Department of Transportation

http://www.dot.gov

Welcome to the DOT WWW Home Page. Thank you for visiting our Web site. You should be able to find most information under "General Information" or under a specific administration's home page in "Browse The DOT Administrations". You can use the DOT Web site as a starting point to reach other DOT web sites and other Federal, State, and International government and transportation related sites.

Links
Browse the DOT Admins • Useful Internet Sites • DOT News And Information • What's New • General Information • Help

119

Energy Information Administration-Data, Analysis, Energy Policy

http://www.eia.doe.gov

This site references publications and data sources relating to Energy, Statistics, Data, and Economic Analysis. While much of the information here is for the upstream side of the business, the downstream analyst will find more than enough to answer most questions about energy production and consumption trends, financial and statistical reports and the ever popular energy forecasts. We can even set up a customized inquiry which will allow us to search various EIA databases interactively and deliver our customized report on the screen. An on-site search engine has been recently added which allows you to quickly find topics of special interest to you.

Links
Petroleum • Natural Gas • Coal • Nuclear • Renewable • Electricity • International • Energy Overview • End Use Consumption • Financial Information • Forecasts • State Energy Statistics • EIA's Web Site Wins Award • Create your own custom reports using the new EIA Interactive Query facility • Greenhouse Gas Emissions Rise in 1994; Slower Growth Seen for 1995 October 18, 1996 • Gore-Chernomyrdin Commission • U.S. Crude Oil, Natural Gas, and Natural Gas Liquids Reserves Annual Report 1995 Advance Summary • Short-Term Energy Outlook Fourth Quarter, 1996 • Alternatives to Traditional Transportation Fuels 1994 - Volume 2, Greenhouse Gas Emissions • EIA Administrator Testifies Growth in Electricity Demand Will Outweigh Environmental Impact of Federal Rule

(9/9/96) • Announcement -- Early Release of the Annual Energy Outlook 1997 • Press Releases • Frequently Asked General Questions • Frequently Asked Technical Questions • Links to other energy related pages • EIA's new CD-ROM -- the Energy Info Disc • Visit the EIA FTP Site • Sign up for the EIA E-Mail list • Energy Events Calendar • Energy Information Administration Contacts • Government Information Locator Service(GILS) • Recent Presentations by the EIA Administrator • Test your knowledge of energy trivia

Environmental Protection Agency - Chemical Emergency Preparedness & Prevention Publications

http://www.epa.gov/swercepp/pubs.html

This site contains publications, fact sheets, technical assistance bulletins, and technical guidance documents useful to those in the chemical industry.

Links
Publications • Accident Histories • Accident Prevention • NCEPI • Q&A database • Update • Q&A Developer • Terra Accident Investigation Summary • Terra Accident Investigation Conclusion • Terra Accident Investigation Recommendations • Terra Accident Investigation Report Review Summary and EPA's Response • EPA Homepage • OSWER Homepage • CEPPO Homepage • Search EPA

Environmental Protection Agency - Chemical Finder

http://www.epa.gov/enviro/html/
emci/emci_query.html

The Environmental Protection Agency's- Chemical Finder uses the EMCI Query Form to obtain the acronyms, chemical identification numbers and chemical names reported by the ENVIROFACTS program system databases (AFS, PCS, RCRIS and TRIS) for the chemical selected by you. For individual chemicals from the output list, you may also see if other chemicals include the selected chemical (using the GROUP search option) or see if the selected chemical is made up of other components (using the COMPONENT search option).

Links
Usage Constraints • User's Guide • Chemical Selection • Chemical Search Option: Chemical Name, Chemical Abstracts Service Registry Number

Environmental Protection Agency - Index of Test Methods

http://www.cais.com/tne/neis/
epa_index.html

The U.S. EPA has formulated hundreds of test methods that must be used by U.S. environmental labs. This site contains a list drawn from the January 1996 edition of the "Index to U.S. EPA Test Methods," an exclusive publication of NEIS.

Links--extensive

Enviroene -- Assisting Pollution Prevention Implementation

http://es.inel.gov

Enviroene is a pollution prevention and environmental compliance assistance network. Its databases offer full-text and multi-site search tools to address technical and regulatory issues. Enviroene's cost effective, cutting edge information comes from a wide spectrum of government, industry, academic, and public interest sources. Enviroene, funded by the Environmental Protection Agency and the Strategic Environmental Research and Development Program, allows those implementing pollution prevention programs, seeking compliance assistance or regulatory guidance, or developing research and development projects to benefit from the experience, progress, and knowledge of their peers.

Links
Prevention Implementation • Enviroene Business Sector Search • National Pollution Prevention Roundtable • Industry Content Guides • Partners for the Environment • EPA Sector Notebooks • American Institute for Pollution Prevention (AIPP) • Animated Pollution Prevention Technologies

Food and Drug Administration

http://www.fda.gov/fdahomepage.html

Welcome to Internet FDA, your electronic source of information about the U.S. Food and Drug Administration.

Links
FDA News • Foods • Human Drugs • Biologics • Medical Devices Radiological Health • Animal Drugs • Cosmetics • Field Operations/Imports • Toxicology • Foreign Language

Los Alamos National Laboratory - Chemical Sciences Technology

http://mwanal.lanl.gov

This site contains general information on the Laboratory, its work groups, and staff experts.

Links--extensive

National Academy of Engineering

http://www.nae.edu

The National Academy of Engineering was established in 1964, under the charter of the National Academy of Sciences, as a parallel organization of outstanding engineers. It is autonomous in its administration and in the selection of its members, sharing with the National Academy of Sciences the responsibility for advising the federal government. The National Academy of Engineering also sponsors engineering programs aimed at meeting national needs, encourages education and research, and recognizes the superior achievements of engineers.

Links
Brief Overview • Member Foreign Associate Public Directory • Calendar • Office Directory • Whom To Call • Suggestion Form: NAE Membership Information • Frequently Asked Ques-

tion • Lifelong Learning for Engineers • For NAE Members ONLY!!! • NAS Home Page

National Academy of Sciences

http://www2.nas.edu/nas/

NAS Members Public Homepage

Links
About the National Academy of Sciences • Membership Listing • Of Current Interest • Activities and Events • Awards Program • Members' Information System • Proceedings of the National Academy of Sciences • How You Can Help the NAS and NRC

National Aeronautical Space Administration - Chemical & Material Projects

http://www.sti.nasa.gov/scan/chem-mat.html

This is the chemical and material portion of a large information database called SCAN (Selected Current Aerospace Notices). It contains data on chemical composite materials; inorganic and physical chemistry; metallic materials; nonmetallic materials; propellants and fuels; and materials processing.

Links
Chemical Analysis • Chemical Processes and Engineering • Luminescence • Photochemistry • Biochemistry • Composite Materials • Reinforced Materials and Fibers • Composite Materials • Inorganic and Physical Chemistry • Corrosion • Metal Crystals • Coatings • Electrochemistry • Metallic Materials • Aluminum • Beryllium • Liquid Metals • Steel • Titanium • Refractory

Metals • Metallurgy • Nonmetallic Materials • Plastics • Adhesives • Ceramics • Elastomers • Graphite • Polymers • Liquid Propellants • Solid Propellants • Materials Processing • Vacuum Technology • Space Commercialization

National Environmental Information Service

http://www.cais.com/tne/neis/default.html

The National Environmental Information Service (NEIS) is a single-source, comprehensive clearinghouse of government environmental documents, including all U.S. Environmental Protection Agency (EPA) and Occupational Safety and Health Administration documents. The EPA maintains nearly two dozen sources of documents; NEIS acts as a central coordinating agent, providing one-call access to these diffuse resources. By providing a comprehensive service, the NEIS precludes the need for long searches and calls to numerous agency distribution points, including EPA and OSHA hotlines, libraries, dockets, and regional offices. NEIS also sells all EPA and OSHA documents sold by the National Technical Information Service for 10 percent or more off the NTIS price.

Links
Index to U.S. EPA Test Methods • Index of Non-Internet Sources of EPA Information • The Chemical Industry Home Page • Current Best Sellers • Air Emissions Documents • EPA Software • Toxicological Profiles • EPA and OSHA Inspection and Enforcement Manuals • Environmental Laboratory Documents • OSHA Documents • Pollution Prevention Documents • Public

Policy Documents • Hazardous Waste Management/RCRA Documents • Superfund Documents • Underground and Above Ground Tanks • Water, Wastewater and Groundwater Documents

National Institute of Standards and Technology (NIST)

http://www.nist.gov:public_affairs/welcome.htm

NIST WWW Home Page. The NIST mission is to promote US economic growth working with industry to develop and apply technology, measurements, and standards.

Links
General Information • Welcome • Tours • NIST Boulder homepage • Site maps • Workshop calendar • Employment opportunities • News • Budget updates • Congressional testimony • Programs • Facilities • Products & Services • Reference materials • Data • Calibrations • Standards information • Gallery • Staff Directory • Search • Keywords • Technical activities • Organizational units • FAQs • Other www Links

National Institute of Standards and Technology - Fundamental Physical Constants

http://physics.nist.gov/PhysRefData/codata86/codata86.html

This document gives the values of the basic constants and conversion factors of physics and chemistry resulting from the 1986 least-squares adjustment of the fundamental physical constants as published by the CODATA Task Group on Fundamental Constants and as recommended for international use by CODATA.

Links
Atomic Mass Constant • Atomic Mass Unit • Avogadro Constant • BIPM Maintained Ampere • BIPM Maintained Ohm • BIPM Maintained Volt • Bohr Magneton • Bohr Radius • Boltzmann Constant • Classical Electron Radius • Cu X-Unit • Deuteron Magnetic Moment • Deuteron Mass • Deuteron Molar Mass • Deuteron-Electron Magnetic Moment Ratio • Deuteron-Electron Mass Ratio • Deuteron-Proton Magnetic Moment Ratio • Deuteron-Proton Mass Ratio • Diamagnetic Shielding Correction • Electron Compton Wavelength • Electron G-Factor • Electron Magnetic Moment • Electron Magnetic Moment Anomaly • Electron Mass • Electron Molar Mass • Electron Specific Charge • Electron Volt • Electron-Alpha-Particle Mass Ratio • Electron-Deuteron Mass Ratio • Electron-Muon Magnetic Moment Ratio • Electron-Muon Mass Ratio • Etc.

National Research Council

http://www.nas.edu/nrc

The National Research Council was organized by the National Academy of Sciences in 1916 to associate the broad community of science and technology with the Academy's purposes of further knowledge and advising the federal government. Functioning in accordance with general policies determined by the Academy, the National Research Council has become the principal operating agency of both the National Academy of Sciences and the National Academy of Engineering in providing services to the government, the public, and the scientific and engineering communities. The National Research Council is administered jointly by both

Academies and the Institute of Medicine.

Links
NAS/NAE/IOM/NRC • What's New • Publications • News • Program Activities • National Academy Press Bookstore • Office of News and Public Information • National Research Council Library • NRC Email Directory

National Science Foundation

http://www.nsf.gov

The National Science Foundation (NSF) is an independent agency of the U.S. Government, established by the National Science Foundation Act of 1950, and was given additional authority by the Science and Engineering Equal Opportunities Act. The Foundation consists of the National Science Board of 24 part-time members and a Director (who also serves as ex officio National Science Board member), each appointed by the President with the advice and consent of the U.S. Senate. Other senior officials include a Deputy Director who is appointed by the President with the advice and consent of the U.S. Senate, and eight Assistant Directors. The Act established the NSF's mission: To promote the progress of science; to advance the national health, prosperity, and welfare; and to secure the national defense.

Links
Recognition Awards for the Integration of Research and Education • NSF FY 1997 Budget Request • Proposals for NSF's Response to the GPRA • NSF Customer Service Plan • Customer Satisfaction Report For Fiscal Year 1996 • Improving Proposal Review • NSF Focus Areas • The NSF World of

Science and Engineering • News of Interest • Hot Topics • NSF Tipsheets • Press Releases • Features • Job Vacancies • Overview • Creation and Mission • Organization and Staff • Program Deadlines • Grants/Funding/Program Areas • Information and Abstracts; Fastlane Project; NSF Regional Grants • Conferences • Federal Demonstration Partnership • Federal Support Electronic Commerce Committee • Information and Publications • Communicating with the NSF • NSF Location and Directions • Publications • Publications (STIS) Search Feature • Graduate Fellowship Applications • NSF Award Search • Proposal Status Inquiry • External Links • Federal Research Centers • Federal Laboratories • Selected NSF-Funded Projects • Federal Agencies • Search the NSF Web

National Toxicology Program

http://ntp-server.niehs.nih.gov/

The National Toxicology Program (NTP) was established within the Public Health Service of the Department of Health and Human Services (DHHS) in November 1978. The continuing broad goals of the NTP are to coordinate and strengthen DHHS basic and applied toxicology research and methods development and validation, and to provide toxicological information for use by health research and regulatory agencies and others in protecting the public health. Overall objectives are to: Broaden the spectrum of toxicological information obtained on selected chemicals; Develop and validate more sensitive and more specific test methods; Develop improved stategies for generating scientific data that strengthen the scientific foundation for risk assessments; and Communicate

Program plans and results to government agencies, the medical and scientific communities, and the public.

Links
Testing Information • Documents & Publications • Chemical Health & Safety Information • News & Events • How Federal Agencies use NTP Data to Protect Human Health • Participating Agencies

Naval Research Laboratory - Chemistry Division

http://chemdiv-www.nrl.navy.mil/

The Chemistry Division conducts basic and applied research and development studies in the broad fields of chemical diagnostics, reaction rate control, materials chemistry, surface and electrochemistry, combustion, and fuels chemistry. Specialized programs within these fields include organic polymeric materials, coatings, dynamics, laser chemistry, tribology, physical and chemical characterization of surfaces and theory of surfaces, chemistry of electronic materials, submarine atmosphere analysis and control, nanometer scale phenomena and solution chemistry. The Chemistry Division staff consists of approximately 100 full-time employees. A number of other personnel work on site in the Division, including Research Associates of the National Research Council and the American Society for Engineering Education, academic scientists and faculty on sabbatical leave or in a part-time status, summer students, exchange students, cooperative programs, Junior Fellows, gifted and talented high school students, research apprentices, and contract scientists. This broad spectrum of scientific talent completes the total complement of approximately 200 personnel who work daily in the Division. Their diverse technical backgrounds include not only chemistry and chemical engineering, but also physics, mathematics, computer science, environmental science, materials science, biochemistry, and electrical engineering. The scientific quality and productivity of this rich mixture of talent is reflected by the numerous awards and recognition accorded members of the Chemistry Division.

Links
Biotechnology Program • Chemical Dynamics and Diagnostics Branch • Molecular Dynamics • Analytical Chemistry • Environmental Chemistry and Sensor Chemistry • Special Projects Group • Materials Chemistry Branch • Publication Lists • Polymer Diagnostics • Materials Synthesis and Processing • Functional Materials • Polymer and Composite Properties • Advanced Materials Group • Surface Chemistry Branch • Gas Surface Dynamics • Tribology • Advanced Surface Spectroscopy • Theoretical Chemistry • Special Research Programs • Navy Technology Center for Safety ; Survivability • Chesapeake Bay Fire Test Detachment • Fuels • Combustion Modeling and Scaling • Combustion Dynamics • Shipboard Fire Scaling

Nuclear Regulatory Commission

http://www.nrc.gov

THE U.S. Nuclear Regulatory Commission (NRC) is an independent agency established by the U.S. Congress under the Energy Reorganization Act of 1974 to ensure adequate protection of the public health and safety, the common defense and security, and the environment in the use of nuclear materials in the United States. The NRC's scope of responsibility includes regulation of--commercial nuclear power reactors; nonpower research, test, and training reactors fuel cycle facilities; medical, academic, and industrial uses of nuclear materials the transport, storage, and disposal of nuclear materials and waste

Links
News and Information • Nuclear Reactors • What Is NRC • Nuclear Materials • Public Involvement with NRC • Radioactive Wastes • Contracting with NRC • Rulemaking • Strategic Assessment Initiative • Search • E-mail • Phonebook • PGP Keys

Oak Ridge National Laboratory - Chemical and Analytical Sciences Division

http://www.ornl.gov/divisions/casd.html

The Oak Ridge National Laboratory, one of the Department of Energy's multiprogram national research and development facilities, is managed by Martin Marietta Energy Systems, Inc., which also manages the Oak Ridge K-25 site and the Oak Ridge Y-12 Plant.

Links
Overview • Mission • Organization and Research • Capabilities • Facilities

The Occupational Safety & Health Administration

http://www.osha.gov/

The mission of the Occupational Safety and Health Administration (OSHA) is

to save lives, prevent injuries and protect the health of America's workers.
To accomplish this, federal and state
governments must work in partnership
with the more than 100 million working men and women and their six and a
half million employers who are covered
by the Occupational Safety and Health
Act of 1970. OSHA and its state partners have approximately 2100 inspec-
tors, plus complaint discrimination
investigators, engineers, physicians,
educators, standards writers, and other
technical and support personnel spread
over more than 200 offices throughout
the country. This staff establishes protective standards, enforces those standards, and reaches out to employers
and employees through technical assistance and consultation programs.

Links
The Assistant Secretary • Information
about OSHA • Directories • What's
New • Media Releases • Publications •
Programs & Services • Compliance
Assistance • Vanguard & Customer
Service • OSHA Software/Advisors •
Federal Register Notices • Frequently
Asked Questions • Statistics & Data •
Standards • Other OSHA Documents •
Technical Information • US Govern-
ment Internet Sites • Safety & Health
Internet Sites • Comments & Info •
OSHA Home Page • OSHA-OCIS • US
DOL Web Site

The Occupational Safety & Health Administration Computer Infomation System - Publications

http://gabby.osha-slc.gov/

Access to OSHA Publications, Regulations, Documents, Technical Info &
Training is provided by this site.

Links
OSHA Standards & Related Docu-
ments • Other OSHA Documents •
OSHA Technical Information • Train-
ing & Registration • The New OSHA •
New Initiatives & Special Emphasis
Projects • OSHA Publications • Salt
Lake Technical Center • Office of
Training & Education • Usage Statis-
tics • Other Government Servers •
Servers of Interest • Web Search Utili-
ties • OCIS Gopher • OCIS FTP site •
OCIS Online • OSHA CD-ROM •
Comments • OSHA-OCIS

Pacific Northwest National Laboratory

http://www.pnl.gov:2080/

Welcome to Pacific Northwest National
Laboratory, a United States Department
of Energy multiprogram national laboratory operated by Battelle Memorial
Institute.

Links
Science and Technology • Partnering •
At A Glance • News/Employment In-
formation • Links to other WWW Sites
• Guestbook • Department of Energy •
Battelle Memorial Institute

Patents & Trademark Office

http://www.uspto.gov/

For over 200 years, the basic role of the
Patent and Trademark Office (PTO)
has remained the same to promote the
progress of science and the useful arts
by securing for limited times to authors
and inventors the exclusive right to
their respective writings and discoveries (Articles 1, Section 8 of the United
States Constitution). Under this system
of protection, American industry has

flourished. New products have been invented, new uses for old ones discovered, and employment opportunities created for millions of Americans. The PTO is a non-commercial federal entity and one of 14 bureaus in the Department of Commerce (DOC). The office occupies a combined total of 1,480,763 square feet, in 15 buildings in Arlington, Virginia. In fiscal year 1994, the office employed 4,977 full time equivalent staff to support its major functions--- the examination and issuance of patents and the examination and registration of trademarks.

Links
What's New • About Patents and Trademarks • US and International Legal Materials • Information by Topic • Information by Organizational Structure • Acquisitions • Search US • Search AIDS Patents • Download PTO Forms • PTO Fees • Order Copies of Patents and Trademarks • Patent and Trademark Related Web Sites • Document Formats and Viewers • Server Statistics • Copyrights: at Library of Congress

Sandia National Laboratory - Combustion Chemistry Laboratory

http://www.ca.sandia.gov/CRF/
Research/Basic/combchem/
Welcome.html

Welcome to the Combustion Chemistry Laboratory Home Page. The Combustion Chemistry Laboratory is one part of the Combustion Research Facility at Sandia National Laboratories. We are a group of kineticists studying elementary chemical reactions important in combustion processes. For the last several years we have been

studying the chemistry of NHx species. This chemistry is important in the formation and destruction of NOx, an important class of pollutants. Our work emphasizes the precise measurement of reaction rate coefficients and reaction product distributions, coupled with high quality theoretical calculations.

Links
Quantum Monte Carlo Evaluation of Chemical Reaction Rate Coefficients • Protodediazoniation of an Aryldiazonium Ion • The Reaction of NH2 with O: A Theoretical Study Employing Gaussian 2 Theory • Kinetics of the NH2 + NO ->; Products Reaction • Recent Publications • First Electronic Conference on Computational Chemistry • First Electronic Conference on Trends in Organic Chemistry • Molecule Visualizer • Other Destinations

Securities Exchange Commission Documents

http://www.sec.gov/

The SEC is an independent, nonpartisan, quasijudicial regulatory agency with responsibility for administering the federal securities laws. The purpose of these laws is to protect investors in securities markets that operate fairly and to ensure that investors have access to disclosure of all material information concerning publicly traded securities. The Commission also regulates firms engaged in the purchase or sale of securities, people who provide investment advice, and investment companies.

Links
Current News • Notice to Small Business Issuers • Fee Rate Advisory: October 1, 1996 • EDGAR Recompetition Notice Released in Commerce Business

Daily, September 20 • About the SEC • What Every Investor Should Know • EDGAR Database of Corporate Information • SEC News Digests and Public Statements • Information for Small Businesses • Current SEC Rulemaking: Proposals and Final Rules • SEC Enforcement Division • About This Site and FAQ (Frequently Asked Questions) • Other Sites of Interest • Search SEC Information • Search the EDGAR Database

STAT-USA/Internet Site Economic, Trade, Business Information

http://www.stat-usa.gov/stat-usa.html

This is a subscription service of the US Department of Commerce. It supplies government sponsored business, economic, and trade information. The National Trade Data Bank (NTDB) is the U.S. Government's most comprehensive source of international trade data and export promotion information. Types of information on the NTDB include: International Market Research, Export Opportunities; Indices of foreign and domestic companies; how-to market guides; Reports on demographic, political, and socio-economic conditions for hundreds of countries; and much more. Very good and worth the cost.

Links
Customize This Page • View Your Customized Page • Mostly Text Version • Select From the Most Popular

Pages • Search Entire NTDB • View Today's Trade Leads • View Most Recent Agricultural Trade Leads • Search the Trade Leads • Search the Market Research Reports • Search the Commerce Business Daily • Search the Country Commercial Guides • Search the International Market Insights • Commercial Service • International Contacts • STAT-USA/Internet • How to Subscribe • Daily Economic News • Frequently Requested Statistical Releases • Information By Subject • Selected Publications of Interest • the Newsletter

USCG Marine Safety Environmental Protection

http://www.dot.gov/dotinfo/uscg/hq/ g-m/gmhome.htm

Welcome to the United States Coast Guard's World Wide Web Site for Marine Safety and Environmental Protection information. In it are documents and other sources of information of general interest to the maritime community.

Links
General • Marine Safety Program Information • Prevention Through People • Lessons Learned and Safety Alerts • Publications, Reports and Forms • Regulatory Notices, Changes and Final Rules • Investigations • Inspection and Compliance • Response • Maritime Security • Marine Personnel • The Sea Partners Program • Other Sites

Colleges and Universities

These are links to the Web pages of the chemistry and chemical engineering departments of colleges and universities around the world and to the special sites they have set up for the chemical industry.

Around the World Sites

Chemistry Department Graduate Programs

http://hackberry.chem.niu.edu/

Chemistry Department Graduate Programs are listed alphabetically. Listing by state is also available.

Links
Arizona State University • Auburn University • Boston College • Boston University • Brigham Young University • Brown University • Carnegie-Mellon University • Case Western Reserve University • City University of New York, Hunter College • Clark University • and many more...

Postdoctoral Openings in Chemistry

http://zn.chem.ndsu.nodak.edu/acs/openings.html

This site contains a listing of persons or organizations seeking postdocs. It is a Theoretical Chemistry Postdoctoral Clearinghouse.

Links
University of Chicago • Australian National University • North Dakota State University • Georgia Institute of Technology • Northern Illinois University • Argonne • Rutgers • Ohio State University • University of Oregon

Asia-Japan

Tohoku University - Molecular Chemistry

http://wwwmater.che.tohoku.ac.jp

Welcome to the Department of Materials Chemistry. These pages are under construction. A Japanese version is also available.

Links
Miyamoto Laboratory • Endou Laboratory • Kobayashi Laboratory • Inoue Laboratory • Tanaka Laboratory • Ozawa Laboratory • Nishiyama Laboratory • Miyashita Laboratory • Kainou Laboratory • Japanese Homepage • World • Department of Applied Chemistry and Chemical Engineering • Faculty of Engineering • Tohoku University • Our city: the modern and active Sendai • Yasunouri Oumi • Stirling

Australia

Curtin University of Technology, School of Chemical Engineering

http://www.curtin.edu.au/curtin/dept/chemeng

Information regarding this university, located in Perth, Western Australia, can be found here. This page contains sections describing the university, its staff and courses, as well as information regarding library and industry sites of interest.

Links--all text

Queensland University of Technology - Centre for Instrumental and Developmental Chemistry

http://www.sci.qut.edu.au/chem/cidc0.htm

The Centre for Instrumental and Developmental Chemistry (CIDC) is a University recognized Research Centre since 1992. Essentially all research carried out in the School of Chemistry is done under the umbrella of the CIDC. The Centre's research efforts are concentrated in three main areas: Analytical /Instrumental Science, Applied Biological Chemistry, and Materials Chemistry. The objectives of the Centre are to promote fundamental studies in modern chemical science and its application to the needs of industry, commerce, government and education; expand the knowledge base in its nominated areas of expertise through high quality research; educate postgraduate students in the intellectual skills necessary to contribute top advances in the field; disseminate information in the field by presentations at conferences, seminars and in internationally recognized journals; utilize and develop staff expertise to service the research and development, consulting, analysis, and testing needs of industry and the community, and to encourage participation of industry in these activities; attract distinguished researchers in the field to engage in joint projects and enhance the experience of Centre staff.

Links
What's New • Search • Jobs • Inquiry/Feedback • School of Chemistry • Consulting and Analytical Services • Centre News • Research Facilities • Postgraduate and Research Opportunities • QUT Home • Faculty of Science Home • School of Chemistry Home • Search

Royal Melbourne Institute of Technology - Department of Applied Chemistry

http://www.rmit.edu.au/

The Department of Applied Chemistry is located at both the City and Bundoora campuses of RMIT. The Department offers three undergraduate courses, and four postgraduate courses. Undergraduate Courses of study are: Bachelor of Applied Science in Applied Chemistry, Bachelor of Applied Science in Environmental Science, and Bachelor of Applied Science in Safety. Postgraduate Courses are: Master of Applied Science in Analytical Chemistry, Master of Applied Science in Toxicology, Master of Applied Science by research, and Doctor of Philosophy (Ph.D.) by research. As well, the Department offers service teaching in each of its three teaching fields. Service teaching in Chemistry is provided to students in the Food Science and Technology, Hospitality, Consumer Science, Chemical Engineering, Metallurgy, Geology, Applied Physics, Applied Biology, Human Biology, Medical Laboratory Science, Ceramics, Chiropractic, Osteopathy, Nursing and Physical Education degrees.

Links
General Information • Course Brochures • Academic Staff • Research • Consulting • Community Service • RACI Research and Development Topics in Analytical Chemistry, 1996 conference • Other Interesting Chemistry, Environment & Safety Sites • Molecular Graphics Laboratory

Royal Melbourne Institute of Technology - Molecular Graphics

http://www.rmit.edu.au/departments/cm/MolGraphics.html

In the past five years in particular, rapidly-increasing access to excellent graphics programs has provided chemists with powerful new tools. This department runs [1] HyperChem, giving access to both quantum and molecular mechanics standard methods, running on a 486-PC. [2] The Biosym suite of programs running on a Silicon Graphics Indy workstation. [3] The Unichem interface to the RMIT Cray Supercomputer facility, which is currently the most powerful installation in Australia, having been commissioned in July, 1995.

Links
Research Page • Home Page

Europe-Germany

University of Bayreuth - MOLGEN - Automatic Structure Elucidation

http://btm2xd.mat.uni-bayreuth.de/molgen/mghome.html

The program system MOLGEN is devoted to the computation of all structural formulae (= connectivity isomers) that correspond to a prescribed brutto formula together with optional further conditions (e.g. prescribed and forbidden substructures). MOLGEN provides an efficient, portable and inexpensive tool for molecular structure elucidation in science and education. The system consists of several components: A generator for connectivity isomers, A graphical molecule editor and 2D-display, A display for 3D-placements using an energy optimization, and A generator for all configurational isomers. MOLGEN serves as the mathematical heart of a program system for automatic molecular structure elucidation, since it provides all mathematically possible candidates that agree with a given set of chemical data. It provides the most capable algorithms due to the recent development of theory and hardware even on a PC.

Links
University of Bayreuth - MOLGEN - Automatic Structure Elucidation • Mathematik • brutto formula • further conditions • A generator for *connectivity* isomers • A graphical molecule editor and 2D-display • A display for 3D-placements using an energy optimization • A generator for all *configurational* isomers • Demos • Pricing and Ordering • Etc.

University of Erlangen - Computer Chemistry Center

http://www.ccc.uni-erlangen.de/
ccc-welcome.html

Also available in German. This page provides links to topics of interest regarding the Computer Chemistry Center at the University of Erlangen.

Links
CCC guiding index • NEW in CCC pages • CCC building and people (groups) • Research topics, products, facilities and manuals • Events in CCC and abroad • Cooperations • Inst. Organic Chemistry • Journal of Molecular Modeling (J. Mol. Model.) • The Encyclopedia of Computational Chemistry • FAUniNET .

University of Karlsruhe - Chemical Engineering Servers in Deutschland

http://www.ciw.uni-karlsruhe.de/
germany.html

This document is also available in German. It provides links to professors and academic and research institutions in Germany.

Links
Aachen Department for Mechanical Engineering • Aachen Lehrstuhl for Process Engineering I and Institute for Process Engineering • Aachen Lehrstuhl for Process Technology • Technical University Berlin • Berlin Process Engineering, Environmental Technology, Material Sciences • Berlin Institute of Technical Chemistry (ITC) • Ruhr-University Bochum - Department for Mechanical Engineering • Etc.

University of Lund - MOLCAS - Theoretical Chemistry

http://garm.teokem.lu.se/MOLCAS/

This page's purpose is to provide users and potential users with information about the MOLCAS-3 quantum chemistry program package developed at the dept. of Theoretical Chemistry at the University of Lund, Sweden. Some of the pages here are still under construction.

Links
MOLCAS-3 release announcement • AIX user's guide • Documentation • News and updates • How to order • Basis sets • Bulletin board • Reference • Homepage of the Dept. of Theoretical Chemistry, Lund, Sweden.

Europe-United Kingdom

Cambridge University - The Cambridge Crystallographic Data Centre

http://csdvx2.ccdc.cam.ac.uk/

CCDC stands for the Cambridge Crystallographic Data Centre. The CCDC develops and maintains the Cambridge Structural Database System. The CCDC is a Registered Charity.

Links
Cambridge Crystallographic Data Centre • Cambridge Structural Database System • Further Information • Instructions for Deposition • Overview of the CSD System • April 1996 Release • Obtaining access to the CSD System • CHANGES FOR OCTOBER 1996 • Citing use of the CSD System • Data Content • Current known prob-

lems and bug fixes • SCIENTIFIC
EXAMPLES • National or Regional
Affiliated Centre • JAICI • CCDC

Cambridge University - Chemical Laboratory

http://www.ch.cam.ac.uk

This page contains a large number of
links to areas of interest in
Cambridge's Chemical curriculum and
outside links of interest. Diese Homepage ist auch in deutsch verfgbar.

Links
Introduction • Academic Staff • Re-
search Profile • Library • Colloquia •
Inorganic • Organic • Physical • Theo-
retical • Melville Laboratory • Chemis-
try Courses • Old Courses • WWW
Servers in the University Chemical
Laboratory • Linux in the PWF •
Melville Laboratory for Polymer Syn-
thesis • Molecular Modelling Research
Group • Physical Methods Section
(NMR and Mass Spectrometry) • Sili-
con Graphics Teaching Laboratory •
Theoretical Chemistry • Theory of
Atomic and Molecular Clusters • Mis-
cellaneous • Search for information on
this server • Cambridge University's
Index of E-mail Addresses @cam.ac.uk
• Jobs Available • New on this server •
Chemical Information from Around the
World • BIDS Literature Search: In-
formation or Connection (requires
password) • Cambridge University Li-
brary • Chemical Data, including Hazard Data • Chemistry Departments and
useful links • Chemistry Journals •
Computational Chemistry List (OSC)

Imperial College of London - Chemical Examples of Virtual Reality Modelling

http://www.ch.ic.ac.uk/VRML

Welcome to the Imperial College, Department of Chemistry, VRML Dem-
onstrator. VR modelling of both individual molecules and reaction products
are shown. Links to publications and
other VRML sites are also included.

Links
Getting Started • Examples • The
3CRO Protein, the world's first VRML
molecule (December, 1994) • Ribbon
Representation of a protein • Connolly
Surface of a protein • VRML in protein
structure determination • Visualization
of the Frontier Orbitals in Diels Alder
Reactions • Publications • Etc.

Oxford University--Physical & Theoretical Chemistry Laboratory

http://physchem.ox.ac.uk/

This page details the Physical and
Theoretical Chemistry Laboratory, its
personnel, and current research activities. Links to areas of interest both
within the Oxford system and from
outside sources are included.

Links
The Department • In Oxford Links •
Out of Oxford Links

Department of Chemistry at the University of Sheffield, England.

http://www.shef.ac.uk/~chem/chemdex

ChemDex is a large index of chemistry-related Internet resources. It is biased toward WWW sites.

Links
Index • Universities • Commercial • Government • Education • Software • Highlights • Periodic Tables • Journals • Societies • SuperList • Newsgroups • Special Interests • Listservs • Conferences • Miscellaneous • University of Sheffield • NCSA Mosaic • Department of Chemistry

University of Bath - WWW Subject Tree - Chemical Engineering

http://www.bubl.bath.ac.uk/BUBL/ Chemeng.html

This is a chemical engineering subject tree containing an information retrieval gopher and chemical engineering resource links.

Links
UDC • Alphabetical • BUBL Home Page • Chemical Engineering • BUBL Gopher Chemical Engineering Resources • Chemical Engineering • AIChE • American Institute of Chemical Engineers Web • ASPEN PLUS VL • AspenTech • Bath University • Buckyball Database (Telnet) • CE Digest • Chemical Engineering • Chemical and Engineering News • Chemical Substance Factsheets • Computational Chemistry • CSIRO • Energy Research • Florida • History of Chemical Engi-

neering and Chemical Technology • Loughborough University • Oklahoma • OpenNet • US DOE • Process Improvement • WWW Virtual Library

University of Bath - WWW Subject Tree - Chemistry

http://www.bubl.bath.ac.uk/BUBL/ Chemistry.html

This is a chemistry subject tree containing an information retrieval gopher and chemistry resource links.

Links
UDC • Alphabetical • BUBL Home Page • Chemistry Resources • American Chemical Society • Australian • Bio-ChemNet • Biophysical Chemistry (BPC) HomePage • Brookhaven National Laboratory • CCDC • CDS • ChemDex • ChemExpo • Chemical Abstracts Service (CAS) • Chemical Information • Chemical Patents Plus • Chemical Substance Factsheets • Chemistry gopher • Chemistry, Chemical Engineering, Materials Research gopher • Chemistry and Industry Magazine • Chemistry Textbooks in Print • Chemistry Today • Chemistry UK • Chemistry and the WWW • Chlorine Chemistry Council • CIBA • Computational Chemistry • Corrosion • CSIRO • CTI • Electrochemical Science and Technology Information Resource (ESTIR) • Electrochemistry Group: University of Liverpool • EXTOXNET • Fertility On The Blink: The Legacy of the Chemical Age • Information systems in Internet Chemistry • Inorganic Materials and Solid State Chemistry • Institute of Biology and Chemistry of Proteins • Internet Resources • Journal of Biological Chemistry • Journal of Computer-Aided Molecular Design • Molecular Modeling • NOAA • Nobel

Prize Internet Archive • NRG • Off-shore Engineering Information Service • Pharmacy Library Catalogue • Physical Chemistry • Physical Chemistry, American Chemical Society Division of • Poly Home Page • Poly-Links • Polymer and Liquid Crystals Tutorial • Polymer Studies • Polymers and Colloids Research Group, Brian Vincent's • Pure and Applied Chemistry, International Union of (IUPAC) • RSC • Servers and Resources, Chemistry • Silicon Graphics: Chemistry and Biological Sciences • Software • Structural Classification of Proteins • Teaching Chemistry on the WWW • THEOCHEM Home Page • TrAC • WebElements • and links to various universities

University of Liverpool - Interdisciplinary Research Centre in Surface Science

http://svr.ssci.liv.ac.uk/homepage.html

The IRC in Surface Science is a fundamental scientific research centre which aims to strengthen the base of understanding of surface processes at an atomic level. The work is, however, very relevant to several major industries. For instance, the the chemical and petro-chemical industries and understanding of the properties of surfaces is central to the search for better, cheaper, more active and more selective catalysts. Surface Science is also crucial in the manufacture and characterisation of semiconductor devices. Knowledge of the behavior of surfaces is necessary in such diverse fields as interfaces, adhesion and wear, friction and wetting.

Links
The IRC • Staff • Scientific plan • Seminars • Papers • www servers • PhD positions • People • www statistics •

MRes at Liverpool • The STM • The University of Liverpool • Information on the DIET 7 conference

University of Manchester - Materials Science

http://info.mcc.ac.uk/MatSci

The study of Materials Science embraces all aspects of these engineering materials and is based on the physics and chemistry of the solid state. Materials Science extends from the extraction of the materials from their mineral sources and their refining and fabrication into finished products; it examines their chemical, crystal, molecular and electronic structure because structure influences not only a material's magnetic and electronic characteristics but also its mechanical properties such as strength, it studies the degradation of materials in service by wear, corrosion and oxidation and is concerned with developing methods of combating these; it considers the proper selection of materials for particular applications and the development of new materials for today's sophisticated technology. Materials Science is an exciting and rapidly expanding subject considered a priority funding area by the EC and the UK government.

Links
What is Materials Science? • Art Gallery • Materials Science at Manchester • Staff List • Researches in Progress • Meetings • News • Undergraduate Prospectus • Postgraduate Prospectus • Student Handbook • Other Useful Sites • Arranging a Visit • Vacancies • UMIST • The University of Manchester • Manchester -The City

University of Southampton - Chemistry Video Consortium Project

http://www.soton.ac.uk/~chemweb/ajrvideo/

These pages describe the activities of the Chemistry Video Consortium Team based at the Department of Chemistry at the University of Southampton. The activities which are funded by the four Higher Education Bodies of the United Kingdom are geared towards producing a comprehensive set of instantly accessible video clips for use in laboratories, lectures and self-paced learning centres. These pages contain general information about the Project, the Consortium University Members, addresses and telephone numbers, e-mail, for communication and information about the video materials that have been produced for 1st year undergraduate laboratory teaching.

Links
Consortium Members and Contact Information • Background of the Project • Aims and Objectives • Organisation of the Project • Achievements • Evaluation • Deliverables • Prices • Materials in Production

University of Strathclyde - Computer Aided Design Centre

http://www.cad.strath.ac.uk/Home.html

The CAD Centre is a postgraduate teaching and research unit at Strathclyde University, in Scotland. Our research is on design methods and computer support of the design process for engineering applications.

Links
University of Strathclyde - Computer Aided Design Centre • Strathclyde University • Scotland • Engineering Information Guide • People • Courses • Research projects • Facilities • Publications • Search • Guide to Internet Services • University master Web server • University campus • Glasgow • Teaching materials • Global Network Navigator

Technical University of Nova Scotia - Chemical Engineering and Chemical Engineers

http://www.tuns.ca/che/aboutche.html

This site discusses the profession of chemical engineering. It answers the following questions: What is Chemical Engineering? How important is Chemical Engineering in today's world? Where do Chemical Engineers work? What type of work does a Chemical Engineer do?

Links
All Text

North America-- United States

Brown University -- Chemical Physics Preprint Database

http://www.chem.brown.edu/chem-ph.html

The Chemical Physics Preprint Database is a fully automated electronic archive and distribution server for the international theoretical chemistry community.

Links

Purpose • Overview • Subscribing •
Listing and Retrieval • Help • Steps for
Submitting an Article • Submission
Commands • Format of Papers for
Submittal • Making Changes/Replacing
your Submitted Paper • Postscript from
the Archives • Frequently Asked Ques-
tions • Beginner's Trouble Shooting •
List of E-mail Commands • What's
New • Etc.

Carnegie Mellon University - Computer Aided Process Design Consortium

http://www.cheme.cmu.edu/
research/capd

The consortium in Computer-Aided
Process Design is an industrial body
within the Department of Chemical
Engineering and The Engineering Design Research Center that deals with
the development of methodologies and
computer tools for the process industries. The CAPD consortium currently
has more than 20 members from
chemical and petroleum companies,
and from a number of hardware and
software companies. Research is directed by Professors Biegler, Gross-
mann and Westerberg and carried out
by about 25 graduate students and researchers. The main areas of concentration include process synthesis, process optimization, process control,
modeling and simulation, artificial
intelligence, and scheduling and planning. Some examples of specific topics
are: Synthesis of energy management
systems, complex nonideal separation
systems and reactor networks; Structural flowsheet optimization and retrofit design; Design, planning and
scheduling of batch processes; Design
of flexible processes; Optimization

strategies for process control; Parame-
ter estimation and profile organization;
Solution and optimization of differen-
tial-algebraic systems; Large-scale
nonlinear programming and mixed-
integer programming algorithms; Representation and processing of qualitative knowledge for process synthesis
and optimization; Advanced environments for the rapid creation, debugging
and solution of large complex equa-
tional-based models; Environment for
capturing, structuring and sharing of
information to support team based engineering design.

Links

Annual CAPD Review • CAPD Software • October 1995 Newsletter • Research Abstracts (consortium access
only) • Recent Publications • CAPD
Short Course • Membership • CAPD
Student Pipeline • Industrial Participants • Membership • Chemical Engineering Research • Chemical Engineering Home

Cooper Union for the Advancement of Science and Art - The Molecular Monte Carlo Home

http://www.cooper.edu/engineering/
chemechem/monte.html

Welcome to the Molecular Monte Carlo
Home Page! This page, sponsored by
the Cooper Union Department of
Chemistry, is meant to serve as an information resource for those who use
"random walks" (stochastic methods) to
simulate and analyze molecular systems
throughout the world. You will find
links to hypertext tutorials on Monte
Carlo methods here as well as software
repositories and other information.

Links

Cooper Union Department of Chemistry • The Schranz group at Australian National University • First Electronic Molecular Graphics and Modelling Society Conference(MGMS EC-1) • Introduction to Monte Carlo Methods • Computational Science Education Project • Introduction to Random Number Generators • Quantum Monte Carlo and the Penn State Imaginary Particle • Metropolis Monte Carlo • Monte Carlo Methods Online Lecture • NCCE Tutorials on Monte Carlo Methods, Introduction to Monte Carlo Device Simulation, etc. • NIH Tutorial on Conformation Sampling • Random Walks, Markov Chains and the Monte Carlo Method • Simulated Annealing • XPLOR Home Page • Chemical Physics Preprint Server • Journal of Molecular Modeling • Journal of Physical Chemistry Online • Markov Chain Monte Carlo Preprint Service • Monte Carlo Methods and Applications • Adaptive Simulated Annealing Codes and Papers • CCP5 - Computer Simulation of Condensed Phases Software Library • FANTOM • FORTRAN 90 for the FORTRAN 77 Programmer • The Helix-Coil Transitions Page • MCSim Simulation Software • Netlib Repository of Mathematical Software at UTK/ORNL • NIST Guide to Available Mathematical Software • Numerical Recipes Home Page • STERIC • XTOYS • Abstracts of Studies of Random Numbers • CCL Discussion on Brownian Dynamics vs MC vs MD for Diffusion • Computational Study of the Structures and Thermodynamic Properties of Ammonium Chloride Clusters Using a Parallel Jump-Walking Approach • Folding of Globular Proteins by Energy Minimization and Monte Carlo Simulations with Hydrophobic Surface Area Potentials • Monte Carlo Simulation of Polymer Interfaces on the T3D • Parallel Monte Carlo Simulation • Path-integral Monte Carlo Simulations of Thin 4He Films on a H2 Surface • Quantum Monte Carlo of Nitrogen: Atom, Dimer, Atomic, and Molecular Solids • Other, Related Sites

Emory Chemistry Library - Net Resources: External

http://www.chem.emory.edu/~library/ chemlink.html

Pointers, gateways, superlists, hyperlinks... Browse this large collection of Chemistry resources and related WWW virtual libraries.

Links

A List List • Organizations • Publishers • Electronic Journals ... • Reference • Library Sources

Harvard University - WebChemistry

http://www-chem.harvard.edu/ webchemistry/webchem.html

WebChemistry is an extremely large index of chemistry-related sites on the Internet. In addition to the traditional resource links, it also indexes software and other resources.

Links

UK mirror • The Queen's University of Belfast • USA mirror • Harvard University • Australia mirror • LaTrobe University, Melbourne • Additions, Corrections, Suggestions Or Comments • Special Announcements • Recent Additions • Academic Sites • Commercial Sites • Chemistry Resources • Jobs Online

Michigan State University - Applied Thermodynamics

http://www.egr.msu.edu/~lira/
thermtxt.htm

An Introduction to Applied Thermodynamics, by J. Richard Elliott and Carl T. Lira. This is a discussion of a chemical engineering undergraduate textbook which is now available for course adoption.

Links
Preface • Overview • Table of Contents • Selected examples • Subject index • Appendix which summarizes the computer programs • How to Purchase • J. Richard Elliott • Carl T. Lira

New Mexico State University - Careers in Chemical Engineering

http://chemeng.nmsu.edu/
brochure/career.htm

This site contains a discussion of chemical engineering as a career and an explanation of the benefits of attending New Mexico State University.

Links
Careers in Chemical Engineering • American Institute of Chemical Engineers (AIChE) • The history of chemical engineering • Application for undergraduate admission • Request more information • Financial Aid information • Resident Tuition at NMSU for Texas Residents

Northern Illinois University - Chemists Directory Search

http://hackberry.chem.niu.edu:70/
0/ChemDir/index.html

The Northern Illinois University Chemistry Directory (NIU ChemDir) is an electronic "phone book" of chemists. With ChemDir, you can quickly find information on chemistry professionals. This is a form based Glimpse gateway for the WWW. Glimpse is an indexing/search program that uses very little space for the index and allows flexible queries. This glimpse interface allows both browsing and searching. A search covers all files in this directory and all directories below it. As you browse deeper, you automatically limit the search to where you are.

Links
Make a search • Information about Glimpse

Rensselaer Polytechnic Institute - Chemical Information Studio

http://www.rpi.edu/dept/chem/
cheminfo/cistudio

Welcome to Chemical Information, a WWW-based, studio course co-sponsored by the Department of Chemistry and the Rensselaer Libraries. CIStudio is a 1995 Excellence in Online Education Award of Merit (sponsored by Knight-Ridder Information, Inc.) recipient.

Links
Chemical Information • Department of Chemistry • Rensselaer Libraries • Syllabus • Overview of Course • Lab Fee • Grading • Homework • Final

140

Project • Student Survey • UNIX Review • Netscape Review • Science Citation Index • CATALOG • CURRENT CONTENTS • The Internet • Citing References • Internet Chemistry Resources • About the Instructors • Etc.

State University of New York at Stony Brook - Buckyball

http://buckminster.physics.sunysb.edu

This is the home page for the Fullerene research groups in the Physics Department at SUNY @ Stony Brook, on Long Island, New York. We are exploring the fundamental properties of Fullerenes (Carbon-60) and doped fullerenes. Many experiments are carried out at Stony Brook, and we also do measurements at the National Synchrotron Light Source at Brookhaven National Laboratory.

Links
Physics Department • SUNY @ Stony Brook • Long Island • Our lab • Seminar room • Guided tour • Doped fullerenes • National Synchrotron Light Source • Brookhaven National Laboratory • List of publications • Fullerene Structure Library • USB Chemistry Department • Widener University Chemistry Department • Patents • Fullerene Gallery • University of Sussex Fullerene Group Home Page • University of Vienna Fullerene Group • Unearthing Buckyballs • Bucky NewsService • Simulations of C60-C240 collisions • White House • Carbon nanotubes • Buckyball Database (University of Arizona Library) • buckybib asciifile (LONG!) • Rapid Single Flux Quantum (RSFQ) Laboratory • X-ray microscopy • Experimental high energy physics • Institute for Theoretical Physics • Nuclear Theory •

American Physical Society • Materials Research Society • European Physical Society • The Electrochemical Society • Fullerenes Group • Institute of Physics • American Institute of Physics • Textbook about problems and solutions • XXX Physics Preprint Server • Chemical Physics PreprintDatabase • High-Tc Update • Graphical Periodic Table of the Elements • The White House • U.S. House of Representatives • Foreign Languages for Travelers

University of California at Berkeley - Departments of Chemistry and Chemical Engineering

http://www.cchem.berkeley.edu

This is the home page for the Departments of Chemistry and Chemical Engineering at the University of California at Berkeley.

Links
A Tour of the College • Chemistry Department • Chemical Engineering Department • Directory of People in the College • Information for Alumni/ae • Resources for Education • Resources for Chemistry • Access Berkeley

University of California at Davis - Chemistry Resources

http://www-chem.ucdavis.edu

This is the home page for the Department of Chemistry at the University of California, Davis.

Links
U.C. Davis • Information about Graduate Studies • How To • Who Does What • Software Archive • Faculty •

Lecturers • NSF Career Planning Workshop • Information about Graduate Studies • Information for Undergraduate Students • Courses - Fall '96 • Classlist Request Form • Facilities and Offices • Bulletin Board • Seminars • Locally Maintained Resources • Other Chemistry Departments • Other Chemistry Resources • Online Databases, Libraries and Facilities • Usenet News Groups • Miscellaneous Items • Search the UCD Whois Directory • White Pages from Netscape • Search the MIT Whois servers list • Search the UCD Faculty/Staff Phonebook • Search local and remote CSO nameservers • Community of Science Expertise Database • Apple Servers • AMUG's • FAQ's • Info-Mac • Resource Lists

University of California at San Diego - Chemistry Visualized

http://www-wilson.ucsd.edu/education/edu.revised.html

This site contains jpeg images of various teaching topics relating to physical and general chemistry.

Links
Physical Chemistry • General Chemistry

University of Florida - Process Improvement Laboratory

http://www.che.ufl.edu

Welcome to the University of Florida Chemical Engineering Department Process Improvement Laboratory which focuses on studying and developing technologies for the continuous improvement of process systems.

Links
Welcome • University of Florida • Chemical Engineering Department • Process Improvement Laboratory • Computer-Aided Process Improvement Laboratory • Gator Power Academic Interface • Computer-Aided Visualization • Advanced System for Process ENgineering (ASPEN) Library • AspenTech Info Library • Real-Time Application Platform (RTAP) Library • Chemical Engineering Department • Undergraduate Online Course Information • American Institute of Chemical Engineers Web • World Wide Web Virtual Library: Chemical Engineering • UFIAC - UF Industrial Assessment Center • SUCCEED - A National Engineering Education Improvement Coalition • SECME Net - Southeastern Consortium for Minorities in Engineering Network • Prototype Development Workshop • Computer-Aided Engineering Tools • Computing Self-Help Resources

University of Florida - Process Thermodynamic Modeling and Analysis

http://www.che.ufl.edu/aspenplus/ThermAnal

This is a text which contains supplemental notes for an undergraduate course on thermodynamic modeling and analysis.

Links
Menu • Tour • News • ASPEN PLUS • AspenTech Info • Help

University of Minnesota - The History of Chemical Engineering

http://www.cems.umn.edu/
~aiche_ug/history/h_intro.html

Welcome to our History of Chemical Engineering Chemical Technology. Our goal is to bring you a history of chemical engineering that encompasses its conceptual origins in Great Britain, subsequent struggle for survival in the United States, and concludes with a cornucopia of contributions made in this Century. Along the way, many tables and figures help illustrate the growth and change in the chemical industry, the chemical engineering profession, and its educational infrastructure.

Links
Table of Contents • What is Chemical Engineering?

University of Oklahoma - Institute for Applied Surfactant Research

http://www.ou.edu/cems/iasr

The Institute for Applied Surfactant Research consists of seven University of Oklahoma faculty members well-known for their research on the properties and applications of surfactants. These faculty, who are members of the School Chemical Engineering and Materials Science, the Department of Chemistry and Biochemistry, and the School of Civil Engineering and Environmental Science, have for many years performed research in such diverse fields as detergent formulation, environmental remediation,

bioseparations, microelectronics, dispersant stabilization and drug delivery systems. This productive group of faculty has made IASR the premier institute dedicated to surfactant research in the world. One indication of this reputation is the selection of the University of Oklahoma to host the 65th Annual American Chemical Society's Colloid and Surface Science Symposium in 1991. In these web pages, we present IASR's research activities, many relating to the study and application of systems in which surfactant aggregates play an essential role. The basic and applied research under the auspices of IASR is useful in solving many problems. Indeed, one of the strengths of the Institute is the capability to apply new knowledge and technological innovations in developing processes and techniques of importance in industry.

Links
Institute Information • Institute Faculty • Surfactant-Based Separation Processes • Consumer Products • Surfactant-Enhanced Environmental Remediation • Ultrathin Films • Fundamental Surfactant Research • Capabilities • Patents and Publications

University of Oklahoma at Norman - Chemical Engineering

http://www.uoknor.edu:80/cems

Welcome to the School of Chemical Engineering and Materials Science World Wide Web server at the University of Oklahoma. Please explore our departmental information regarding the graduate and research programs in chemical engineering. We are involved in many areas of chemical engineering research including Surfactants, Bioengineering, Energy, Polymer Science and Engineering and, Environmental Engineering.

Links
Chemical Engineering Departmental Information • at OU • Faculty Profiles • Research Areas • Graduate Studies • Research Support • General Information • AIChE Student Chapter • Research Institutes within CEMS • Institute for Applied Surfactant Research • Institute for Gas • Utilization Technologies • Chemical Engineering Research • Tools on the Internet • Online Scientific Journals • The Chemical Engineering Virtual Library • AIChE Home Page • Industrial and academic database resources in Chemical Engineering Research • United States and State Government Research Institutions • Constantly updated listing of web sites in the Chemical Industry • Online catalogs from suppliers of laboratory equipment and chemicals • U.S. Patent Info at CNIDR • University of Oklahoma Libraries • Searching the World Wide Web for Information • The Lycos Internet Directory • The Yahoo Internet Directory • The WebCrawler Internet Directory • DejaNews - search the full text of the Usenet news groups for recent worldwide discussion on practically any research topic • The Whole Internet Catalog • A Compilation of W3 Search Engines

University of Oklahoma at Norman - Institute for Gas Utilization Technologies

http://www.uoknor.edu/
engineering/igupt

The Institute for Gas Utilization Technologies (IGUT) is an interdisciplinary

research unit at the University of Oklahoma whose objectives are to develop technologies that will enhance the value and use of our natural gas resources. The focus of the Institute is research and development to take advantage of the environmentally friendly nature of natural gas as a source of fuel and chemical feedstocks. A collaborative, multidisciplinary, approach involving the technical talents of personnel from chemical engineering, mechanical engineering and chemistry provides the broad perspectives needed to work toward achieving the best possible solutions.

Links
General • Information • Research and Development Activities • Faculty Involved • Current Events and Seminars • National and International Events • Funding information in current research programs • International Efforts • Related Links

University of Missouri at St. Louis - Education Resource Shelf

http://www.umsl.edu/divisions/
artscience/chemistry/books/
welcome.html

Welcome to the Chemical Education Resource Shelf. This resource archive, once called "Chemistry Textbooks in Print- Online!", is now being produced under the auspices of the Journal of Chemical Education Online. This space has changed dramatically in the last few months, as we have become the source for the Journal's printed "Book Buyer's Guide" scheduled for September, 1996. Some of the big changes we have been working on include the addition of hyperlinks to virtually all of the publishers who maintain Web pages, and links to pages devoted to many of the individual titles. We have added new categories, including ones for safety, demonstrations, and methods of teaching (all in the Teaching Chemistry menu), and now have a list of software suppliers in addition to expanded lists of book and journal publishers.

Links
About this archive • Addresses of Publishers • Hal's Picks of the Month • Hal's Picks in 1995 • Index to Chemistry Textbooks in Print • Journals of Interest to Chemical Educators • References for Chemistry Teachers • Suppliers of Software for Chemical Education • UMSL Chemistry • JCE Online

University of Pittsburgh Medical Center - Petrochemical Disaster Study

http://www.upmc.edu/news/petro.htm

The mental health effects of petrochemical disasters on surviving workers is the focus of study at the University of Pittsburgh Medical Center through a five-year $2.8 million grant from the National Institute of Occupational Safety and Health and the National Institute of Mental Health. The study, led by principal investigator Andy Baum, Ph.D., professor of psychiatry and psychology, examines disasters including explosions and fires in settings such as railways, oil refineries and chemical manufacturing plants. As part of the project, investigators will interview people employed in petrochemical facilities, including those who were on duty during a disaster and some who were not on duty. The researchers will study mental health out-

comes of survivors of several disasters beginning soon after they happen.

Links
Top of page • Psychiatry • Background • Information

University of Tennessee at Knoxville - ATHAS (Advanced THermal Analysis System)

http://funnelweb.utcc.utk.edu/~athas/

Available on the ATHAS WWW are the following: Our detailed communication addresses and an organization list covering approximately the last two-year period. For the ATHAS publications you can look at the new publication list, (1988 to date). Earlier publications contains papers from 1988 back to 1957. A list of available reprints (by number of the publication) is compiled and continually updated. Occasionally articles will be slated for display under the heading present research. The teaching effort of ATHAS allows you to download lectures and full college courses. A listing of the present research topics is also given. The ATHAS Data Bank of thermal properties is in the process of transfer. Check for polymers already available Goals, abilities and plans are detailed and general ATHAS Information is presented.

Links
University of Tennessee at Knoxville - ATHAS (Advanced THermal Analysis System) • Picture of the "ATHAS family" • Communication addresses • Organization list • New publication list • Earlier publications • Reprints • Heading present research • Teaching effort • A listing of the present research topics • Data Bank • Goals, abilities

and plans • ATHAS Information • List of thermal analysis instruments • Etc.

University of Tennessee at Knoxville - Molecular Based Study of Fluids and Amorphous Materials

http://flory.engr.utk.edu/ldrd/w.html

This is the LDRD (Laboratory Directed Research and Development) Homepage. This project involves the development of new molecular simulation codes. It is sponsored by Oak Ridge National Laboratory (ORNL) and managed by Lockheed Martin Energy Research Corp. for the U.S. DOE. The research is a collaborative effort between ORNL, the University of Wisconsin, and the University of Tennessee.

Links
Introduction • Personnel • Overview • Manuscripts • Presentations • Codes • Movies and Images

University of Texas - Investment Opportunities in the Venezuelan Petrochemical Industry

http://lanic.utexas.edu/la/venezuela/con apri/resume/petro.htm

Petrochemical industry experts maintain that an oil industry can generate downstream petrochemical investments as large as the investment in production and refining of crude oil. Based on figures from the Venezuelan oil and petrochemical industry, there are still multiple opportunities for a low-cost, reliable supply of raw materials from the Venezuelan oil industry. Venezuelan state intervention in the petrochemical industry along with import-replacement policies, restraints on foreign investment and high taxes until the early 1990s, restricted the size of petrochemical industry.

Links
References and footnotes

University of Texas - Mallet Chemistry Library

http://www.lib.utexas.edu/Libs/Chem/

Internal and external library sources and general University of Texas information are available here.

Links
Mallet Chemistry Library • The University of Texas at Austin • Collections and Services • Finding Information • Chemistry on the Internet • UT Dept. of Chemistry & Biochemistry: Faculty Research Profiles • UT Dept. of Chemistry & Biochemistry: Home Page • UT Dept. of Chemical Engineering: Home Page • What's New

Magazines, Books, and Newsletters

These links are to those magazines, journals, newsletters, newpapers, newsgroups, listserves and book sites of particular interest to chemical industry personnel.

Albion Woods

http://www.ibisweb.com/chandler.htm

The first edition of WOODS' Illustrated English-Russian Petroleum Technology Dictionary is a comprehensive, single-volume resource for the petroleum industry professionals working in Russian language environments. Given the multidisciplinary character of the modern hydrocarbon industry, the dictionary draws vocabularies from Geology, Geophysics, onshore and offshore drilling, production, Reservoir Engineering, refining and transportation. The most current Petroleum technologies are included as are commercial and legal terminologies. Descriptions of oilfield equipment and industry vernacular, new technologies, market concepts and colloquialisms are presented. Our Dictionary contains the most current technology and has a practical vocabulary of over 35,000 petroleum industry terms.

Links
Question or Request • To Ibis Web

American Chemical Society Publications

http://acsinfo.acs.org:8008/

This is a hot links page of all ACS articles and publications. If it's about

chemistry and on the Internet, you can find it here.

Links
What's New! (9/17/96) • Customer Service Directory • Hot Articles • Journal Home Pages (TOC's, Instr. to Authors, Supp. Info., Ordering Instr., etc.) • The Journal of Physical Chemistry • Environmental Science & Technology • Biochemistry • Supporting Information • Publication Descriptions/Ordering Information • Instructions for Authors and Editors • About ACS Electronic Editions • C&EN Hot Articles • Meeting Information • ACS Classified Ads • ACS Books Home Page • ACS Books Catalog (gopher) • Recent Titles • ACS Style Guide • Reagent Chemicals • Listing by Product/Service • Company Listing by Product/Service • How to Advertise • LabGuide 1996-1997 Edition • Chemcyclopedia 1996-1997 Edition (coming in October) • ACS Job Bank • Pittcon '96 • ACS Software • ACS Publications Newsletter • Expositions and Meetings • ChemCenter • ACS Home Page • CAS Home Page

American Crystallographic Association-Newsletter

http://nexus.hwi.buffalo.edu/ACA/Newsletter/winter94.html

ACA Newsletter (ISSN 1058-9945). Published four times per year in the spring, summer, fall and winter for the membership of the American Crystallographic Association, PO Box 96, Ellicott Station, Buffalo, NY 14205-0096. Membership in the ACA includes a non-deductible charge of $1.75 from membership dues to be applied to a subscription to the ACA Newsletter.

No links--full text

American Scientist

http://www.amsci.org/amsci/amsci.html

American Scientist is an illustrated bimonthly magazine about science and technology. Each issue is filled with feature articles written by prominent scientists and engineers, reviewing important work in fields that range from molecular biology to computer engineering. The articles are carefully edited and accompanied by illustrations that are developed to enhance the reader's understanding and enjoyment.

Links
About American Scientist • Current Issue of American Scientist • Past Issues • Subscriptions • The Scientists' Bookshelf • Sigma Xi • The American Scientist

Applied Spectroscopy

http://esther.la.asu.edu/sas/journal.html

This page contains references to the table of contents for recent issues of Applied Spectroscopy. Follow the links to the specific issues. You can also search all the references by keyword.

Links
Volume 48 (1994) January - December • Volume 49 (1995) January - December • Volume 50 (1996) January - June

Australian Journal of Chemistry

http://www.publish.csiro.au/journals/ajc/index.html

The Australian Journal of Chemistry has achieved international standing for its publication of original research in all branches of chemistry: theoretical, physical, inorganic, organic, organometallic, structural. Before acceptance, all articles are assessed on the basis of their original contribution to chemistry and chemical technology. The Australian Journal of Chemistry is one of the series of journals produced by CSIRO Publishing with the cooperation of CSIRO and the Australian Academy of Science.

Links
What's New • Author Information • Subscriptions • Contents Pages • Corrigenda • Selected Papers • Editorial Committee

Baltzer Science Publishers

http://www.NL.net/~baltzer/

Baltzer Science Publishers, established in 1980, publishes a widerange of highly regarded scientific journals on Mathematics and Computer Science, Chemistry, Physics and Medical Sciences.

Links
Catalogue of our Journals • Ordering information • Author instructions • FTP archives

Bulletin of the Chemical Society of Japan

http://www.syp.toppan.co.jp:8082/

The Chemical Society of Japan (CSJ) presents full text database of its research journal, Bull. Chem. Soc. Jpn. with graphics images as a free-of-charge, experimental service over a limited period of time until the end of January, 1995.

no links

Business Communications Company

http://www.vyne.com/bcc/

Here you will find information on BCC's in-depth and critically acclaimed market analyses and monthly newsletters covering a broad range of technologies, as well as our scheduled conferences. BCC...the place to come for the hard-to-find information you need.

Links
What's New • Business Opportunity Reports • Internet Related Publications • Monthly Newsletters • Energy Magazine • Register For Our Upcoming Conferences • Search Our Archive • About BCC

Business Wire Corporate News

http://www.businesswire.com/cnn/

Business Wire is a leading source of news on major US corporations, including Fortune 1000 and NASDAQ companies. We electronically disseminate full-text news releases for public and investor relations professionals simul-

taneously to the news media, online services and databases, the Internet and the investment community worldwide. Our Strategic Information Services division provides relevant information to public relations and investor relations professionals in a meaningful and useful manner.

Links to all companies in their searchable index, company profiles available as well.

Links
many to all companies

Cambridge Scientific Abstracts

http://www.csa.com/

Cambridge Scientific Abstracts (CSA), a privately owned information company, has been producing bibliographic databases for over 25 years. Located in Bethesda, Maryland, CSA makes available 39 databases in formats that include print, magnetic tape, CD-ROM, online, via the Internet, and in some cases, fiche. CSA bibliographic records go beyond citations to furnish valuable summaries of the original material, allowing researchers to identify precisely the articles they need to acquire.

Links
Who we are • Our Products and Services • What's New • Access to Internet Database Service • Access to Environmental RouteNet • Free Demonstrations

Chemical Abstracts Service

http://www.cas.org/

Chemical Abstracts Service: A Scientific Information Resource. CAS is the producer of the printed Chemical Abstracts and corresponding indexes. CAS also operates the STN International online service which provides access to over 200 databases covering topics such as chemistry, engineering, medicine, patents, business, regulatory data, and much more. CAS also produces topical current awareness publications, CD-ROM, and software products such as STN Express. CAS provides full customer training with regularly scheduled workshops and user meetings throughout the world.

Links
About CAS • CAS Products and Services • Customer Support and Training • What's New • CAS Releases • CAS Technical Days • CA on CD • New and Expanded CAS • Using CAS Registry: Structure

Chemical Communications

http://www.ch.ic.ac.uk/clic/

The CLIC Consortium. A Flagship Chemistry Electronic Journal for Chemistry--The consortium operates between the Royal Society of Chemistry, and the chemistry departments at the Universities of Leeds and Cambridge and Imperial College. Each partner has a well defined role in the project. This is another fantastic source of chemical information on the Internet.

Links
Authoring Environment • Illustrated Contents Lists • Molecular Multimedia Keynote Articles • Chemical Program Collection for authors and readers • ECTOC-1 • ECHET96 • CLIC in the Library • The Chemistry Markup Language (CML) Project • The Chemistry

Java Project • HyperSpec • The Chemistry Virtual Reality Modelling Language Project • Chemistry Webmasters • Discussion Forum • The Chemical MIME Project • The LaTeX2HTML Project • Publisher Item Identifiers • Checksum Calculator and Verifier • etc. etc.

Chemical & Engineering News

http://acsinfo.acs.org/hotartcl/cenear/cen.html

With full text of articles back to 1995, this is one of the American Chemical Society's magazines designed for chemical engineers.

Links
Search for full text by date or title, hypertext index.

Chemical Week

http://www.chemweek.com/

This is one of the premier sites for the chemical publications industry. Chemical Week has been the mainstay of industry information for many years. Now it is available online in full text articles with plenty of extras, including its line of newsletters.

Links
Search Chemical Week's Web Site • Chemical Week Index: WWW Edition • Chemical Week Buyers' Guide: WWW Edition • Executive Edition • Micropatent Search • Chemical Week CD-ROMs • Chemical Industry Directory • Meeting Place • Hot Links

Chemistry & Industry Magazine

http://ci.mond.org/

Published twice monthly, Chemistry & Industry is an international magazine that provides news and features on chemistry and related sciences, as well as on the commercial and political aspects of these subjects. Broadly speaking, we are interested in new advances in science and technology, in the industries that make use of such advances and in associated issues like the environment, education, business trends and safety. The magazine is published by the Society of Chemical Industry, a learned society founded in 1881 to promote the application of chemistry and related sciences. SCI is not a trade association, and has no corporate members, only individual members. Its main activities are to hold conferences, publish journals and books, award medals and other honors to individuals, and give grants to projects that meet its aims.

Links
Current Issue • News • Magazine Archive • Job Search • Meetings • Only Connect • What is C&I? • Free Sample Issue

Chem Sources: The Chemical Source Directory

http://www.chemsources.com/

Here you may order a variety of chemical buyer's guides and other sources of chemical information.

Links
Chem Sources USA • Chem Sources International • Chem Sources Europe • Chem Sources CD ROM • Chem Sources Online

ChemTech Publishing

http://www.io.org/~chemtec/

Here is a source of hard-to-find chemical books, journals and software, like *Ukrainian Polymer Journal* and *Recycling of Plastic Materials*. It is worth a look, if you don't find what you need elsewhere.

Links
Journals • Books • Software • How to Order

Cherwell Scientific Publishing

http://www.cherwell.com/cherwell/

Cherwell Scientific brings specialist software to scientists and engineers around the world as both publisher and distributor. Our mission is to publish and market what we believe to be the best software applications in niche scientific and engineering markets giving real benefit to the end user. The company, founded in April 1990, uses a publishing business model, tailored to the special requirements of marketing software. We don't develop software in-house: instead we focus on sales and marketing, offering developers a complete publishing service. We work with software developers in many countries, marketing over 10 products world wide as a publisher, and several others in the UK, Germany and other European countries as an exclusive distributor.

Links
Home • Software List • What's New •
Support • Contact • Prices • About
Cherwell • Customer Service •
Alchemy • gNMR • StatView • Model-
Maker • ChemWindow/ChemIntosh •
ChemWeb • Prism • PROCEDE • pro
Fit • Ball & Stick • DIMPLE • EndNote
• EasyPlot • Cyrillic • Demos Available

Critical Reviews in Analytical Chemistry

http://www.crcpress.com/jour/crac/
crac.htm

Critical Reviews in Analytical Chemistry is a journal which presents in-depth,
but critically crafted reviews, on topics
of current importance to the chemical
areas of quantitative and qualitative
measurement science. Subscribers to
the Journal have access to recent papers
using this WWW-server to read titles
and abstracts and to download the exact
paper as it appears in the archival
printed paper form. Viewing of complete papers is possible using the Adobe
Acrobat Reader distributed as part of
the subscription to individuals and to
site subscribers as well; you can download Acrobat Reader at no charge. Accepted papers are typeset and made
available to the subscriber community
immediately in electronic form - often
well in advance of the paper edition.
Volume number, Issue and page numbers are exactly as they will appear in
the archival edition and are thus cit-
able.

Links
Letter from the Editor • Guide for
Authors • Free Demonstration • Current
Subscribers

Elemental Discoveries

http://homepages.enterprise.net/
bradley/elem1.html

This is the first edition of a new section
in New Elements. In it I hope to bring
you some of the more novel, or at the
very least intriguing, chemical discoveries. Not everything reported will necessarily have made it into the refereed
journals, which means there might be
items from conferences, poster sessions
or even personal contacts! Elemental
Discoveries is therefore open to offers
from researchers who feel their work
deserves a bit of free publicity.

Links
Issue 1 • Issue 2

Engineering News Record

http://www.enr.com/

Engineering News-Record provides the
business and technical news needed by
anyone who makes a living in or from
the construction industry. We cover
major projects, technological achievements, business conditions, markets,
finance, costs, legislation, government,
management, labor, construction methods, equipment and materials. We give
readers the weekly news and analysis
they need to make decisions in their
work, covering all sectors of the industry from buildings to highways to hazardous waste cleanups. We highlight
significant events worldwide. Good
ideas don't stop at political boundaries
nor does the business of construction.

Links
Search Engine • Directory of Firms •
Meet ENR • What's new • Subscribe to
ENR • Shopping Mall • Find a Job

ECTOC-1: Electronic Conference on Trends in Organic Chemistry

http://www.ch.ic.ac.uk/ectoc/

Welcome to the first fully electronic conference with organic chemistry as the main theme. Papers and posters are accessed exclusively through the World-Wide Web and were discussed using electronic mail.

Links
Keyword Search • ECTOC-1 What's New • ECTOC-2: Electronic Conference on Heterocyclic Chemistry (ECHET96) • Conference Starts here • Invited Keynotes • Synthetic Papers and Posters • Physical, Mechanistic, and Biological Papers and Posters • List of Participants • Conference Photograph • E-mail discussions • Submit a Molecule • Citing ECTOC • Publisher Identifier

Electronic Journal of Theoretical Chemistry

http://ejtc.wiley.co.uk/

EJTC is the first totally electronic publication covering theoretical chemistry and molecular modelling. It represents a new generation of research publishing in a central discipline which is strong and growing. The journal maintains a rigorous peer-review system under a full international editorial board. The public access area of the journal is freely available over the Internet with full information for subscribers and contributors. Please use the feedback form to let us know what you think and what you need. For full subscription details go to `How to Subscribe'.

Links
Aims and Scope • How EJTC Operates • Editors and Editorial Board • Reviews • Information for Contributors • How to Submit an Article • Subscription Information and Order Form • Terms of Service Agreement and License • Feedback Form • Table of Contents for Public Access • Table of Contents for Subscribers

Elsevier Science Publications-Chemistry and Chemical Engineering

http://www.elsevier.nl:80/homepage/saa/

Elsevier Science is a leading information provider in the field of chemistry and chemical engineering. Offering a wide variety of scientific and technical literature in the core disciplines of chemistry (and at interfaces with physics, engineering and life sciences), we provide a vast resource to the scientific and technical community. Our free contents alerting services will keep you informed of the most recent research - even before publication. Examples include: Fullerenes-Alert, Chromatography Pipeline, Separation, Colloids & Surfaces Preview, Catalysis Pipeline, Catalysis Hotline, Mass Spectrometry-Alert and Theochem-Alert.

Links
Chemistry, General • Analytical Chemistry • Inorganic Chemistry • Organic Chemistry • Physical and Theoretical Chemistry • Spectroscopy • Chemical Engineering

EurekAlert!

http://www.eurekalert.org/

Welcome to EurekAlert!, a comprehensive news server for up-to-date research in science, medicine, and engineering. Whether you're interested in cancer treatments, gene mapping, global warming, or space probes, you will find the latest advances. News is posted daily on EurekAlert! by the world's major research providers - universities, corporations, non-profit organizations, and peer-reviewed scientific journals. EurekAlert! is produced by the American Association for the Advancement of Science; technical assistance is provided by Stanford University and creative support by Duke University.

Links
News Releases • Archives • Search • Bench Notes • Journals • Institutions • Science Media • Inside Science Television • Journalism Groups • Submissions • EurekAlert! News • Behind EurekAlert • FAQ Sheet

Gower Chemical Reference

http://www.ashgate.com/gower/

Gower is widely recognized as one of the world's leading publishers in business management and information science. Gower titles range from paperback guides on business practice to Gower's Chemical Reference Series, a highly sophisticated source of chemical information available in both print and electronic formats. Gower also offers specialized lists in library and design management.

Links
Gower Chemical References • News and Information • New series • New Releases • Search the Online Catalogue • Manuscript Submissions • Add Your Name to Our Mailing List

Gulf Publishing Company

http://www.gulfpub.com/

Gulf Publishing Company is the leading publisher to the oil and gas industry. Our specialized publications reach over 100,000 people involved in energy industries worldwide. Our magazines, books, and catalogs help readers keep current with information important to their field and allow advertisers to reach their customers in all segments of petroleum operations. Gulf Publishing Company was founded in 1916 by Ray L. Dudley. He was a man with a vision who insisted on producing the highest quality technical editorial in all of his publications. To achieve this goal he reached into the industry itself. Today, more than half of Gulf Publishing Company's editorial staff have engineering degrees.

Links
GPC Overview • World Oil • Hydrocarbon Processing • Pipe Line & Gas Industry • Composite Catalog • Russian Composite Catalog (Cyrillic) • OneSource • Energy Events Calendar • Conferences • Scientific and Technical Books • Business and Professional Books • Consumer and General Interest Books • Juvenile Books • Video • Software • Oil and Gas Technology (Simplified Chinese) • Oil and Gas Technology (Cyrillic)

Internet Science Journal

http://www.sci-journal.com/ed/

Standard scientific journals are the best way to publish scientific research because they give clear credit to who published what and when. The ISJ is a new journal which supplements these regular journals by offering special services: The ISJ is FREE to authors and readers, thanks to sponsors and volunteer editors; Entire articles can be presented, not just abstracts; Authors can present preprints and discussion papers quickly for scrutiny by world scientists; Authors can present their ideas creatively using hypertext, including complex linking and color pictures; Authors have their articles on their own website, and control the article and copyright; Authors can still publish their articles elsewhere; the ISJ only links to articles, it does not "publish" them; Students (grad and undergrad) can present their exceptional science research, submitted by their professors; Controversial ideas, which normally would not pass refereeing, can be published in a special section; Amateur scientists can present their ideas and research for scrutiny by professionals.

Links
Topics • FAQ • Submit articles • Editors • Volunteer as Editor • Sponsors

Japan Chemical Week

http://www.chemnews-japan.com/index.html

Strategic information source for Japan and Asian chemical industries air delivered on a weekly basis from Tokyo. On this site we can get the full text of the headline article only.

Links
Headline of this week • Back Numbers list • Chemical-Metal-Digital • Hot Topics

John Wiley & Sons, Inc.

http://www.wiley.com/

John Wiley & Sons, Inc. publishes books, journals, and electronic products for the educational, professional, scientific, technical, and consumer markets. The oldest independent publisher in North America, Wiley is in the forefront of electronic publishing, with more than 200 products and services on disk, CD-ROM, or available by network. Wiley has 9,953 active book titles and 300 journals. The company publishes 1,000 new titles in a variety of formats each year. The company has approximately 1,700 employees worldwide.

Welcome to Wiley • Wiley Worldwide • Access to Online Products and Services • Product and Ordering Information • Information for Authors

Journal of Chemical Education - Resource Shelf

http://www.umsl.edu/divisions/artscience/chemistry/books/welcome.html

This resource archive, once called "Chemistry Textbooks in Print - Online!", is now being produced under the auspices of the Journal of Chemical Education Online. This space has changed dramatically in the last few months, as we have become the source for the Journal's printed "Book Buyer's Guide" scheduled for September, 1996. Some of the big changes we have been working on include the addition of hyperlinks to virtually all of the publishers who maintain Web pages, and links to pages devoted to many of the individual titles. We have added new categories, including ones for safety, demonstrations, and methods of teaching (all in the Teaching Chemistry menu), and now have a list of software suppliers in addition expanded lists of book and journal publishers.

Links
About this archive • Addresses of Publishers • Hal's Picks of the Month • Hal's Picks in 1995 • Index to Chemistry Textbooks in Print • Journals of Interest to Chemical Educators • References for Chemistry Teachers • Suppliers of Software for Chemical Education

Journal of Chemical Physics

http://jcp.uchicago.edu/

JCP Express is provided by the American Institute of Physics. Manuscripts submitted by authors for distribution by JCP Express have been accepted for publication in the Journal of Chemical Physics and will be available prior to publication only. They may be copied electronically and printed for individual use only.

Links
JCP Express mailing list • JCP Titles mailing list • tables of contents • How to contribute

Journal of Chemical Physics Preprint Database

http://www.chem.brown.edu/
chem-ph.html

The Chemical Physics Preprint Database is a fully automated electronic archive and distribution server for the international theoretical chemistry community. This database is intended to provide a means for rapid and efficient preprint distribution within the international chemical physics community. This project is a joint effort by the Department of Chemistry at Brown University and the Theoretical Chemistry and Molecular Physics Group at the Los Alamos National Laboratory. It has been made possible by funding from the Camille and Henry Dreyfus Foundation.

Links
Overview • Getting Started • Subscribing to Receive Notification of New Preprint Entries • Listing and Retrieval of Papers • Help • Submitting Articles • Steps for Submitting an Article • Submission Commands • Format of Papers for Submittal • Making Changes-Replacing your Submitted Paper • Postscript from the Archives • Frequently Asked Questions • Beginner's Trouble Shooting

Journal of Chemistry and Spectroscopy (Pre-prints) - Wave of the Future

http://kerouac.pharm.uky.edu/
ASRG/wave/wavehp.html

Wave of the Future provides online peer-review of manuscripts on a Web page as part of a vision of a new scientific publication system, comprising a large number of computer servers linked logically by search engines, with each server storing years of quality articles, graphics, and data from a handful of researchers for easy retrieval.

Links
Vision • Table of Contents • Instructions for Authors • Editorial Staff • Advertising

Journal of Computer-Aided Molecular Design

http://wucmd.wustl.edu/jcamd/jcamd.html

ESCOM Science Publishers in collaboration with the Center for Molecular Design are proud to present an experimental electronic version of the Journal of Computer-Aided Molecular Design. This server will attempt to carry complete articles, including figures and tables, along with enhancements such as molecular coordinates for viewing with RASMOL. You are welcome to freely access Volume 9 Number 1 (February 1995) and Number 2 (April 1995). Thereafter we shall post on an ongoing basis, information on articles that have been accepted for publication in advance of their appearing in printed form. Access to full text searchable files will be made available to subscribers of the printed journal who provide us with the required documentation for issuing a password.

Links
Aims & Scope • Instructions for Authors • Subscription Information • Table of Contents • Editors and Editorial Board

Journal of Corrosion Science and Engineering

http://www.cp.umist.ac.uk/JCSE/JCSE.htm

The journal will be published for a trial period by members of the Corrosion and Protection Centre on behalf of the International Corrosion Council (ICC). A Management Board provides overall control of the journal, while the technical management of the Journal is undertaken by an Editorial Board nominated by the Management Board. Papers for publication in the journal must meet normal standards for a refereed scientific publication; this is ensured by a conventional refereeing procedure. Papers are published (i.e. made available online to readers) as soon as the refereeing process is completed. There is no upper or lower limit on the number of papers published over a particular period.

Links
Submission Instructions and Journal Management • Volume 1 (4 papers now fully published) • Corrosion Information Server • Centre for Electrochemical Science and Engineering, University of Virginia (JCSE Mirror Site)

Journal of Cyber Chemistry

http://www.u-net.com/ukchem/cybrchem/home.htm

Welcome to our new Journal - forget your old ideas about science publishing, this is the future and part of a technology shift as significant as the invention of type. The Internet gives a revolutionary medium for publishing scientific papers. This is a proposal for publishing a journal on Chemistry related topics that will blaze a trail for the general publishing of Chemistry papers on the Internet. Everything and anything that relates to the Internet and Chemistry. Papers should be about the Internet and its use in Chemistry or be of material covering Chemistry research in its widest sense that can take specific advantages of the possibilities the Internet offers.

Links
Contents • Latest epapers • List of epapers • Editors email

Journal of Molecular Modeling

http://derioc1.organik.uni-erlangen.de/info/JMOLMOD/jmolinfo.html

The aim of the Journal is to be over all a good scientific publication. The quality of the contributions is therefore checked by highly commended specialists. The layout and all data provided by the authors are carefully checked by the editorial office at the Computer-Chemie-Centrum at the Univeristy of Erlangen-Nürnberg. The production and distribution of the final product is done by the Springer-Verlag. If you want to keep pace with leading edge research in the field of molecular modeling and experience the rapid development of scientific publishing the Journal of Molecular Modeling is a must for you.

Links
Editor in Chief • Editorial Board • Aims & Scope • Notice to Authors • (Volume 1, 1995 ; Volume 2, 1996) • Examples of published papers in PDF format • Events dealing with Molecular Modeling

Journal of Physical Chemistry

http://acsinfo.acs.org/plweb/jrpublic/jpchax/

The Journal of Physical Chemistry (JPC) publishes original experimental and basic research targeted to scientists in the physical chemistry of molecules, condensed phases, materials and biomolecules. Weekly coverage includes rapid dissemination of new findings and full-length studies in spectra, structure, and molecular dynamics . . . laser chemistry and chemical kinetics . . . surface science, clusters, micelles, and interfaces . . . statistical mechanics and thermodynamics . . .condensed phases and macromolecules . . . physical chemistry of materials and biophysical chemistry. In addition, JPC features invited papers that review the status of a particular topic, clarify controversies, or explore future directions. Proceedings of selected symposia and special thematic issues appear throughout the year. Rapid publications for urgent and new results appear in the Letters section.

Links
About the Journal and its Editors • Release Notes • Table of Contents • Author Index • Search The Journal of Physical Chemistry • Supporting Information [Subscribers Only - Help] • Instructions for Authors • ACS Ethical Guidelines

Journal of the Serbian Chemical Society

http://ihtmceh4.tmf.bg.ac.yu/htdocs/shd.htm

The Journal of the Serbian Chemical Society formerly Glasnik Hemijskog drustva Beograd publishes articles from the fields of theoretical and applied chemistry. The Journal is financially supported by the Ministry of Science and Technology of Serbia. Journal of the Serbian Chemical Society - JSCS is published continuously over 60 years by the Serbian Chemical Society.

Links
Overview Of This Year Issues • Detailed Information • Instructions For Authors

Journal of Synthetic Organic and Natural Product Chemistry

http://science.springer.de/molec/molecule.htm

Molecules is a journal of synthetic organic and natural product chemistry. It covers mainly small- and medium-sized molecules and their preparation (synthesis, biosynthesis, extraction, etc.), structural elucidation (X-ray crystallography, NMR, etc.), their properties (chemical and biological activities) and applications (functional materials, additives, catalysts, etc.). Authors are encouraged to submit samples of the relevant chemical species to an MDPI storage center. Papers describing combinatorial synthesis, engineering and robotics of multi-step synthesis and natural product isolation, applications of compound collections such as high throughput screening and combinatorial compound libraries, molecular diversity assessments, compound archives management, and compound database design and management, are also welcome.

Links
Examples of published papers in PDF format • Examples of published papers in PostScript format • Table of Contents • New: List of Forthcoming Papers • Editorial • Editorial Board • Aims and Scope • Subscription Information and Order Form • Notice to Authors • Advertisement • Manuscript submission form • Conference Announcements

Hydrocarbon Processing

http://www.gulfpub.com/hydro/index.html

Hydrocarbon Processing is the leading magazine for the huge Hydrocarbon Processing Industry - refining, petrochemical / chemical, gas and synfuels processing. Technical buying power in this market (with $38.1 billion in annual capital spending alone) is spread worldwide among thousands of HPI plants, plus engineering departments, engineer - constructor firms and original equipment manufacturers. Editorial coverage of new HPI developments and ever-changing technology makes Hydrocarbon Processing essential to over 34,600 subscribers each month. It reaches more HPI planners, specifiers and buyers than general publications because its market directed coverage is specifically edited for the HPI.

Links
Contents • Editorial • HP Insight • HP in Control • HP in Processing • HP in Reliability • HP Internet • Advertisers' Index • Advertising Sales Contacts • Subscribe

Labtrader Magazine - Laboratory Equipment Exchange

http://www.magic.mb.ca/~econolab/

Welcome to Labtrader Magazine. This is a buy, sell and trade Internet media for used scientific equipment and deals on new equipment. If you are interested in any of the advertised items in our magazine, please click on the underlined item numbers to email the advertiser directly, or contact us at labx@mts.net if you need assistance. You can also place an ad on our entry form. Our goal is to provide you with a comfortable medium to advertise your buying and selling needs for scientific equipment. Labtrader Magazine is only an advertising medium. We do not buy or sell equipment because then we would be competing with you. Revenue we receive from the listings is used to market and advertise this magazine. By pooling the small fees we receive from the many ads, we are then able to provide our advertisers with serious, consistent and substantial exposure.

Links
Analytical Consumer • Great Deals • Guess The Molecule • Lab Equipment Dealers • Labsavers • Medical Equipment • Service Companies • Our Sponsors • Become A Sponsor • Subscribe To Our Email Newsletter

Mass Spectrometry Online

http://www.elsevier.nl:80/section/chemical/msonline/menu.htm

The Table of Contents listing of forthcoming issues of the International Journal of Mass Spectrometry and Ion Processes (IJMSIP) and the Journal of the American Society for Mass Spectrometry (JASMS) is supplied free of charge by Elsevier Science B.V. Amsterdam, the Netherlands. Issues will be sent out on a single basis, i.e. IJMSIP and JASMS issues will arrive separately and with a different frequency, due to the journals' different publication schedules. For each paper the titles, author(s) and pages numbers are given. Due to technical restrictions the information for IJMSIP is given in TeX format, but also those people without a TeX viewer will have no difficulty to read the files.

Links
Mass Spectrometry Alert • Elsevier Mass Spectrometry Books

The Molecular Modeling e-Conference - TMMeC

http://stark.udg.es/agora/welcome.html

An electronic conference and multimedia publication established with the aim of providing a setup for fast and continuous display of current work in Molecular Modeling and Computational Chemistry. All the applications of Quantum and Statistical Mechanics to Chemistry are within the scope of this multimedia publication. Acceptable articles for TMMeC are those that deal with both methodological and computational developments that allow or facilitate the computing of structure, reactivity and properties of isolated or interacting molecules (from a few atoms to macromolecules), both in gas phase and condensed phases. The emphasis is on articles that benefit from the possibilities of the Web, such as molecular dynamics, potential energy surface calculations, chemical reactivity, docking, etc.

160

Links
Main Entrance • NEWS! • Papers • Current Reviews • Meetings • Books of Abstracts • Societies • FCTL • THEOCHEM

National Academy of Sciences Proceedings

http://journals.at-home.com/PNAS/

The National Academy of Sciences is a private, non-profit, self-perpetuating society of distinguished scholars engaged in scientific and engineering research, dedicated to the furtherance of science and technology and to their use for the general welfare. Upon the authority of the charter granted to it by the Congress in 1863, the Academy has a mandate that requires it to advise the federal government on scientific and technical matters. This site contains the proceedings of the organization.

Links
Masthead and Subscription Information • Information for Contributors • Copyright Assignment Form • Information about the National Academy of Sciences • The National Academy of Sciences Home Page

Nature

http://www.america.nature.com/

Nature is the world's most cited science journal, covering all fields of research, from cell biology to quantum mechanics. Nature has the highest impact factors in immunology, molecular biology, physics, earth sciences, astrophysics and space sciences, and chemistry. In 1995, Nature published the world's six most popular research papers, which were cited five times more than papers in any other scientific publication. As well as an extensive science-policy news database, Nature's website also publishes hundreds of up-to-date science jobs and events. In addition to regular coverage of Nature's contents, the website has regular features on recent research. All this has made Nature's website one of the most visited by researchers and students around the world.

Links
What's new in Nature • Table of Contents and summaries for the last four issues • News • Science-policy news, including searchable news archive • Archives and indexes • Supplementary information and PDF index • International science jobs • Scientific vacancies around the world • International events and announcements • Comprehensive database of forthcoming meetings and exhibitions • World Market • Products and advertisers • Nature science update • Nature past

New Scientist: Planet Science

http: //www.newscientist.com/

Register first, it is free and then you can enjoy this online magazine of science. Planet Science is the online voice of New Scientist, the world's leading weekly magazine of popular science. It contains news, features, reviews and comment drawn from the magazine each week, plus the answers to questions about puzzling scientific phenomena in everyday life and, of course, contributions from our readers. It also contains an increasing number of features developed specially for the site.

Links
Magazine • No Limit • Big 3 • CD-
ROM • Subscribe • Grand Tours •
About Us • This Week • Appointments
• Daily News • Top Selling Science •
Books • Strange • Ways • Science City

NewsPage - Company Tracking

http://www.newspage.com/
NEWSPAGE/cgi-bin/walk.cgi/
NEWSPAGE/info/d20/

NewsPage is a single-user online information service from Individual, Inc.
It is designed to provide World Wide
Web users with current, pre-sorted
news across a broad array of topics and
industries. With more than 25,000
pages, all refreshed daily, NewsPage is
one of the deepest, most comprehensive
sites on the Web.

Links
Main • Register • Search • Stocks • Hot
Topics • InfoSeek • Freeloader • Indi-
vidual, Inc. • Questions? • NewsPage
Direct • Sources • Advertising • Topic
Index

Newsletter of the International Fission-Track Community

http://www.lib.utexas.edu/Libs/
GEO/OnTrack10www.html

On Track is a biannual newsletter of
the international fission-track community. It is printed in the months of
May and November. The views ex-
pressed in On Track are those of the
authors and do not necessarily reflect
those of the fission-track community or
the editor(s) of On Track.

Links
Editors' Notes • 8th International
Workshop on Fission-Track Dating •
A new irradiation facility for fission-
track dating in the University of Pavia
reactor • A New Track on the Horizon •
Monte Trax • Annealing, Objects, and
Distributed Computing • On Track and
the WWW • Short Tracks: News •
Timing and thermal characteristics of
Sevier belt thrust faulting and synoro-
genic sedimentation in the Pavant and
Canyon Ranges, central Utah • Recent
Fission-Track Papers • 1995 Directory
of the International Fission-Track
Community

The Oil & Gas Journal Online

http://www.ogjonline.com/

OGJ Online is Oil & Gas Journal in
electronic form, but it's also much
more. Technology, industry news, statistics, special reports and analysis exclusively for OGJ Online, and information from other exclusive, proprietary
services are just a few of the resources
industry decision-makers access to
analyze operations and company performance, design and operate facilities,
and plan strategy.

Links
Oil & Gas Journal • OGJ Calendar •
Offshore Magazine • Offshore Calendar
• General Search • Information Mall •
Products & Services • User Profile

PennWell Publishing Company

http://www.pennwell.com/

PennWell Publishing Company is a
highly diversified global business information provider serving a broad
spectrum of industries and technolo-

gies. The company has a long history of magazine publishing with roots that date back to 1910 when the company began publishing an oil journal serving the emerging petroleum industry in the United States. With an aggressive strategy for diversification and a vision for growth, PennWell came from this humble beginning to a company that today serves computer, laser, electronic, municipal, energy and environmental fields through business and technical magazines, along with conferences, exhibitions, books, maps, database resources, and market research for these markets. PennWell publishes 39 business-to-business trade and technical magazines and newsletters. These publications provide up to the minute industry information to 1.5 million professionals in more than 120 countries.

Links
Magazines • Newsletters • Conferences And Exhibitions • Information Products And Services • Petroleum, Dental, Electric Power • Water; Fire Engineering • Books and Videos • PennWell Research • PennWell Directories • Oil & Gas Journal Energy Database • International Petroleum Encyclopedia • OGJ Online

Petroleum Chemistry

http://www.elsevier.nl:80/
catalogue/SAA/210/06345/
06350/284/284.html

There is a vast world literature on petroleum and its products and the contributions in the field emanating from Russia are of great importance. Petroleum Chemistry is a cover-to-cover translation of the Russian journal Neftekhimiya, dealing mainly with the chemistry of petroleum and its use as a base for the manufacture of industrial products. These papers are of value and interest to the researcher, the laboratory chemist and to all those dealing with the practical aspects of petroleum technology. Petroleum Chemistry has a wide coverage and includes papers on the analysis, physical and chemical properties, and behavior of individual petroleum constituents. Complementary papers cover the mechanism and application of a wide spectrum of processing reactions, featuring particularly catalytic oxidation and reduction. Neftekhimiya is published six times a year.

Links
Orderform • Ordering Information for Librarians, Booksellers and Subscription Agents

PR Newswire

http://www.prnewswire.com/cnoc.html

Company News On-Call gives you the latest news from hundreds of the most exciting public and private companies. Get the full-text news minutes after it is transmitted by PR Newswire or find stories stored for up to one year. Releases are from participating PR Newswire members. For the latest news, just enter a company name below; or click on the first letter of the company name to search; or click for a complete list of companies.

Links
Today's News • Company News On-Call • Feature News • Industry Focus • Money Talks' • About PRN

The Referee Online

http://www.aoac.org/pubs/
referee/referee.htm

Welcome to AOAC INTERNA-
TIONAL's Referee (a newsletter for
analytical laboratories) page. For a
limited time, AOAC INT'L will be
placing The Referee online for all
viewers. After December 31, 1996, The
Referee Online will only be available to
AOAC members. To learn more about
membership in the AOAC INT'L, visit
our Membership Information page.
Each month, members of AOAC
INTERNATIONAL turn to The Referee for articles on methods, regulations,
scientific innovations, laboratory processes, laboratory management, and
technologies, and for news about activities and programs of AOAC and
related organizations worldwide.

Links
Membership Information • Back Issues
• Return to AOAC INTERNATIONAL
Home Page

Science Online

http://www.sciencemag.org/

SCIENCE, the global weekly of re-
search, is published by the American
Association for the Advancement of
Science. SCIENCE ONLINE is pub-
lished with the assistance of Stanford
University's HighWire Press.

Links
SCIENCE Online • SCIENCE •
SCIENCE NOW • SCIENCE'S Next
Wave • SCIENCE Professional Net-
work • Electronic Marketplace •
American Association for the Ad-
vancement of Science

Scientific American

http://www.sciam.com/WEB/
index.html

Here, on the World Wide Web, we are
creating a new publication that pushes
Scientific American into the frontiers
of publishing in an electronic medium.
Just as Scientific American has tracked
key changes in technology for the past
150 years, we are now participating in
the radical transformation driven by
computer technology. We invite you to
take a look. Each month, we will bring
you the best of the current issue --
augmented to take advantage of the
unique capabilities of the WWW. You
will find many of your favorite magazine features here, as well as at least
two major articles in their entirety, with
links that let you connect directly to the
researchers and their work.

Links
Current Issue • Articles • News and
Analysis • Reviews • Commentaries •
50, 100 and 150 Years Ago • Amateur
Scientist • Previous Issues • Weekly
Web Features • Explorations • Exhibits
• Ask the Experts • Interviews • Book-
marks • Marketplace • Product selec-
tions • Scientific American Frontiers •
Children's books • Medical publications
• CD ROMs • Reprints and back issues
• Single topic issues • Subscriptions

The Scientist Newsletter

gopher://ds2.internic.net:70/11/
pub/the-scientist

This is a searchable gopher site of the
newsletter, The Scientist. The Scientist
is a biweekly tabloid newspaper, published in Philadelphia (Pennsylvania,
USA) and distributed internationally to

research scientists, managers, and administrators in industry, academia, and government. Although it is targeted at all science professionals, the majority of the 30,000 subscribers are associated with the life sciences and the burgeoning biotechnology marketplace.

Links
gopher menu

Tetrahedron Information System

http://www.elsevier.com/pluto/
Projects/TIS5/Menu.shtml

The Tetrahedron Information System (TIS) provides a unique focal point for all chemists wanting immediate access to research published in Tetrahedron, Tetrahedron: Asymmetry, Tetrahedron Letters, Bioorganic & Medicinal Chemistry and Bioorganic & Medicinal Chemistry Letters. Following the successful launch of Tetrahedron Alert in February 1996, future developments to TIS will include access to the full online journals.

Links
Tetrahedron Alert • Other TIS Services • Tetnet • Notes for authors • About TIS • Message from the Chairman of the Board of Executive Editors • Further information on the TIS products and services • Technical requirements and recommendations • Other Elsevier Science Services

Theory and Modeling in Chemistry

http://www.elsevier.nl:80/section/
chemical/theochem/menu.htm

THEOCHEM publishes research related to the theory and modelling of molecular systems. This includes, but is not limited to: electronic structure, ab initio and semiempirical, graphical approaches to structure and properties, molecular modelling, reaction dynamics and scattering, spectroscopic and experimental studies that test and evaluate theories and models, statistical mechanics, unique computational techniques. High quality, original reports of significance in theory and modelling are invited. Reports on new theoretical methods and/or their applications are especially welcome. The molecular problems within the scope of the journal range from structural aspects of small, isolated molecules to inorganic complexes, organic reactions, polymers and biopolymers, protein structure, molecular aggregations, nonlinear phenomena, surface chemistry, spectroscopic properties, and materials and drug design.

Links
Launch of THEOCHEM-Alert • Publication of Proceedings of 2nd Electronic Computational Chemistry Conference (ECCC-2) • THEOCHEM and TMMeC announce a joint project • THEOCHEM Supplementary Material

Trends in Analytical Chemistry

http://www.elsevier.nl:80/section/
chemical/trac/menu.htm

TrAC is a scientific publication comprising short reviews that cover the latest advances in the analytical sciences. They are written in such a way that they allow the non-specialist to understand the principles and applications of the topic. Consequently, articles are broadly based and practically oriented. The fields covered include analytical instrumentation, biochemistry, biotechnology, clinical chemistry, environmental chemistry, forensic science, laboratory automation, materials science, pharmaceutical chemistry, process analysis, surface science, and toxicology.

Links
Supplemental material • Background information • Special Issues • Single cell analysis • Biosensors for environmental analysis • Analytical methods for monitoring industrial effluents and waste • Table of Contents of recent issues • Forthcoming Articles • Guide for Authors

Ultrasonic Non-Destructive Technology Journal

http://www.ultrasonic.de/

More than an online journal, this site is a global meeting place for the practitioners or non-destructive testing techniques.

Links
Articles • Virtual Exhibition • News Flashes • Virtual Library • UT by Country • UT by A-Z • Workshops • Newsgroup • Abstracts • Publications • Calendar • Editorial • and many more

Chemical Resources Pages

These web pages are home for vast amounts of links and other special services for the chemical industry.

A.C.T.E.D. Services - Chemicals in Australia

http://www.vianet.net.au/~acted/

This page is both a telephone directory and a chemical "Buyers Guide" for Australian chemical manufacturers. Australia has a population of 18 million, a huge natural resource base with increasingly export-oriented manufacturing industry and growing market for specialist chemicals. Australia's R&D intensity is well above average, and near top for graduates in science and engineering. Here you will find important information via color coded BUSINESS, REGULATIONS, ORGANIZATIONS and NEWS buttons. As you will see, the A.C.T.E.D. consultancy can help you with market assessments, feasibility studies, regulatory compliance, training, publications and strategy assessments.

Links
Business • Regulations • Organizations • News • Buyers Guide • Commerce

The Analytical Chemistry Springboard

http://www.anachem.umu.se/jumpstation.htm

Brought to us by Knut Irgum at Umeå University. This is an attempt to present a comprehensive list of analytical chemistry resources on the Internet. You are invited to submit pages for indexing, as well as to correct errors you may find in the links.

Links
Atomic Spectroscopy • Automated Methods • Chemical Sensors • Chemometrics • Chromatography • Electrochemistry • Electron Spectroscopy • Electrophoresis • Elemental Analysis • Good Practices [GLP/GMP] • Lab Info Management Systems • Mass Spectrometry • Materials Science • Miscellaneous Techniques • Nuclear Magnetic Resonance • Optical Molecular Spectroscopy • Radiochemical Methods • Sample Preparation • Standardization • Surface Analysis • Thermal Methods • X-Ray Spectroscopy • etc.

ARI ChemLink

http://www.ari.net/chemlink/chemlink.html

Your #1 Resource for Chemistry Information, Products, and Services from the ARInternet Corporation in Landover, MD. This site is more weighted toward educational links.

Links
Internet Resources • Databases • Software • Chemistry Supplies and Services • Education Resources • Publications • Meetings and Announcements • Other Chemistry Internet Guides

Australian Chemistry Network (OzChemNet)

http://apamac.ch.adfa.oz.au:80/
OzChemNet/

This is an evolving World Wide Web site at the School of Chemistry, University College (UNSW). The University College is a faculty of the University of New South Wales and is located at the Australian Defense Force Academy in Canberra, Australia's capital city.

Links
Search • Recent Additions & Late Breaking News • The Australian Science Olympiads • Electronic Resources for Chemistry and related disciplines • Teaching Resources • Research Resources • Administrative Resources • Software Resources • Other Chemistry sites on the WWW • Microscale Chemistry in Australia • Chemical Abstracts Down • Web Educational Software Tools (WEST) - Authorized Users Only Please

Beilstein CrossFire

http://www.camsci.com/others/
beilstein/crossfire.html

The CrossFire in-house information system provides chemists and information specialists with easy access to more than six million structures and their associated chemical, physical properties, preparative methods, chemical behavior, and literature references. The CrossFire concept is based on client-server RISC technology -- the client has a graphical interface running on a PC or Macintosh -- in combination with a new structure indexing system, and a revolutionary search engine. You can

now search multi-million files on your local workstation, in seconds. Cross-Fire allows searching of the entire Beilstein file with more than 6,000,000 heterocyclic, acyclic and isocyclic compounds, covering the literature from 1779 to the present. Substructure query types can include bond and stereo-chemical descriptors, atom types, generic groups (e.g. acyclics, heterocycles, etc.).

Links
No links, just a full description of this product

BetaCyte List of Chemistry Journals

http://www.betacyte.pair.com/
journals.html

For the last 6 months we have grown to be the most popular source of information about Chemical and BioChemical journals on the WWW. We have now well over 200 journals listed, and we have decided to change the format a little bit. Instead of weekly updates, we have started a Journal Alert Mailing List. As soon as we find more journals that use the WWW as a way to publish their articles, we will update this site and send out an email to everybody on the list. The site groups journals into the following headings: Complete online Journals that do not require any payment (yet); Online Journals that have some limitations; Journals that show the Table of Contents and/or abstracts of their paper edition; and Others. If you want information on chemical journals, this is the place to visit.

Links
200+ links to chemical journals

Biocatalysis/Biodegradation Database

http://dragon.labmed.umn.edu/
~lynda/index.html

From the University of Minnesota, this database contains information on microbial biocatalytic reactions and biodegradation pathways for primarily xenobiotic, chemical compounds. The goal of the UM-BBD is to provide information on microbial enzyme-catalyzed reactions that are important for biotechnology. The reactions covered are studied for basic understanding of nature, biocatalysis leading to specialty chemical manufacture, and biodegradation of environmental pollutants. Individual reactions and metabolic pathways are presented with information on the starting and intermediate chemical compounds, the organisms that transform the compounds, the enzymes, and the genes. The present database has been successfully used to teach enzymology and use of biochemical Internet information resources to advanced undergraduate and graduate students, and is being expanded primarily with the help of such students.

Links
Search • Index • About the UM-BBD • What's New • Guest Book • Contributors • Guided Tour • Publications • Useful Internet Resources • Conferences • What's New? • Pathways

Biological and Chemical Sites

http://www.ciit.org/WWW/
biochem.html

CIIT is located in Research Triangle Park, North Carolina. Founded in 1974, CIIT is a not-for-profit toxicology research institute dedicated to providing an improved scientific basis for understanding and assessing the potential adverse effects of chemicals, pharmaceuticals, and consumer products on human health. CIIT is supported by 36 industrial organizations. This is their list of WWW sites of interest. The list is grouped as follows:

Links
Academic • Associations, Organizations • Databases • Government • Laboratories • ListServes and Newsgroups

ChemExper (Belgium)

http://www.chemexper.be/0

The ChemExper Chemicals Directory-- This directory containing the chemicals available in the world is intended to be freely available to researchers in academic and industrial laboratories. Searching the chemicals directory: The directory can be searched by--registry number, molecular formula (exact and non-exact), chemical name (and synonyms). Searching for a producer-- Users are able to quickly find a producer, contact address, etc.

Links
Who are We ? • Experbib • Expereact • Chemicals Directory • Job opportunity • Chemical companies • French IUPAC rules • Commercial • databases • FW Calculator

ChemExpo Virtual Trade Show

http://www.chemexpo.com/

This excellent site is presented by Chemical Marketing Reporter. ChemExpo, is a virtual trade show for the chemical industry, providing worldwide, in-depth information and communications. Whether you are searching for chemical manufacturers, or reading the industry's news, ChemExpo will let you work smarter, not harder. The ChemExpo Lobby provides shortcuts to find the information you need. Visit the Lobby to learn what's new in ChemExpo and for help in navigating the virtual trade show. The ChemExpo Show Floor is where trade show visitors conduct commerce. Search 2,000 leading companies selling more than 20,000 products and services. The ChemExpo Info Booth will provide an industry-wide calendar, trade association news, a Help Desk and answers to frequently asked questions. The ChemExpo Industry News provides the latest chemical news. In the future, it will also contain company press releases and new product announcements. Feature articles and white papers, product profiles and historical records on chemical issues will track industry trends. ChemExpo Forums will enable the ChemExpo community to consult with industry leaders on industry breakthroughs, environmental programs, and recycling issues. Comments and reactions to state and federal regulations and advocacy efforts will be posted and shared across the ChemExpo community.

Links
Lobby • Show Floor • Info Booth • Help Desk • Industry News • Forums • People Connections

Chemical Companies on the Web

http://pages.prodigy.com/CT/jakiela/chemcomp.html

This is Dr. Dennis J. Jakiela's favorite chemical sites on the Internet.

Links
Chemical companies • Specialty Material Companies • Service Companies • Software Companies

Chemical Database Service - Daresbury Labs

http://gserv1.dl.ac.uk/CDS/cds.html

The primary aim of the service is to help chemists solve their problems. This is done by providing chemical databases, help, training and information - free of charge to all UK "academics" . The Chemical Database Service is a National service, funded by the Chemistry Program of the EPSRC.

Links
How to navigate these pages • Review the CDS Databases • Examples of how CDS can help you • Expert help available • Becoming a user • Other information

Chemical Engineering Sites All Over the World

http://www.ciw.uni-karlsruhe.de/siteworl.html

The following list was partly withdrawn from the book Chemical Engineering Faculties 1994-1995, Volume 43, Ed. James B. Rawlings, A Publication of the Chemical Engineering Education Projects Committee of the American Institute of Chemical Engineers which is now available in HTML-Format named Chemical Engineering Faculty Directory.

Links
All Chemical Engineering Departments at every College and University in every country in the world!

Chemical Industries Newsletter

http://piglet.sri.com/CIN/cin_home.html

Welcome to the Chemical Industries Newsletter home page. This service is provided by the Chemical Business Research Division at SRI Consulting (a wholly owned subsidiary of SRI International.) New issues are published on a bi-monthly basis.

Links
Current issues and archives beyond 1994

The Chemical Industry

http://www.neis.com/

A service of the National Environmental Information Service, this is an extensive collection of valuable sites for the chemical Internet searcher.

Links
Chemical Industry Associations • Management Resources • Chemical and Process Engineering Resources • Chemical Sales Resources • Environmental Resources • Analytical Chemistry Resources • Chemical Companies' Websites • Miscellaneous Chemistry Resources

Chemical Mailing Lists (Australia)

http://131.236.60.11/OzChemNet/lists_overview.html

The following is a list of mailing lists which deal with chemistry. There is a description of each list, how to subscribe and how to use the archives. The whole list (all mailing list descriptions) is quite big (~75 K), so it might be better to look for the one-line descriptions of each mailing list, which are linked to smaller parts of the main list.

Links
A to Z links (about 100 mailing lists)

Chemical Mailing Lists (Canada)

http://gpu.srv.ualberta.ca/~psgarbi/mailing_list2.html

A shorter list than the one from Australia, but more detail is provided on each mailing list.

Links
BUCKY -- Fullerene News • Computational Chemistry List • Chemical Information Sources • High Resolution Infrared Spectroscopy • Natural Products • Organic Chemistry • Postdoc International • Laboratory Safety •

World Association of Theoretical Chemists • CHEMLAB-L

Chemical Marketing Online

http://www.chemon.com/

ChemOn is a place for visitors from around the world in the chemical industry. Use ChemOn to find buyers and sellers for your products and services. Let us put your company on the World Wide Web! Advertising available.

Links
Chemicals For Sale • Chemicals Wanted • Chemical Equipment and Services • Chemical Employment Listings • Frequently Asked Questions

Chemical and Process Engineering

http://www.fdgroup.co.uk/neo/fsi/chempro.htm

Flow Simulation develops and markets software for scientists and engineers, both academic and industrial, including leading universities and blue-chip companies. The company is a SMART competition winner, and has received SMART Stage 1, Stage 2 and other awards from the UK Department of Trade and Industry. The company is based at the Sheffield Science Park. This is their list of chemical and process engineering sites on the Internet.

Links
Professional Bodies • Other sites of interest • Academic • Major chemical companies • Newsgroups • Mailing Lists

Chemical Recycling

http://www.sonic.net/chemsearch

Online Surplus & Byproduct Chemicals and Chemsources Inc.'s list of recycled and recyclable chemicals (and a few other things).

Links
Chemicals we are offering by type • An alphabetical index • Your needs or usage • Your surplus or excess • We are trying to find sources for these • Recycling forum

Chemical Week's Cool Links

http://www.chemweek.com/marketplace/links/coollinks.html

Chemical Week is positioned like no other magazine. Every week we can make the links in this vast and diverse industry in a way no other chemical industry journal can. That is because of our global positioning and in-depth coverage of all sectors of the worldwide chemical business. Their "Hot Links" are links to their advertisers; "Cool Links" are to the rest of the chemical industry.

Links
Trading Post - Marketing, Sales, Traders and Equipment • Publishers and Information Providers • List of Lists - a directory of other lists of chemical industry sites • Unified Search Page • Chemical Companies • Chemical Distribution, Transportation and Storage • Computer • Consultants • Education and Government • Environmental • Professional Organizations

Chemist's Art Gallery

http://www.csc.fi:80/lul/chem/
graphics.html

Welcome to the Chemist's Art Gallery
containing spectacular visualization
and animations in chemistry done at
the Visualization and Animation Laboratory at CSC by the Visualization
Group and groups at other locations.

Links
Small Molecule Diffusion In Polymers •
Animations Of The Protein Cellobio-
hydrolase I (CBH1) • Visualization Of
Volumes Of Chromosomes And
Viruses Based On Electron Microscopy
Tomography • Visualization Of Mi-
celles • Visualization Of The Dynamics
Of Spreading Of Small Droplets Of
Chainlike Molecules On Surfaces •
Visualization And Animation Projects
At CSC • Etc., Etc.

Chemistry Internet Index

http://www.chemie.fu-berlin.de/
chemistry/index/

From Burkhard Kirste at the Freie Uni-
versität in Berlin, Germany, we find
one of the most comprehensive collections of chemical sites on the web.
These are technical sites, not industrial
sites.

Links
Analytical Chemistry and Chemomet-
rics • Biochemistry • Biographies of
Chemists • Chemistry and Develop-
ment of the Web • Chemistry Databases
• Chemistry Indexes • Computational
Chemistry • Conferences • Crystal-
lography • General Chemistry • Inor-
ganic Chemistry • Internet Chemistry
Sites • Macromolecular Chemistry,

Polymers • Mineralogy • Miscellaneous
• Molecular Modeling and Visualiza-
tion • Organic Chemistry • Physical and
Theoretical Chemistry • Re-
print/Preprint Databases, (Electronic)
Journals • Software • Spectroscopy

Chemistry Information on the Internet

http://hackberry.chem.niu.edu:70/0/
cheminf.html

This WWW site is a pilot project
funded by the Camille and Henry
Dreyfus Chemical Informatics Program
to determine the utility of making
chemical information available via the
Internet. Since this is an experimental
server, some aspects may not work
quite right for all users and information
available will constantly be changing.

Links
New and Exciting Chemistry Web De-
velopments • Chemistry Databases and
Related Information • Electronic Jour-
nals • Chemistry World-Wide Web
Sites • Commercial Sites • University
Web Sites • Government Web Sites •
Chemistry Gopher Sites • University
Chemistry Department Sites • Other
Lists of Chemistry Resources on the
Internet

Chemistry on the Internet: The best of the Web 1995

http://hackberry.chem.niu.edu:80/
Infobahn/Paper38

A selection of high quality chemical
information on the Internet, presented
as a poster at the ACS Symposium in
Chicago on August 21, 1995 as part of
the "Chemistry on the Infobahn" ses-
sion. In compiling this selection, we

have focused on the work of key individuals who we believe have shown a vision of the future in creating innovative and original chemistry Internet resources for us all. This is a collection of about 100 sites organized along the following lines:

Links
The best "World Collections" of pointers • Chemical Internet Standards • "Value added" Processing of chemical information • Conferences and Talks • Visual Sources and Programs • Teaching Resources • Electronic Journals • Organizations

Chemistry (Science) -- Galaxy

http://galaxy.einet.net/galaxy/
Science/Chemistry.html

Galaxy is a guide to worldwide information and services and is provided as a public service by TradeWave Corporation. In addition, Galaxy guest editors bring you their wide-ranging information and insight. This is their chemical page. They have about 200 links along the following topic areas:

Links
Subtopics • Related Topics • Articles • Guides • Events • Software • Collections • Periodicals • Discussion Groups • Directories • Organizations • Government Organizations

Chemical Online Presentations, Talks and Workshops

http://www.ch.ic.ac.uk/talks/

You are invited to contribute the URL of any chemically orientated talk, poster or workshop presentation that

you have made or will make to an audience.

Links
Currently 55 talks (links) are reproduced full text at this site, concerning chemistry and the chemical industry.

Chemistry Today - Internet Resources

http://chemistry.mond.org/

Chemistry Today is a daily service bringing you the latest chemistry news, jobs, meetings and other information.

Links
News • Jobs • Meetings • Apropos

Coatings

http://www.umr.edu/~jstoffer/
Coatings/

From The University of Missouri-Rolla, we have this database of coatings. The database is searchable as well as indexed. The links below are the index categories.

Links
Categories Of Organic Coatings Substances • Performance Objectives Of A Coating • Reaction Rates • Paint Appearance • Pigments And Hide • Polymerizations • Examples Of Polymers Used For Coatings • Miscellaneous

Commodities--Chemical

http://www.commodities.net/
chemic.html

This site is published by OnLine Trade Association with permission of Tradewinds Publishing Company.

Buyers and sellers of commodity chemicals and minerals post their offerings or needs. There is a monthly charge, or a membership.

Links
No Links, but a long continuos list of chemicals for sale

Community of Science Web Server

http://cos.gdb.org/

The Community of Science World Wide Web server contains information about scientific Expertise, funded scientific research, and funding opportunities for research. The COS philosophy is to provide working researchers with valuable information tools to help them: 1) complete work underway; 2) secure funds for the next project. COS is a consortium of research institutions and one of the largest repositories of searchable scientific information available on the Internet. Total access to this site is limited to member institutions.

Links
Expertise, Inventions, and Facilities • Medline • The U.S. Patent Citation Database • Federally-Funded Research in the U.S. • Commerce Business Daily • The Federal Register • Funding Opportunities Database • Add or Update an Expertise Profile • The Canadian Community of Science

Computational Fluid Dynamics OnLine

http://www.tfd.chalmers.se/ CFD_Online/

Version 1 of this document was announced in the beginning of 1995. It all started as a hobby project in December 1994. Gradually version 1 became quite popular, with about 800 requests per week for the original URL http://eru.dd.chalmers.se/~f88jl/CFD/cfd_online.html. Version 2 was announced Sept. 1, 1995. This was a major revision. The document had been split into many smaller sections, and it also had forms support at several levels. As of version 2 the URL has been http://www.tfd.chalmers.se/ CFD_Online/.

Links
Intro. • News • Homes • Proj • Users • Topic • Soft • Refs • Docs • CMC • Conf • Jobs • Meta • Misc. • About • etc. • and many more

Cosmetic & Toiletry Industry Email Directory

http://www.skypoint.com/ members/mhevey/emaildir.htm

The Email Directory for the Cosmetic and Toiletry Industry is sorted by last names. Choose the appropriate sub directory, double click the name and you are ready to send email to that person.

Links
Links A-Z

COSMOS OnLine--Mexican Companies

http://www.cosmos.com.mx/

This is a Mexican Chemicals Buyers Guide with a Trade Center with hundreds of companies, suppliers of thousands of products, equipment and services, grouped in different industrial areas. Find quickly and easily the companies, the products and the services you are looking for, with our powerful search engine. Register your organization in COSMOS OnLine*, get your username and use our free services. Request quotations of products directly from possible suppliers, wherever they are located. Fill in only one form that our system will send simultaneously to each supplier. They shall contact you directly, we are not mediators, nor charge for this service. The database is searchable and is bi-lingual (English/Spanish).

Links
Food • Graphic Arts • Automotive • Financial • Leather And Shoes • Construction • Containers • Equip. & Material • Housekeeping • Hospital • Rubber • Laboratories • Office • Plastics • Chemicals • Services • Fabric

Derwent Scientific and Patent Information

http://www.derwent.co.uk/

Derwent Information, part of The Thomson Corporation, is the world's leading provider of global patent and scientific information products. For over 40 years Derwent has been providing critical information solutions to organizations throughout every stage of the innovation process. Every day you make strategic decisions that are critical to the future of your business or research. Whether you are devising company strategy, exploring new research areas or developing or patenting new products, top quality information in the right format and at the right time is essential.

Links
Derwent Scientific and Patent Information • About Derwent • About Patents • Products and Services • What's New • Recruitment • Subscriber Area • Patent Copy Ordering • Search the Site

Dialog/Knight Ridder Information Services

http://www.dialog.com/dialog/dialog1.html

Welcome to DIALOG a service of Knight-Ridder Information, Inc. Knight-Ridder Information's World Wide Web server provides you with: an electronic version of many of our DIALOG Publications; with help selecting the correct DIALOG databases; links to download our premiere telecommunications software, DialogLink, with answers to some Frequently Asked Questions (FAQs) about DIALOG; information on the Custom DIALOG(tm) product, including Quickstart Applications; answers about our Services, Products, and Commands; and, how to sign-up for DIALOG and complete copies of our DIALOG Subscription Form (Domestic U.S.) and DIALOG Subscription Form (International).

Links
DIALOG • Knight-Ridder Information, Inc. • DialogFAQ • DIALOG Publications • selecting the correct DIALOG

databases • DialogLink • Frequently Asked Questions (FAQs) about DIALOG • Custom DIALOG(tm) product, including Quickstart Applications • Services, Products, and Commands • sign-up for DIALOG • DIALOG Subscription Form (Domestic U.S.) • DIALOG Subscription Form (International) • What's New • Search hotlink • Telnet Link to DIALOG

Ecosse Group

http://www.chemeng.ed.ac.uk:80/ecosse/

The ultimate goal of the Ecosse program is better chemical processes through better design. In this context "design" encompasses the whole range of activities carried out by engineers to improve the final product: in this case, the chemical plant. The database carries both an instructional course and technical papers written concerning chemical process engineering since 1991.

Links
1995 Directory • 1994 Directory • Technical reports are available for 1996, 1995, 1994, 1993, 1992 and 1991 • Some live web reports are available • The Ecosse Process Engineering Environment • The KBDS design support system • The ECOSSE control course. (restricted access) • A Taster of The ECOSSE control course.

Electronic Research Resources for Chemistry

http://131.236.60.11/OzChemNet/ResearchResources.html

More from our Australian friends in electronic resources for research in

chemistry. This site contains hundreds of links to sites in the following areas:

Links
Electronic Journals • Electronic Conferences • E-mail lists, discussion groups etc. • Newsgroups • Information Databases

The Industrial Research Institute, Inc.

http://www.iriinc.org/

The Industrial Research Institute (IRI) is a non-profit organization of over 260 leading industrial companies. These companies --representing such industries as aerospace, automotive, chemical, computer, and electronics -- carry out over 80 percent of the industrial research effort in the United States, employ some 500,000 scientists and engineers, and account for at least 30 percent of its gross national product.

Links
IRI • Networks • IRI News • RTM • What's New • PDP • Publications • Audio Tapes • Committees

Keidanren--Japanese Companies

http://www.keidanren.or.jp/

Keidanren (Japan Federation of Economic Organizations) is a private and non-profit economic organization which represents virtually all branches of economic activities in Japan. Keidanren, maintaining close contact with both public and private sectors at home and abroad, endeavors not only to find practical solutions to economic problems but also to contribute to the sound development of the economies of

Japan and other countries around the world. Its membership stood at 970 corporations and 123 association members, as of October 1994. The corporate members are leading Japanese enterprises and 53 foreign companies operating in Japan. The association members include trade associations and regional economic organizations. This is a searchable database and bit-lingual (English/Japanese).

Links

What's New • It Is Not Too Late--Yet • Fifty-Years Young • Keidanren Appeal on Environment- Declaration on Voluntary Action of Japanese Industry Directed at Conservation of Global Environment in the 21st Century • An Attractive Japan • Search Company Database

LabInfo

http://www.labinfo.com/labinfo/Welcome.html

Labinfo is the World Wide Web Site designed to create a laboratory community online by bringing together information resources supportive to laboratory professionals and the users of laboratory services. LabInfo is dedicated to providing individuals and businesses associated with laboratories a fast easy means of communication through utilization of the Internet. Laboratories can browse suppliers' homepages to find the laboratory equipment they are looking to purchase, customers can browse staff profiles, types of analysis done, and laboratory locations on individual company homepages, and interested parties can read online industry periodicals or society newsletters. Quite simply if you are looking for something associated

with laboratory analysis you will find it on the LabInfo.

Links

What's New! • About LabInfo • Calendar of Events • Products • Journals • Laboratories • Associations/Societies • Classifieds • Software • Links of Interest • Employment

LEXIS-NEXIS Communication Center

http://www.lexis-nexis.com/

The LEXIS®-NEXIS® services, the world's premier online legal, news and business information services, are the cornerstone of an array of enhanced information retrieval, storage and document management products and services from LEXIS-NEXIS. Serving customers in more than 60 countries, sales representatives are located in 50 U.S. cities and around the world, including in London, Frankfurt and Toronto. The company is a division of Reed Elsevier Inc., part of the Reed Elsevier plc group, one of the world's leading publishing and information businesses. Reed Elsevier is headquartered in London. LEXIS-NEXIS is based in Dayton, Ohio and employs 4,275 individuals worldwide.

Links

About LEXIS-NEXIS • Products & Services • Customer Service • Communications • Employment • What's New

Planet Earth - Chemistry Information

http://www.nosc.mil/planet_earth/
chemistry.html

This military site (Space and Naval Warfare Systems Command) lists some very good, and interesting, chemical servers from around the world.

Links

ChemEd: Chemistry • UCSD S&E Library - Chemistry • San Diego State University - Chemistry • The WWW Virtual Library • EINet Galaxy Server • North Carolina State University Server • Yahoo Server • Rice University Information Server • The World Guide to Chemistry • Chemistry from Fedworld • Chemistry Related Jobs in Industry • Chemistry at CSC • School of Chemistry, Queensland University of Technology • MIME Types for Chemistry • Fundamental Physical Constants • Scientific Constants • Periodic Table 1 - Berkeley • Periodic Table 2 - Sheffield • Metric Conversion Factors • Weights and Measures • Data Powers of Ten

Plasnet Home Page - The Plastics Industry in Australia

http://www.plasnet.com.au/
plasmain.htm

Eighteen months in gestation, Plasnet is an initiative of the brothers Maloney from Melbourne. Peter, with twenty five years plastics Industry Experience and Chris, with similar years spanning Computing, Corporate Communications and Design. The system has been developed primarily for people in the Plastics Industry in Australia and the

Asia Pacific Region - although we expect significant use by the International Community and students of all ages.

Links

Processors • Raw Materials Suppliers • Machinery & Equipment • Research & Development • Buy • Swap • Sell • Service Industries • Employment • Education & Training • Toolmakers & Engineers • Plastics & Environment • Prototyping • Miscellaneous • An Overview of The Australian Plastics Industry

The Plastics Network

http://plasticsnet.com

This fantastic Internet community is brought to us by Commerx, Inc., an Internet development company. The Plastics Network is a huge website devoted to the plastics industry and contains information on over 4,500 companies in the industry. A visitor to this site can collect information from companies in the raw material feedstock area to used blow molding equipment, including chemical additives and plastics recycling companies. You can visit forums and discussion groups to learn what others are doing in the plastics industry. This one is a must for members of the Plastics Industry; it is a members only database, but membership is free.

Links

Hundreds of links, including a business center; business card directory; Plastics Buyer's Guide; MarketPlace; technical training and an online magazine for the industry

Plastics Technology Center

http://www.lexmark.com/ptc/ptc.html

The Plastics Technology Center is a commercial enterprise providing design, engineering, prototyping, tooling, and production services for plastic parts and products. The PTC is comprised of approximately 30 designers, engineers, analysts, and support personnel with diverse backgrounds and many years of experience in the plastics industry. In addition to our permanent staff, we also have a rotating staff made up of retired industry experts, graduate and undergraduate students, international assignees, and visiting professors. This site is listed in the resources because of its extensive information for the plastics industry.

Links
Design Services • Injection Molding Simulation • Structural Analysis • Material Selection • Rapid Prototyping • Prototype and Production Tooling • Part Production, Finishing, and Assembly • An Introduction to Plastics • Polymers FAQ • Polymer Abbreviations • Tradenames Database • Language Index • etc.

Polymers DotCom

http://www.polymers.com/dotcom/home.html

You are on the main page of the plastics industry's oldest and busiest industry-wide mega server. This triumvirate server is offered to the industry on a free subscription basis by WorldWide WebLabs, an award winning web developer and publisher of plastics and polymer information. We have been providing service to the Internet plas-

tics community since 1994! Referred to as an Internet MEGA-SITE, The Internet's oldest and largest index of polymers and plastics web sites! Members only, but the subscription is free for the first year.

Links
PDC Magazine • Polycontent • Polylinks • Subscribe • Our FAQ • Plastics Primer • etc. etc.

PolySort

http://www.polysort.com/pts.html

Welcome to PolySort, the most comprehensive polymer industry site on Internet. Browse through our menu, or use the PolySort Search to quickly locate the information you need. PolySort now offers excerpts of polymer industry news stories from the current issue of Chemical Week. See our new Chemical Week page. The page will be updated each Monday with the latest on stories appearing in the following Wednesday edition of Chemical Week.

Links
PolySort Search • Database Input Form • What's New? • Industry News • Industry Events • Industry Access • Internet Links • Classified Ads • Discussion Groups

Quadnet

http://www.vyne.com/qnetwww/

Quadnet is an online news service representing research universities and technical centers. We distribute science and technology, medicine, environment, business/economic and education news to a selected list of reporters and editors. This home page provides news and resources to the press and the interested public. It also contains information about Quadnet for reporters and writers who might be interested in receiving the Quadnet service, and for prospective contributing members.

Links
Quadnet's Developments To Watch • Research Resources • About Quadnet • Contacting Quadnet

Questel-Orbit

http://www.questel.orbit.com/patents/oqovw.html

A world leader in online information systems. For more than 20 years, we've been the right place to turn for intellectual property, scientific, chemical, technical and business information. Questel-Orbit is the online information service of choice for more than 20,000 information professionals around the world. We should be your choice too. Our comprehensive selection of databases is unmatched in the industry. Questel-Orbit is an international online information company specializing in patent, trademark, scientific, chemical, business and news information. There are links to our Database Catalog, Price List, search commands and features, as well as links to other sites we hope you will find helpful. We are a subscriber service. As a subscriber, you will be able to conduct online searches yourself.

Links
Subscription Information • PATService • How to Contact Us • Why You Should Use Us • Overview

Refining, Petrochemical & Chemical WWW Sites

http://www.processassociates.com/sites/links.htm

This resource page is brought to us by Process Associates of America. It contains about 400 links to information sources and companies, plus the wacky patent of the month.

Links
Information Sources • Technical Humor • Companies

Resources of Scholarly Societies - Chemistry & Chemical Engineering

http://www.lib.uwaterloo.ca/society/chem_soc.html

This is one of a set of subject pages created by compilers at the University of Waterloo Library to facilitate access to webpages and gophers maintained by or for scholarly societies across the world. A set of guidelines is used in determining whether to include resources. When a society maintains both a webpage and a gopher, only the webpage is included. Links to electronic resources of scholarly societies in Chemistry & Chemical Engineering are given below. This excellent site contains about 400 links to associations and societies in the field of chemistry and chemical engineering, some with brief descriptions.

Links
Many

SOCMA Member Companies - Commercial Profiles

http://www.socma.com/commprof.html

This is a searchable database of SOCMA member companies. You can search by company name, or by equipment, or capabilities. The entire list is also searchable by drill down index.

Links
A-Z • Market Place

STN International

http://www.fiz-karlsruhe.de/stn.html

Knowledge is the most important resource in high-tech countries. For research and development, for the daily scientific work, appropriate information - comprehensive and easily accessible - is a fundamental prerequisite. The direct route to scientific information leads via STN International, The Scientific and Technical Information Network. This network is operated cooperatively by Fachinformationszentrum (FIZ) Karlsruhe, Chemical Abstracts Service (CAS) of the American Chemical Society (ACS), and the Japan Information Center of Science and Technology (JICST). Service Centers in Karlsruhe, Columbus and Tokyo are linked by sea cable (TAT8). Thus, the users have access to one worldwide information service with up-to-date databases in science and technology. The STN centers have many years of experience in the field of scientific information.

Links
What's new • Advantages of going online • Our services to your advantage • STN software products • All STN on-line databases • All file clusters • Database producers and their databases • MESSENGER Prices • connect to STN • Guide to STN Patent Databases • Workshops • User meetings and exhibitions • Search Service • Frequently asked questions • A list of STN Representatives around the world

Technology and Engineering Services

http://www.techexpo.com/

This is the Home Page of TechExpo, a WWW site geared for Hi-Tech in the Engineering and Medical/Life Sciences: the most visited technical web site.

Links
Internet Business 500 • JOM - A publication of the Minerals, Metals & Materials Society • Journal of ASM • Science & Engineering Network News • The Egyptian Government List of Preferred Sites • INFOWEEK Magazine List of Hot Sites

VRML, Visualization of PDB files

http://ws05.pc.chemie.th-darmstadt.de/vrml/pdbvis.html

Select one of the molecules listed (stored in PDB format) and select one of the representations on left side. The PDB file will be converted into VRML after clicking on Prepare Model. Visualize these molecules on your screen, turn them around, etc.

Links
Acenaphthene to p-Xylene

182

Waste Treatment Technology

http://www.vyne.com/bcc/
bcc_waste.html

From the consultants at BCC, you will find a list and summaries of all the reports in our catalog. If you have any questions about our report, or are interested in ordering a report, click on the title. This list contains BCC reports only, with a description and order info for each.

Links
About 25 sites on Waste Treatment

World Wide Engineering/Construct Projects

http://www.odyssee.net/~wwp/

WWP Market Intelligence Reports monitor engineering/construction undertakings valued at between $5 million and $40 billion per project. In so doing, the international business activities of American, Canadian, European, Japanese and Australian companies active in developing country markets are reported on. And, the operations of leading domestic firms based in emerging nations are also monitored. Reports cover project plans, feasibility studies, advance bidding information, low bids and negotiations, letters of intent, contract awards, construction start-ups, and related joint venture opportunities. And, every major economic sector is closely scrutinized for project opportunities. These include general infrastructure & plant operations, mining, metal making & conversion as well as oil, gas, chemicals and petrochemicals, on a world wide scale.

Links
WWP Quick Site Tour • Region • Industry • Frequently Asked Questions (FAQ) • Sample project reports

World Wide Web Links to Chemistry pages

http://www.cm.utexas.edu/cejones/
Linkpage.html

This fantastic collection of good links for the chemical industry is brought to us by the University of Texas.

Links
General Chemistry • General Physics • Materials Science • Electrochemistry • Superconductivity • Polymer Chemistry • Fullerene Chemistry • Computational Chemistry • Funding Agencies and Information • Other Research Groups • Teaching Related Sites • Computer and Software • Organizations • National Labs and Government Agencies • Instrument Manufacturing Companies • Commercial Sites • Informational Databases

The World-Wide Web Virtual Library: Chemical Engineering

http://www.che.ufl.edu:80/WWW-
CHE/outline.html

A part of the WWW Virtual Library project, this subject catalog lists information resources relevant to Chemical and Process Engineering. The site is maintained for us by the folks at the University of Florida.

Links
Meeting and Conference Announcements • Analytical Methods, Products and Services • Biomedical • Biotechnology • Ceramics • Chemical Produc-

ers and Suppliers • Databases • Education Resources • Electrochemical • Energy, Conservation and Efficiency • Engineering and Construction • Environment • Fluid Mechanics • Forest Products • Heat Transfer • Mass Transfer • Materials and Properties • Nuclear Particle Technology • Petrochemicals and Fuels • Polymers • Reactions • Process Control • Process Design • Process Modeling • Safety and Hazards • Software Products and Suppliers • Standards • Statistics and Experimental Design • Teaching Topics and Resources • Technical • Water Technology • Organizations • Academic Institutions • Professional Organizations • Research Organizations and Laboratories • Consultant and Service Providers • etc.

The World-Wide Web Virtual Library: Chemistry

http://www.chem.ucla.edu/chempointers.html

A part of the WWW Virtual Library project, this subject catalog lists information resources relevant to Chemistry. The site is maintained for us by the folks at the University of California at Los Angeles.

Links
Academic Institutions • Non-profit Organizations • Commercial Organizations • Other Lists of Chemistry Resources and Related WWW Virtual Libraries • Special Projects • Chemistry Software Ads • Specialty Ads • Chemical Industry Consultants • Other Chemistry Services • Chemistry Gopher Servers • Chemistry FTP Servers • Chemistry and Biochemistry USENET News Groups

The World-Wide Web Virtual Library: Wastewater Engineering

http://www.halcyon.com/cleanh2o/ww/welcome.html

Also from the Virtual Library Project, this site concentrates on Wastewater sites and is brought to us by Industrial Wastewater Engineering in Seattle, Washington.

Links
Buckman's Micro 101 • Link to wastewater info • Municipal Wastewater Resources • Academic and Research Institutions • Professional & Trade Organizations • Commercial Orgs. - Consultants • Commercial Orgs. - Suppliers • Resource bases, company listings, mags, other

WWW Chemicals

http://www.chem.com/

This is a searchable directory of chemical companies present on the World Wide Web. The left frame window lists the names of all companies in the directory. Use the scroll bar to see more company names. You can also use 'Find' command in the 'Edit' menu of the Netscape browser for searching. Click on a company name to visit this company's Home Page on the Web.

Links
Company directory • Catalogs • Company Home Pages • Chemicals on sale • Chemicals wanted • MSDS • 127,000 3D structures • Resumes • Membership

Miscellaneous Sites of Particular Interest

These are links to web sites of special interest to the chemical industry and not included in any other chapters. They include sites on the Internet for finding MSD Sheets and patent information.

MSDS Information

Chemical Safety - MSDS

http://www.portal.com/~austin/chemsafe/

Welcome to Chemical Safety, makers of the award-winning Environmental Management Systems (EMS) environmental, health, and safety computer tracking and control database. At Chemical Safety, we are proud to help provide environmental management solutions for all organizations, regardless if you are big corporation, or a small facility. Chemical Safety has tailored the EMS program specifically to meet the environmental, health and safety needs of your organization.

Links
Environmental Management Systems (EMS) • New Product Announcements • EMS - Environmental, Health and Safety Software • Material Safety Data Sheet Management • Spotlight on MSDS View for Windows • Spotlight on Container Barcode Tracking • Regulatory Alert! • Get to Know Chemical Safety • Contact the Chemical Safety Staff • Download a Demo of MSDS View for Windows.

Chempliant

http://www.chempliant.com/

Chempliant International Inc., headquartered in Raleigh, North Carolina, designs, develops, and markets Material Safety Data Sheet management software and services throughout the world. With Chempliant software, your MSDS transaction costs will plummet while your productivity soars. Chempliant's automatic creation, integration, distribution, and tracking tools save you valuable time. And that translates into money. Chempliant was developed by experts who know and understand the MSDS process. From regulatory compliance issues to product development considerations. MSDS compliance is our only business - not a sideline.

Links
For More Information • What We Do • Products • FAQ's • Download Demo • MSDS Sheets • Customers Only • Who We Are • Dealer Inquiries/Job Opps

Enviro-Net MSDS Index - Univ. of Utah Mirror

http://www.enviro-net.com/
technical/msds/

This is a searchable index. Please type all or part of the chemical name you are searching. You can also search for a chemical manually. To do this please choose a letter. The ENVIRO-NET MSDS database is a mirror of the University of Utah MSDS database. We will be establishing a bulletin board for MSDS information, so let us know of any problems.

Links
A - Z

The Fisher Scientific Internet Catalog--MSDS

http://www.fisher1.com/index.html

Announcing Fisher Scientific's Participation in ProcureNet, the Mall designed specifically for business to business transactions. U.S. Fisher Scientific Customers can now place orders using this WWW. The catalogs listed below are complete electronic versions of their printed counterparts. Each catalog offers an intuitive table-of-contents navigation tool, full-text searches, as well as part number, page number, and manufacturer searches. Almost 100,000 quality Fisher Scientific products and 10,000 images are represented here in over 4,000 catalog pages. You can search for any MSDS from our popular database within the Fisher Chemical and Acros Chemical catalogs. We hope you find our electronic catalogs convenient, comprehensive, and informative!

Links
The Fisher Catalog 95/96 • Fisher Safety America 95 • The Fisher Chemical Catalog 95/96 • Fisher What's New Catalog • Acros Chemicals Catalog 95/96 • Help on using this site • Ordering Information • Phone and Email Directory • Fisher Scientific Locations • About Fisher Scientific • Employment Opportunities

MSDS by Company

gopher://Quasar.Tach.Net:70/11/msds

This contains several hundred MSD Sheets of proprietary products. Several companies market chemical products under a special name or tradename. This database carries those MSDS. Caution, this database is often very slow to respond.

Links
A-Z

MSDS--Gopher Page - University of Utah

gopher://atlas.chem.utah.edu/11/
MSDS

This is one of the largest and most copies collections of MSDS on the net. The collection is a gopher, so just scroll down until you find what you want.

Links
A - Z

MSDS Manager

http://www.io.org/~jpn/msds.html

The MSDS Manager is a Windows application organizations can use to manage their MSDS (Materials Safety Data Sheets) in compliance with government regulations (WHMIS in Canada, OSHA in the U.S.). Unlike the costlier packages that actually store each MSDS document on the computer (with extensive demands placed on both the user and the user's hardware), the MSDS Manager only requires the user to input the certain elements of each sheet, which is made easier with the use of pick lists, drop-down boxes, etc. Some other features: Able to manage multiple sites with the Multiple Site Management feature; Comprehensive context-sensitive online help; Automatic 'Fax Format' Renewal Request generation; Customized Report Generator; One-touch quick reports; Multiple security levels; Various data integrity checks and verifications; Network version available

Links
What is the MSDS Manager v2.0? • What are some of its features? • Who needs it? • How does it work? • Why Version 2.0? • What are the System Requirements? • How much does it cost? • How do I get a DEMO or more information?

MSDS Index--Indiana University of Pennsylvania

http://www.py.iup.edu/college/
chemistry/msds/

The University of Utah Chemistry Department is currently developing an archive of unlicensed, unrestricted publicly distributable Material Safety Data Sheets (MSDS) in ASCII text file format. In collaboration with several other sites we will be electronically scanning our existing paper MSDS and

Optical Character Recognition (OCR) processing them to extract the text content into ASCII text file format. Suppliers of materials provide the required MSDS on paper in many data formats and not all are easy to read. This project should eventually address the variety of data formats and create a series of filters to convert them into a single "standard" data format. The current effort, however, is to convert the MSDS data into ASCII text file format regardless of the data format. The text files will be given the common, or product, name of the material. This is a gopher search tool.

Links
A-Z

MSDS Rx Home

http://home1.gte.net/msdsrx/index.html

This site offers vital information concerning Hazard Communication and Workers' Right-to-Know. It is of immediate interest and importance to the following people (choose a category): I. Employers whose employees use any chemical products in the workplace. II. End Users of workplace chemicals. III. Safety; Compliance Managers. IV. Chemical Manufacturers and Distributors. V. EHS and OSH Professionals. Please note that MSDS Rx is NOT a publicly accessible MSDS database. If that is what you're looking for, our annotated Links provide a plethora of excellent resources which we ourselves rely on.

Links
Mfrs • Pros • Sample • Starter

MSDS Unlimited

http://users.aol.com/RTNmsds/
home.html

The MSDS Unlimited™ system continues to set the standards by which all other MSDS authoring tools are judged. Economical enough for the small manufacturer, yet loaded with enough optional features to satisfy the needs of even the largest chemical suppliers. Our MSDS Unlimited™ software package was written with the environmental manager in mind to help ease the burdensome chores involved with Material Safety Data Sheet management. It generates and maintains 16 part documents in multiple languages, links container labels directly to the MSDS information, and keeps track of who's gotten what and when do they need updates . This is true Windows® software (Windows® 3.1 or higher, Windows NT™, Windows® 95, etc.) for the PC environment.

Links
Vermont SIRI MSDS Archive • MSDS Rx • Material Safety Data Sheet Searches • Fisher Chemical Company Chemicals Catalog and MSDS • University of Utah Trade Name Material Safety Data Sheets • Oxford University Department of Theoretical Chemistry Laboratory Material Safety Data Sheet database • Chemical Abstracts Service Links • EPA Chemical Substance Factsheets Environmental Protection Agency Factsheets • University of Toronto Department of Chemistry • The College of Chemistry at Berkeley • Chemical Resources on the Net • TEXT-Trieve Home Page

Vermont SIRI MSDS Collection

http://hazard.com/msds/

Provides Services and Training for Use of Safety Information Resources on the Internet. The Vermont SIRI Material Safety Data Sheet (MSDS) collection is searchable by manufacturer, CAS number, and by product proprietary names. An excellent source of MSDS by company with over 100,000 MSDS files. Also, this site is a guide to using the Internet to find occupational and environmental safety information. It includes: information about and access to the archives of the safety-related e-mail lists; the Vt. SIRI Safety File Library of text and graphics files; information about MSDS's available on the Internet; and links to other safety and health web sites. (SIRI = Safety Information Resources on the Internet).

Links
About this archive • New MSDS Archive on a second host • Search the SIRI MSDS • NFPA codes for common liquids • Manufacturer's MSDS Data (doesn't include the main archive above) • BNZ Materials • Dojindo Laboratories Biological and Analytical Reagents • MSDS and EPA data on Pyrotechnic Chemicals by John Ray • Hazardous Chemical Database at U of Akron • MSDS at the University System of Georgia • Pointers to MSDS web sites(at Kansas State Univ.) • MSDS at U of Utah • MSDS at Macquarie University • EPA Toxic Substances Data Sheets • MSDS Software • MSDS Rx

Text-Trieve Online MSDS Resource Project

http://www.halcyon.com/ttrieve/
msdshome.html

This is actually a resource page of links to other sites regarding MSDS.

Links
Vermont SIRI MSDS Archive! • MSDS Rx • Material Safety Data Sheet Searches • Fisher Chemical Company Chemicals Catalog and MSDS • MSDS, University of Utah • Oxford University • Chemical Abstracts Service • EPA Chemical Substance Factsheets • University of Toronto Department of Chemistry • Chem & Biochem WorldWide Connections • The College of Chemistry at Berkeley • Chemical Resources on the Net

Toxic Chemical Factsheet - Gopher - University of Virginia

gopher://ecosys.drdr.Virginia.
EDU:70/11/library/gen/toxics

This gopher database is maintained for the U.S. Environmental Protection Agency and contains their toxic chemical factsheets. These factsheets contain much more information than does a MSDS. However only a limited number of them have been prepared. This gopher file may be browsed until you find the chemical of interest.

Links
A - Z

National Oceanic and Atmospheric Administration

http://research.nwfsc.noaa.gov/
msds.html

Here are links to publicly accessible MSDS information. The first form allows searches of a local database of chemical names linked to MSDS pages hosted on gopher servers at the University of Utah Department of Chemistry and Oregon State University. The link to the Case Western Reserve University Department of Biochemistry Gopher searches the same Utah database. Individual MSDS's can be printed or saved using the appropriate Web Browser commands.

Links
MSDS Sheets, University of Utah Department of Chemistry • MSDS database, CWRU Department of Biochemistry Gopher, searches the Utah database • Chemfinder Database Searching (a service of CambridgeSoft Corporation) • Online MSDS Project • Chemical Abstracts Service • The Fisher Scientific Internet Catalog

Hazardous Chemical Database- Univ. of Akron

http://odin.chemistry.uakron.edu/
cgi-bin/wwwwais

Information can be retrieved by entering a keyword in the form below. Preference is given to names, synonyms, formula and registry numbers (CAS, DOT, RTECS and EPA) in conducting a search. Note: This service can only be used from a forms-capable browser.

This is a WAIS Search engine.

MSDS Gopher-Stanford Univ.

gopher://portfolio.stanford.edu:
2270/1GOPHER%
20SHOWINDEX%20TCHEM

This is a searchable gopher site. You can look for MSDS by name, CAS number or phonetic name. If you work at Stanford University, you can access the database by Stanford Chemical Number.

Links
A-Z

MSDS Database-University System of Georgia

http://www.ps.uga.edu/rtk/msds.htm

Welcome to the University System of Georgia MSDS Database! This database is searchable by selecting the first letter of the chemical name, then scroll down to the target product.

Links
A to Z

MSDS Gopher-Oregon State Univ.

gopher://gaia.ucs.orst.edu:70/11/
osu-i+s/osu-d+o/ehs/msds/Product

Another very good source of MSDS on a gopher database.

Links
A-Z

Data and Information Network (ECDIN) -- Europe

http://ulisse.ei.jrc.it/Ecdin/Ecdin.html

Quality of life in Europe is at the heart of the Environment Institute's research and support activities which focus on: Health of EU inhabitants; Quality of EU products; Quality of air, water and soils; Global change and its impact on Europe; The Institute's objectives; Providing neutral scientific support for the preparation and implementation of EU directives. This is a fantastic source of information similar to U.S. MSDS on products made in the EEC. Certain pesticides, etc. not found in the U.S. databases, may be found here.

Links
This is database is searchable by:
ECDIN Number; Names-Synonyms;
CAS Number; Molecular Formula

Agency for Toxic Substances and Disease Registry (ATSDR)

http://atsdr1.atsdr.cdc.gov:8080/
atsdrhome.html

The mission of the Agency for Toxic Substances and Disease Registry (ATSDR), as an agency of the Public Health Service in the U.S. Department of Health and Human Services , is to prevent exposure and adverse human health effects and diminished quality of life associated with exposure to hazardous substances from waste sites, unplanned releases, and other sources of pollution present in the environment. ATSDR is directed by congressional mandate to perform specific functions concerning the effect on public health of hazardous substances in the environment. These functions include public health assessments of waste sites, health consultations concerning specific hazardous substances, health surveillance and registries, response to emergency releases of hazardous substances, applied research in support of public health assessments, information development and dissemination, and education and training concerning hazardous substances.

Links

 Jobs • Announcements • Search • Browse • Examples • Search the Internet HazDat Database - for specific site and contaminant data • ATSDR Announcements • ATSDR Job Opportunities • ATSDR Summary • Fiscal Year 1994 Agency Profile • Background and Congressional Mandates • Organizational Structure • Goals • Statement of Values • ATSDR Glossary of Terms • EPA Glossary of Terms • ATSDR Locations (addresses and phones) • ATSDR Datasets/Resources • The HazDat Database • Contacts and References • ATSDR Science Corner • Tox-FAQs(tm) • Public Health Statements (Text Search) • ATSDR/EPA Top 20 Hazardous Substances • Minimal Risk Levels (MRLs) for Hazardous Substances • Information Center Bookmarks to Web Resources • Environ-

mental Data Needed for Public Health Assessments (Guidance Manual) • Hazardous Substances ; Public Health (Newsletter) • A Primer on Health Risk Communication Principles and Practices • Case Studies in Environmental Medicine (CME/CEU credit) • ATSDR Great Lakes Human Health Effects Research Program • ATSDR Mississippi Delta Project • ATSDR Minority Health Program • Biennial Report to Congress: 1991-1992 (Executive Statement) • ATSDR Cancer Policy Framework • Congressional Testimony • CLUSTER version 3.1 (Disease cluster analysis software) • Related Organizations and Internet Resources • U.S. Department of Health and Human Services • Agency for Health Care Policy and Research • Commissioned Corps / Surgeon General • Sanitarian Officer Category • Centers for Disease Control and Prevention (CDC) • National Institute of Environmental Health Sciences (NIEHS) • NIEHS Superfund Basic Research Program • National Toxicology Program (NTP) • U.S. Environmental Protection Agency (EPA) • The Association of Occupational and Environmental Clinics (A.O.E.C.) • CIESIN (Consortium for International Earth Science Information Network) • ATSDR Contacts

Patent Searching

Affordable Patent Searching, Affordable Trademark Searching, Affordable Copyright Searching

http://www.neca.com/~breffni/

Patents and more. We search both patent and non-patent publications that might invalidate a patent; this is a crucial point if the prior art most similar to your invention is not a patent. Our searches are not limited by the date of an electronic database; we search as far back in time as needed and we search paper literature which predates electronic databases. Our approach is to send you not only copies of the relevant prior art, patents and non-patent publications, but also a letter noting the relationship between your invention and the art. Imagine the benefit of having this letter written by a patent attorney so that he/she can determine for you the likelihood of your success at the next stage (patent filing, litigation, licensing, etc.).

No links

BUBL WWW Subject Tree - Patents

http://www.bubl.bath.ac.uk/BUBL/Patents.html

This is a resource page of links to areas of interest, around the world, to the field of intellectual property and patents. This is an excellent source page.

Links
Chemical Patents Plus • Derwent • EPO • High Technology Law Journal • In-

formation Law Alert • Intellectual Property Law for Multimedia Developers • Intellectual Property Magazine • Inventions - Investment Opportunities - Patents • IPD • JOLT • MIT's Invention Dimension • Patent, Trademark and Copyright Information and Resource Links • Patents on the Internet • Questel Orbit • Searching • Searching System • SPO • USPTO • USPOBBS

Patents on the Internet--World Patent Offices

http://www.aber.ac.uk/~dgw/patent.htm

This is a great resource page which includes links to most of the patent offices of the world.

Links
Swedish Patent and Registration Office • United Kingdom Patent Office • United States Patent and Trademark Office • World Intellectual Property Organization • Other Intellectual Property Offices on the Web • Servers of other patent offices • EPO member states • Inventions for Sale or License • Technology Transfer; Business Development • Patent Portal: Internet Patent Resources • Segrest's Select Resource on Intellectual Property

STO's Internet Patent Searching

http://sunsite.unc.edu/patents/intropat.html

This is the home page for Source Translation & Optimization's (STO) Internet Patent Search System, a way for people around the world to perform patent searches, and access information on the patenting process. The US Patent and Trademark Office uses a classification scheme with 400+ main classes, and tens of thousands of subclasses, to classify all of the 5,300,000+ patents issued since the 1800's. With a few clicks of your mouse, you can obtain a list of titles to patents in any class/subclass. The first is to locate the class that pertains to your technology area. The 400+ main classes are divided into four supergroups: electronic, chemical, engineering and mechanical, each of which are divided into 5 to 7 groups. A master list of all the classes is also provided. The Manual pages at this Mosaic site are current as of December 1993.

Links
Manual of Classification • Index to Classification • Class • Patent number • Patent documents • US Code Section 35 • IPNS • Archive of stories • Prior art • Master list • Design patent • Electronic • Chemical • Engineering • Mechanical

Chemical Patents Plus: From CAS

http://casweb.cas.org/chempatplus/

Chemical Patents Plus: FREE searching of fulltext U.S. patent documents from 1971, with complete patent page images from 1993, and many JAVA-rotateable 3D chemical structures, from CAS.

Links
Account Set-up • Easy online registration • Locate the U.S. patents you need • Free Demo • CAS Home Page

The European Patent Office

http://www.epo.co.at/epo/

Welcome to the European Patent Office; patent information products, patent information products on CD-ROMs, databases, databases, CD-ROMs, CD-ROM collections of patent documents; European patents, etc. The European Patent Office (EPO) is your partner in all matters concerning European patents. The EPO's task is to grant European patents using a unitary and centralized procedure. By filing a single patent application in one of the three official languages (English, French or German) it is possible to obtain patent protection in all 18 member states of the European Patent Organization.

Links
Register online • PATLIB Info. Centres • EPO databases • CD-ROM collections • Japanese patent information • Press releases • Notices from the President of the EPO • Patent information news • What is the EPO? • Important addresses • EPO member states • EPO publications • EPO Annual Report 1995 • What is a European Patent? • Obtaining a European Patent • Important publications for obtaining a European Patent • What is patent information? • Where to find patent information • Available patent information products • Online information on European patent applications • EPIDOS News - your patent newsletter • Education and international conferences/exhibitions • Patent information on the Internet

Search the European Patent Register online Database

http://www.epo.co.at/epo/
epidos/epr.htm

The Register of European Patents provides detailed information on all European and Euro-PCT patent applications. The system provides bibliographic data such as title of the invention, classification, publication dates, name and address of the applicant, inventor, attorney and the latest information about the status of the granting procedure of the patent application. The Register is provided in the three official languages of the EPO: English, French and German.

Links
Costs and request for a one month free access trial • How to access the database • Basic description • Search criteria • Major advantages and coverage of the online Register • Available training courses • apply for a free password • EPO home page • Recent updates • Request info • Patent information on the Internet

INPI - Instituto Nacional da Propriedade Industrial (Brazil)

http://www.bdt.org.br/bdt/inpi/english

Brazil has been participating in the Industrial Property System since 1809, being the fourth country to recognize a national law on patents. The National Institute of Industrial Property is the competent national authority dealing with Industrial Property in Brazil. INPI was established in December 1970, with the responsibility for the implementation of legal rules on industrial

property, regarding its social, economic, legal and technical function and for the adoption of measures in order to accelerate and regulate the transfer of technology. INPI is also in charge of making recommendations concerning the signing, ratifying or withdrawing from conventions, treaties and other national and international agreements on industrial property and transfer of technology. In the last 25 years, the Brazilian National System has been developing to be a effective instrument of industrial, technological and trade polices in Brazil, focusing on the development of innovation concepts in local industry.

Contacts and addresses, but no links.

ISTA--Japanese Patents

http://www.netaxs.com/~aengel/
ista.htm

This company provides CD ROM products of Japanese patents in English and more.

Links
ConvertedKokai(tm) - Machine Translations of Japanese Patent and Utility Model • Professional Translations • Up-to-Date Legal Status • Expert Searches • Patent Abstracts of Japan on CD-ROM in English • Directory of Science & Technology Organizations in Japan • Patent and Trademark Information Resources on the Internet • Using Online and CD-ROM Patent Databases to Obtain Japanese Science and Technology Information

Japanese Patent Office

http://www.jpo-miti.go.jp/

In the Year 1996, the JPO intends to make efforts to achieve the following policy objectives: Firstly, the JPO will continue to endeavor to process examination promptly and adequately by means of various measures, including the development of the Paperless Project. The pendency of patent and utility model applications has been reduced to shorter than 24 months by the end of 1995. A post-grant opposition system and a new system for accelerating the examination of patent applications filed in more than one country, which were introduced in January this year, are also expected to shorten the pendency. With regard to designs, the JPO will continue to study measures for speeding-up the examination procedure, including the introduction of electronic application system. The JPO will also try hard to expedite the processing of trademark applications by developing an efficient online retrieval system, increasing the number of examiners, and so forth.

Links
JPO Overview • Statistics • Patent Abstracts of Japan NEWS • Summary of the ICIPC* Final Report • APEC Industrial Property Rights Symposium • Request for Comments on Draft Implementing Guidelines for Inventions in Specific Fields etc.

Search the U.S. Patent Database

http://cos.gdb.org/repos/pat/pat.html

Search the U.S. Patent Database by field, or by using Boolean language. This site provides patent abstracts back to 1975. This site has very effective search engine and good report formatting.

No links

MicroPatent Web Services

http://www.micropat.com/

Welcome to MicroPatent®, Home of PatentImages ® and The Trademark Checker. In 1989, when we first began to think CD-ROM might be the perfect medium for publishing patent information, CD-ROM's sold for about $2,000 per disc. We knew we could bring the retail price down to $50 - $100 per disc if we could offer a patent information product that was fast, frequent, and friendly. Our first product, APS -- Automated Patent Searching, was a monthly abstract search disc. Although we were warned it was impossible for us to produce 12 CD-ROM discs per year, we did it anyway. Today, we are still doing it in the form of "US PatentSearch Claims and Abstracts", and it remains one of our most popular products. Since 1991, over 1000 clients worldwide have accessed text and images faster and friendlier than ever before. Recently, the three most frequent requests have been: Internet, Internet, Internet. Look at our free FullText product. New patents are available just two days after issue from the U.S. Patent Office.

Links
US PatentSearch Claims and Abstracts
• Images, Images, Images • Paten-
tImages • FullText product

Access U.S. Patent Database

http://patents.cnidr.org:4242/
access/access.html

This page contains links for accessing
the U.S. Patent Database. This site is
excellent and highly recommended for
abstract searching.

Links
Boolean Search Page • Browse the U.S.
Patent Classifications Database

World Intellectual Property Organization

http://www.uspto.gov/web/offices/
nonpto/wipo

The World Intellectual Property Organization (WIPO) is a specialized
agency of the United Nations system of
organizations. It is an intergovernmen-
tal organization responsible for the
promotion of the protection of intellectual property throughout the world. The
WIPO Arbitration Center is an administrative unit of the International Bureau of WIPO. The establishment of the
Center was approved by the General
Assembly of WIPO in September 1993
and commenced operations in Geneva,
Switzerland, in October 1994.

Links
Introduction • Handbook on Industrial
Property Information and
Documentation • International Patent
Classification Information • Patent Co-
operation Treaty (PCT) information •
Laws, treaties, and agreements con-
cerning International intellectual prop-
erty rights • Order WIPO Publications •
Patent Cooperation Treaty (PCT)
Forms which are publically available •
WIPO Arbitration Center

Internet Search Engines

These are hot links to our list of recommended Internet search engines. Remember to read the FAQ, hints or help files, because search engines are all different

AltaVista: Main Page

http://altavista.digital.com/

Brought to us by Digital Equipment Corporation, AltaVista gives you access to a large Web index: 30 million pages found on 275,600 servers, and four million articles from 14,000 Usenet news groups. It is accessed over 18 million times per weekday. You may search the web, or the Newsgroups. You may conduct a simple keyword search, or an advanced Boolean search. Remember that AltaVista does not rank its findings by relevancy, so force your key words to the top of the list. Be sure to read the help files on each type of search. Having done that, you will find that AltaVista is probably the best search engine on the net today.

Links
Help with Query • Usenet • Surprise • FAQ • Advanced Query • Simple Query • Private eXtension Products • Help with Query • Major Worldwide Expansion • AltaVista Visionary Club

Archie Request Form

http://hoohoo.ncsa.uiuc.edu/archie.html

Also from Digital Equipment, this search engine helps us to find FTP sites on the Internet. This is a form based Archie gateway for the WWW. Please remember that Archie searches can take a long time... You might just want to check out the Monster FTP Sites List instead. "Archie" is a database of anonymous FTP sites and their contents. "Archie" keeps track of the entire contents of a very large number of anonymous FTP sites, and allows you to search for files on those sites using various different kinds of file-name searches.

Links
Monster FTP Sites List • Digital Equipment Corporation

Best search engines for finding scientific information in the Internet: comparison list of their efficiency

http://www.chem.msu.su/eng/comparison.html

Brought to us by Dr. Alexander Lebedev, Moscow State University, we have a very good comparison of the ten most widely used search engines for finding scientific information. This is one of the best comparisons on the net and it demonstrates each of the ten search engines.

Links
History of the document • Experiment • Results and discussion • Multi-threaded search engines • Search engines and professional databases • Information about different search engines •

BigBook Directory Search

http://www.bigbook.com/

BigBook, Inc. was founded in 1995 to build a whole new kind of Yellow Pages. A Yellow Pages that would include all the business information that consumers need - and features to let them get to the information quickly and easily. At the same time, BigBook helps local businesses provide details about their products and services, cost-free. BigBook makes it easier for consumers and businesses to hook up with each other, and provides "value-added" information to help consumers make better, more informed decisions. The great thing here is that you can have a map drawn for any location in the U.S., so you can find exactly where that chemical plant is located.

Links
BigBook Network • Jobs • Category Finder • BigBook3D • BigBook Short List • BigBook Free Page • Registration • Vote • Maps

DejaNews Research Service

http://www.dejanews.com

DejaNews is a unique search engine which searches all the Usenet groups (approx. 30,000) on the Internet for your key words and returns all the actual e-mail messages containing your search criteria for the last 30 days. Along with this you get the message string, information about the author of the message and the newsgroup where the message was found. This enables you to determine where topics of interest to you are being discussed and to locate experts in any field. This is a definite candidate for your hotlist.

Links
Quick Search • Power Search • Post to Usenet • New Users! • Newsgroups?! • Features • Why use DN? • Advertising Info • New Features!

Welcome to The Electric Library

http://www.elibrary.com/

The Electric Library makes it possible to conduct real research over the Internet, using a deep database of reliable sources. Never before has finding the information you need been so fast and so easy! With The Electric Library, any person can pose a question in plain English and launch a comprehensive, simultaneous search through more than 150 full-text newspapers, nearly 800 full-text magazines, two international newswires, two thousand classic books, hundreds of maps, thousands of photographs, as well as major works of literature and art. The Electric Library is the best way for students and families to do research. The content is as safe as a local public library, and the information it contains is always up-to-date. The Electric Library is updated daily via satellite! This is ultimately a fee-based service.

Links
About Electric Library • Research vs. Net Search • Free Trial Offer • Download Software • Common Questions • Search Tips • Help Index

Europages - The European Business Directory

http://www.europages.com/
home-en.html

Europages offers you a database of 150,000 companies carefully selected from 25 European countries. Make an open-text search or a search by activity sector, or alternatively search for the name of the company in which you are interested! European Economic Data: A global macro-economic analysis of the European market which traces the main trends of the European economy, the expected developments and their consequences for companies. You can visualize or download nearly 100 pages of the economic indicators relating to the main activity sectors. Multi-lingual in French, German, Italian, Spanish and English.

Links
Search by activity sector • Search by company name • CD-ROM Europages • Chambers of commerce • Contact Europages • Dialing codes • Europages awards • European economic data • Fairs and exhibitions • Market survey • Standardization organizations

excite Netsearch

http://www.excite.com/

Excite's primary goal is to raise users' expectations of information retrieval. We believe that our information retrieval tools mark a significant advance in both sophistication and ease-of-use. Excite, formerly known as Architext, was founded in September 1993 by six Stanford University graduates who were tired of making keyword searches.

This is one of the best search engines on the net, bookmark it.

Links
Search mechanism and index available.

FTP search v3.1

http://ftpsearch.unit.no/ftpsearch

This search engine will locate FTP sites for you based on a number of technical criteria.

Links
FTP search v3.3 • Searching parameters • What's new? • Mirrors

Harvest Broker

http://www.town.hall.org/Harvest/
brokers/www-home-pages/query.html

This Broker was built using the Harvest system, and uses WAIS, Inc.'s WAIS server (version 2.1.1) as a backend indexing and search engine. Enter your query in the box below. You may access help for formulating queries; or example queries. We use a variety of methods to discover home pages and we currently have approximately 110,000 WWW home pages indexed in this Broker.

Links
Harvest • WAIS, Inc.'s WAIS server (Version 2.1.1) • Help For Formulating Queries • Example Queries • Forms • Author • Keywords • Title • URL • Help

HotBot

http://www.hotbot.com/

Search the entire Web with 54 million documents, HotBot is one of the most complete Web indexes online. Simple Boolean parameters can be easily added to your search via drop down menu.

Links
search

InfoSeek Net Search

http://www2.infoseek.com/

InfoSeek Corporation is dedicated to making information easy to find. The company's services benefit all Internet users, whether they are casual World Wide Web surfers or business professionals whose jobs depend on up-to-date market information. By capitalizing on the public's increasing access to the Internet and the availability of information online, InfoSeek has pioneered a revolutionary way of accessing information. InfoSeek's services feature rich content collections and powerful search technology which allow users to find precisely the information they need quickly and easily. InfoSeek's search and news services are among the most popular information search services available on the Internet, processing millions of information requests a day. InfoSeek is increasingly becoming the first stop on the Internet. Multilingual in German, Spanish, French, Japanese and English.

Links
New Search • Big Yellow • Fast Facts • World News • Your News.......extensive index to choose from

Inktomi Web Services

http://inktomi.berkeley.edu/

The core technology that powers this site has been used to build a new ad-

vanced commercial search engine, HotBot. Through the use of the Inktomi scaleable architecture, initially developed at U.C. Berkeley, the HotBot search service provides the world's most comprehensive database of Web documents. Check it out at www.hotbot.com, or read the Inktomi Corporation technology white paper at http://www.inktomi.com/whitepap.html

Links
Instructions for searching • Add a URL • Linking to Berkeley Inktomi • Truth in Document Counting • More info on our scaleable web server research • Where does the name come from?

The Internet Sleuth

http://www.isleuth.com/

The Internet Sleuth is a bit different from the other search engines you might have used. While Alta Vista or Lycos search a local database of keywords and URLs, The Sleuth maintains a "database of databases". Most of these can be searched directly from The Sleuth, making the search for information a very simple process. There are hundreds of searchable databases on the net. However, finding them and then generating a search can be extremely cumbersome. The Internet Sleuth solves this problem by finding the databases for you, and allowing you to perform your search without leaving The Sleuth. To improve your chance of success, try to search for the broadest category that contains your goal.

Links
About. • Add URL • Sleuth forum • Awards • Sponsorship • Make you Site

Searchable • hundreds of index categories

Lycos: Hunting WWW Information

http://lycos.cs.cmu.edu/

Lycos™ is the catalog of the Internet
brought to us from Carnegie Mellon
University. The Lycos web explorer
searches the World Wide Web every
day (including Gopher and FTP space),
building a database of all the web pages
it finds. The index is updated weekly.
The Pursuit search engine provides
probabilistic retrieval from this catalog,
taking a user's query and returning a
sorted list of hits (the list is sorted by
match score, and only documents with
scores above the threshold are retrieved). You need a browser that can
use forms, then you run the Forms-
based Lycos Search and choose the
maximum number of hits. On October
24, 1996, Lycos found 14,407 documents concerning "organic chemicals"
in its directory of 66,557,959 known
web pages.

Links
What Is Lycos? • How Big Is The Web?
• How Can I See More Than 10 Hits •
When Will You Have Boolean Search?
• What's The Difference Between Serv-
ers Lycos1, Lycos2, And So Forth? •
What Did I Do Wrong To Get A 500
Error? • How Can I Search With Lynx? •
• How Can I Put My Own URLs Into
The Lycos Catalog? • Why Is Lycos So
Slow? • Forms-Based Lycos search •
Current Estimate Of The Web • Forms-
Based Lycos Search • Lycos Search

MetaCrawler Searching

http://metacrawler.cs.washington.
edu:8080/index.html

The MetaCrawler is a free World Wide
Web search service. The MetaCrawler
differs from other services in that it
doesn't maintain any internal database.
Rather, it relies on the databases of
Open Text, Lycos, and others. The
MetaCrawler sends your queries to nine
different services: Open Text, Lycos,
WebCrawler, InfoSeek, Excite, Inktomi, Alta Vista, Yahoo, and Galaxy.
The MetaCrawler works by querying a
number of existing, free search engines,
organizes the results into a uniform
format, and displays them. With the
MetaCrawler, you also have the option
of scoring the hits, so that the sorted
list that is displayed can be sorted by a
number of different ways, such as lo-
cality, region, and organization.

Links
Search • Examples • Fast Search •
Comprehensive Search • Help • Prob-
lems

NlightN Search Tool

http://www.nlightn.com/

NlightN is the Web's largest library of
meaningful information. It is the fast
and easy way to find anything you want
to know. This is a fee based, subscription service. It is also the only one we
know of that not only searches the web,
but also 400 databases not presently on
the web. Free examples are available.

Links
Log In • Sign Up • More Info • Link
NlightN • Contact NlightN • New for
Libraries

The Open Text Index

http://index.opentext.net/

The Open Text Index is an Internet search engine. It's a way of finding specific information - words or phrases - on the World Wide Web. You type a word, or a group of words, or a phrase of any length, into a search form. Then the Open Text Index searches every word of every page of the World Wide Web for occurrences of your search terms, and shows you a list of pages that include them. It also lets you link to those pages.

Links

Simple Search • Power Search • Current Events • Newsgroups • Email • Other Languages • Webpulse! • Cool Sites • OTI in the News • Submit your URL • Search Tips • FAQ • More Help

SavvySearch

http://savvy.cs.colostate.edu:2000/

Welcome to SavvySearch, an experimental search system designed to query multiple Internet search engines simultaneously. Use the Search Form to enter your query, indicate whether you would like to search for all or any of the query terms, and indicate the number of results desired from each search engine. When you submit your query, a Search Plan is created wherein the nineteen search engines are ranked and divided into groups. Ranking factors include: The text of your query, Sources and types of information selected, Estimated Internet traffic, Anticipated response time of remote search engines, and The load on our computer. A parallel search is performed when a group of search engines is selected from the

search plan. The groups are displayed in order of anticipated usefulness from left to right (top to bottom), so the leftmost (top) entry contains the most favored group, and the rightmost (bottom) contains those predicted to be least useful, based on the above factors.

Links

Links to all popular search engines

Search.com

http://WWW.search.com/

The Internet is full of great information. But there's so much out there, and so much of it's junk! SEARCH.COM is a collection of tools designed to find all kinds of information...from World Wide Web sites to phone numbers to movies to stock quotes, and all points between. But SEARCH.COM is more than just a collection of search forms culled from the Internet. We also add feature stories to help you find what you're looking for, searching tutorial help, reliability ratings for each site, a chance to vote on your favorite site (or one that you hate), and a whole lot more.

Personalize • What's new • About • Help • Find a search • A-Z Index List

U.S. Gazetteer

http://www.census.gov/
cgi-bin/gazetteer

This gazetteer is used to identify places to view with the Tiger Map Server and obtain census data from the 1990 Census Lookup server. You can search for a place by entering the name and state abbreviation (optional), or 5-digit zip code. After you identify your location with the gazetteer, you can develop all sorts of 1990 census bureau information...the complete 1990 U.S. census. This is a fantastic and little used site.

Links
search by city, or zip code

Wall Street Research Net

http://www.wsrn.com/home/index.html

Wall Street Research Net consists of over 110,000 links to help professional and private investors perform fundamental research on actively traded companies and mutual funds and locate important economic data that moves markets. Wall Street Research Net is proud to present CompanyWatch, a new research tool for investors. CompanyWatch allows investors to maintain a list of companies that are in their portfolio. The list allows for easy access to company information such as press releases, quotes and charts for each of the companies that appear in their own CompanyWatch.

Links
Register • Research A Company • Research The Economy • The Markets • Business News • Research Publications • Mutual Funds • Brokers & Services • About WSRN.com • Search • Quick Question • WSRN.com FAQ • Press Releases • About WSRN Remote • About WSRN Company Watch

WebCrawler

http://webcrawler.com/

WebCrawler comes to us from America Online. The WebCrawler is a tool for searching the Web. It operates by traversing the Web and either building an index for later use, or by searching in real-time for a query. The index built by the WebCrawler is available for searching via the WebCrawler Search Page.

Links
Webcrawler Search Page • News About The Webcrawler • Hints For Searching • Frequently Asked Questions • Top 25 List • Technical Description Of The • Submit It For Indexing • Other Web Indexes • Paper Describing The Webcrawler • Postscript • Acrobat

Yahoo

http://www.yahoo.com/

Yahoo! is a hierarchical subject-oriented guide for the World Wide Web and Internet brought to us from Stanford University. Yahoo! lists sites and categorizes them into appropriate subject categories. Yahoo! is a database of Links to other sites. Yahoo! does not provide any original content, so we can only reference sites that already exist. This is one of the finest manual indices on the Internet. It is also great fun to search. Be sure to bookmark this site. It is free.

Links many

White Pages, Software and Other Sites of Interest

These are very interesting sites; they just didn't fit well in any of the above chapters.

Indonesian Petrochemical Industry (Outline Report)

http://www.idola.net.id/dc/petroch.htm

In the last two year, Indonesia's petrochemical industry has grown robustly, covering almost all branches of the industry aromatic, olefinic and natural gas-based petrochemical industries - from upstream to downstream. Viewed from its market size, in the last five years, it has grown at annually by 12.3%, from US$ 3.46 billion in 1990 to US$ 5.47 billion in1994. A tremendous increase - 25.2% over the previous year - took place in 1994. The market size of upstream aromatic petrochemicals which shrank in 1993, swelled again to US$ 231 million in 1994. It was spurred by xylene import which is the basic ingredient for PTA, following the operation of Bakrie Kasei's PTA plant. Upstream olefinic products which, until 1994, prior to the operation of PT Chandra Asri, were entirely imported, experienced fast growth because of the operation of new plants in downstream industry. Ethylene glycol and polyethylene resin plants which began to operate in the middle of 1993 have expanded their production to full capacity. The market size of upstream olefinic petrochemicals grew at a fantastic rate of 47.3% per year in the last five years. in 1994,

its market size was worth US$ 249 million.

Links
Outline Of The Report • Order Form • Executive Summary • Upstream Aromatic Petrochemicals Industry • Midstream Aromatic Petrochemicals Industry • Upstream Olefinic Petrochemicals (Olefin Centre) • Midstream Olefinic Petrochemical • Upstream Natural Gas Based Petrochemicals Industry • Midstream Natural Gasbased Petrochemicals Industry • Downstream Aromatic/Olefinic/Natural Gas-Based Petrochemicals

The Chemical Industry in Korea

http://www.iworld.net/Korea/text/f207.html

Korea's petrochemical industry has made remarkable growth throughout its short history of 20 years, in tandem with rapid national economic growth. Korea has three petrochemical complexes with a total annual capacity of 3,570,000 MTA based on ethylene, the fifth largest capacity in the world. The first is the Ulsan Petrochemical Complex, located in the southeastern part of the peninsula, which boasts two naphtha crackers with a total ethylene capacity of 870,000 MTA. The second is the Yochun Petrochemical Complex, located in southwestern Korea, which has five naphtha crackers with a total ethylene capacity of 1,900,000 MTA. The third is the Daesan Petrochemical Complex located in the middle of the west coast. Daesan contains two naphtha crackers with a total ethylene capacity of 800,000 MTA. With the facility expansion of naphtha crackers, production capacities of derivatives are also increasing greatly.

Links
Supply and demand for major petrochemicals in Korea • Overall supply and demand for fertilizer elements in Korea • Production of fertilizer elements in Korea • Consumption of fertilizer elements in Korea

Biodegradable Polymers and Plastics in Japan

http://144.126.176.216/biopoly/toc.htm

The Japanese Technology Evaluation Center (JTEC) and its companion World Technology Evaluation Center (WTEC) at Loyola College provide assessments of foreign research and development in selected technologies under a cooperative agreement with the National Science Foundation (NSF). Loyola's International Technology Research Institute (ITRI), R.D. Shelton Director, is the umbrella organization for JTEC and WTEC. Paul Herer, Senior Advisor for Planning and Technology Evaluation at NSF's Engineering Directorate, is NSF Program Director for JTEC and WTEC. Other U.S. government agencies that provide support for the program include the National Aeronautics and Space Administration, the Department of Energy, the Department of Commerce,

and the Department of Defense. JTEC/WTEC's mission is to inform U.S. policy makers, strategic planners, and managers of the state of selected technologies in foreign countries in comparison to the United States. JTEC/WTEC assessments cover basic research, advanced development, and applications/commercialization. Small panels of about six technical experts conduct JTEC/WTEC assessments. Panelists are leading authorities in their field, technically active, and knowledgeable about U.S. and foreign research programs. As part of the assessment process, panels visit and carry out extensive discussions with foreign scientists and engineers in universities and in industry/government labs.

Links
JTEC/WTEC Staff • Abstract • Foreword • Executive Summary • Background • Introduction • Analysis and Conclusion • Reports On Organizations, Companies, And Ministries

Mitsubishi Petrochemical-- Biodegradable Polymers

http://144.126.176.216/biopoly/ mitsub.htm

The Mitsubishi Petrochemical Co. (MPC) has principal research centers at Yokkaichi and at Tsukuba. The former is devoted to market-oriented research and the latter to long-term basic research, including biotechnology. The company had sales of approximately $3.7 billion dollars in 1992 in five major areas: (1) industrial chemicals (45%); (2) plastics (45%); (3) fine chemicals (e.g., components of consumer products); (4) electronic components; and (5) bio-related products (especially L-aspartic acid, fungicides, and amino acids). Their plastic products are of three principal types: (1) polyolefins, especially polypropylene; low-density, linear low-density, and high-density polyethylene; and ethylene-vinyl acetate copolymers; (2) specialty polymers, including propylene-based thermoplastic elastomers, poly(acrylic acid), polymers for adhesives, and conducting polymers; and (3) engineering plastics, especially fiber-reinforced PET and poly(phenylene ether)-nylon blends.

Links
JTEC/WTEC Hyper-Librarian

Chemistry and Science on the Internet

http://www.inform.umd.edu:8080/EdRes/Topic/Chemistry/ChemConference/BackgroundReading/Internet_Chemistry.txt

This paper briefly describes the main Internet information access tools, including gopher, World Wide Web, FTP, newsgroups, and e-mail discussion groups (listserv lists), and gives examples of the sites that have chemistry and other science-related material.

Links
While there are no links, there are plenty of valuable URLs listed in the document

ChemPen+

http://users.aol.com/hfevans/chempen.htm

With ChemPen+ copy 1995 chemists, chemistry students and chemistry educators can create illustrations like to the one below without breaking the budget.

Copy and paste drawings into your favorite MS Windows(TM) word processing applications. ChemPen+ combines menu driven drawing with special object editors to make drawing quick and easy.

Links
More...

Composites

http://www.advmat.com/

COMPOSITES: An Insider's Technical Guide to Corporate America's Activities. This book contains corporate intelligence on Polymeric-, Ceramic-, and Metal-matrix composites, Used in Aerospace, Automotive, and Industrial applications. Locate product and component manufacturers, new constituent suppliers, materials fabricators, users of various processes. Learn who is doing what research, learn about your competitors corporate structure, and much more!

Links
Explore Major Portions Of The Book • Learn Why This Book Is Unique And Useful • Order A Copy • Table of Contents • Prelude • A Listing Of 497 Business Entities • etc.

Common Equivalent Weights and Measures

http://www.cchem.berkeley.edu/ChemResources/Weights-n-Measures/weights-n-measures.html

An Internet conversion table for chemists...metric, engineering constants, etc.

No links

Conversion of Temperature Units

http://www.cchem.berkeley.edu/
ChemResources/temperature.html

This is a temperature conversion program. It converts Kelvin, Celsius and Fahrenheit units. Temperature may be defined as the condition of a body which determines the transfer of heat to or from other bodies. Particularly, it is a manifestation of the average translational kinetic energy of the molecules of a substance due to heat agitation. The customary unit of temperature is the Centigrade degree, 1/100 of the difference between the temperature of melting ice and that of water boiling under standard atmospheric pressure. The Celsius temperature scale is a designation of the scale also known as the centigrade scale. The degree Fahrenheit is 1/180, and etc.

Conversion Of Units

Error Messages

http://www.signweb.com/main/
netnews/ERROR.html

They sound so loud and intimidating. It's hard not to take them personally. Bad request! Unauthorized! Forbidden! The error messages that pop up on the Net aren't exactly designed to put you at ease. But there's something worse than their tone. Those error messages and mysterious dialog boxes you keep running into are often not clear, and they're seldom helpful. And that's a match made in cyberhell. Here's what they mean.

Links
Bad request • Unauthorized • Forbidden • Not found • Service unavailable • Bad file request • and more....

Fundamental Physical Constants / Naturkonstanten

http://www.chemie.fu-berlin.de/
chemistry/general/constants.html

Links
From Avogadro's number to Planck's constant .....they're all here for you.

GIFs and PNGs of 2D-Plots of Chemical Structures

http://schiele.organik.uni-
erlangen.de/services/gif.html

GIF (Graphical Image Format) is a portable encoding standard for image data. Chemical WWW pages employ GIFs to show the structures in the text because there is no other portable method to insert a structure plot short of adding a Java widget. However, as a general rule, one should always add a link to the image which leads to a structure file in one of the Chemical MIME types in order to ensure that the structural information is reusable. GIFs are for human browsing only (or chemical OCR as a last resort)....more discussion.

Links
Chemscape Chime • PNG • ChemWindow • ChemIntosh • ChemWeb • CACTVS editor • Daylight Depict service • and many more

MINEQL - Chemical Equilibrium Modeling Systems

http://www.agate.net/~ersoftwr/
mineql.html

Chemical equilibrium models allow you to calculate how chemical entities interact with each other. These models use thermodynamic data (e.g., equilibrium constants or Gibbs Free Energy) and mass action expressions to determine the distribution of chemical species in solution. MINEQL+ is a powerful, user-friendly modeling program that uses the chemical equilibrium program, MINEQL (Westall et al., 1976) as its numerical engine. Its thermodynamic database is identical to the EPA's MINTEQA2, so all calculations will produce results compatible with EPA specifications.

Links
Download MINEQL+ • Main Page • Other Available Software

MOBY - Molecular Modelling Software

http://science.springer.de/
newmedia/chemist/model.htm

You can do "intelligent handling" with the molecule using RasMac (for Macintoshs) or rasmol (for PCs). If you don't have these programs installed on your computer, simply click on the appropriate name to download it from the server. A description is displayed under README

Links
MOBY - Molecular Modelling on the PC • QC for MOBY

Molecular Weight Calculation

http://www.chemie.fu-berlin.de/
cgi-bin/molform

Type in a chemical molecular formula...get the molecular weight back in response.

Links
MW Calculator

The Nobel Prize in Chemistry 1995

http://www.nobel.se/announcement95-chemistry.html

The Royal Swedish Academy of Sciences has decided to award the 1995 Nobel Prize in Chemistry to Professor Paul Crutzen, Max-Planck-Institute for Chemistry, Mainz, Germany (Dutch citizen), Professor Mario Molina, Department of Earth, Atmospheric and Planetary Sciences and Department of Chemistry, MIT, Cambridge, MA, USA and Professor F. Sherwood Rowland, Department of Chemistry, University of California, Irvine, CA, USA for their work in atmospheric chemistry, particularly concerning the formation and decomposition of ozone. There follows an extensive review of their work and the history of the ozone layer research.

Links
To The Royal Swedish Academy of Sciences home page • To The Nobel Foundation home page

Publishing Chemistry on the Internet

http://www.awod.com/netsci/
Issues/Mar96/feature4.html

Imagine the reaction of a practicing chemist of the turn of the century if he or she was suddenly transported into a modern chemical research facility. Outside of the odd pieces of glassware and the occasional Bunsen burner, the modern laboratory would be barely recognizable. Modern instrumentation has dramatically transformed the laboratory and the practices of chemists. IR, UV, and NMR spectrometers allow chemists to identify structures without destroying the sample. X-ray crystallography affords a detailed structure with bond distances and angles. Chromatography in its many variants allow for the separation of complex mixtures. While it is perhaps a simplification to call these techniques routine they are everyday workhorses in the modern research environment. Our visitor from the past would no doubt be amazed! Now imagine he or she stepping into the research library. Whilst our time traveler might be in awe of the number of journals, the sheer volume of material published every year, the computer access to databases and the search tools, he or she would be perfectly comfortable with the primary means for disseminating chemical information - the printed journal! In fact, the chemical journal has changed very little this century. Except for the occasional inclusion of a color graphic, an issue of any chemistry journal looks very much the same as it did in 1900. Considering the remarkable innovations in communication sciences over the century, i.e. film, radio, television, computer graphics, digital audio, digital video,

etc., the static nature of chemical communication is striking.

Links
Introduction • Standards in Chemical Publishing • E-conferences and Journals • References • MIME (Multipurpose Internet Mail Extensions) • VRML (virtual reality markup) • Java • Chemical Markup Language • Electronic Conferencing and Journals

WebElements

http://www.shef.ac.uk/uni/academic/
A-C/chem/web-elements/
web-elements-home.html

WebElements is the periodic table on the World-Wide Web. This page contains links to chemical data for the first 112 elements. I've made every effort to ensure accuracy of the data but you and I both have to accept there are still plenty of errors. Time permitting, I'm still working on them. Therefore use all data obtained here at your own risk. Information concerning the names of elements 104-108 is available.

Links
General • Chemical • Physical • Nuclear • Electronic • Biological • Geological • Crystallographic • Reduction potentials • Isotope abundances • Electronic configurations • Ionization enthalpies • names of elements 104-108 • also each element on the table....

A
AAAS, 94
ACA, 148
ACA Newsletter, 148
Academic Institutions Non-profit Or-
    ganizations Commercial Organiza-
    tions Other Lists, 184
Academy's purposes of knowledge, 124
Acrylic alloys, 37
ACS articles, 147
ACS Software National, 95
    ACS Symposium, 173
    Acta Chemica Scandinavica, 100
Additive Blends, 21
Additive plants, 11
Adhesives business, 33
Ads Specialty Ads Chemical Industry
    Consultants Other Chemistry, 184
Advancement of Science, 164
Aerosols, 82
Africa, 114
AgrEvo Canada, 23
Agricultural applications, 25
Agricultural chemicals, 46
Agricultural products, 15
Agriculture, 7, 21, 23
    AIChE 95
Air boards, 78
Air sensitivity, 38
Akzo Nobel, 20
    business units of, 1
Alchemy gNMR StatView ModelMaker
    ChemWindow/ChemIntosh Chem-
    Web Prism, 152
Alcohols, 12, 28
Aldrich Chemical Company
Alias Wavefront TM entertainment, 86
Alkylate
    biodegradable detergent, 12
    detergent, 12
Alle
    Dienstleistung für, 113
Allied Chemical, 3
Alumina, 12
Aluminum, 1

Aluminum nitride ceramics, 30
America 95
    Fisher Catalog 95/96 Fisher Safety,
        186
American Association for the Ad-
    vancement of Science, 94, 164
American chemical companies, 3
American Chemical Society, 94
American Chemicals Company, 3
American Institute of Physics, 156
American Refractories Company, 54
Amines, 28
Ammonia, 36
Ammonia/urea plant, 36
Amoco Corporation, 3
Amoco investments, 4
Amoco's status, 4
Analytical Consumer Great Deals
    Guess, 160
Analytical methods
    environmental analysis, 166
Analytical Reagents MSDS, 188
Animation Laboratory, 173
Animation Projects, 173
Annual American Chemical Society's
    Colloid, 143
Annual Book of ASTM Standards, 96
Anthium Dioxcide, 91
Antibody production, 9
Anticancer drug therapy, 26
Antimony-based polymer additives, 4
AOAC INT'L, 164
API separators, 78
Application Data Application Software,
    64
Application FREE EXSYS Demos, 67
Applications/commercialization, 205
Applied Biology, 132
Applied Chemistry, 100
Applied Chemistry Department of Uni-
    versity of Salford, 49
Applied Physics, 132
Applied Surfactant Research, 143
Applied Surfactant Research Institute,
    144

Aquapal group
  customer profile, 55
Architectural components, 5
Architectural Finishes Store Photo-
  chromics 1995 Annual Report, 38
Argus Chemicals, 4
Aromatics, 15
Aromatics division, 35
Aromatics production, 10
Aromax technology, 10
Art Gallery Materials Science, 136
Artificial Intelligence group, 88
ASCII text file format, 187
ASEAN, 36
Asia, 2, 48, 49
Asia Pacific region, 36, 179
ASM, 95
ASQC Quality News Membership
  Services Ten Reasons, 95
ASSE org site, 96
Association of Water Technologies, 97
ASTM, 96
ASTM standards, 96
Astrophysics, 161
ATHAS Data Bank of thermal proper-
  ties, 145
ATHAS Information List, 146
Atomic level, 136
Atomic Mass Constant Atomic Mass
  Unit Avogadro Constant, 124
ATSDR Announcements ATSDR Job
  Opportunities ATSDR
  contaminant data, 191
Australia, 19, 179
Australia/New Zealand, 29
Australian Academy of Science, 148
Australian Defense Force Academy,
  168
Australian Journal of Chemistry, 148
Automotive products, 3
Awards of Society, 99
AWT Industry Events, 97
A-Z Index List, 202

B
Badische Anilin, 6
Baker Hughes Inc

chemical division of, 6
Baker Industrial Chemicals, 6
Baker Jardine, 57
Baker Performance Chemicals Incorpo-
  rated, 6
Baltzer Science Publishers, 148
Bangkok, 48
Bangladesh, 7
BASF, 6
BASF Aktiengesellschaft, 6
BASF Corporation, 6
BASF Group, 6
Battelle Memorial Institute, 127
Bayer Group, 7
Beijing Yanshan Petrochemical Corpo-
  ration, 51
Beilstein file, 168
Belgium, 49
Benzene, 10
Beograd
  Glasnik Hemijskog drustva, 159
Bethesda, 149
Biocatalysis, 169
Biocatalytic reactions
  microbial, 169
Biochemicals, 9
Biochemistry, 49, 166, 184
Biodegradation of environmental pol-
  lutants, 169
Biodegradation pathways, 169
Biological control needs, 16
Biological markers
  fluorescent, 11
Biological Papers, 153
Biology
  molecular, 148, 161
Biology Tools Magnifiers Molecular
  Models Sets Kits Components, 70
Biomedical Engineering, 71
Biomolecules, 158
Biopharmaceutical manufacturing, 76
Bioscience group
  international, 51
Bioseparations, 143
Biotechnology, 23, 42, 166, 169, 205
Biotechnology marketplace, 165
Biotechnology products, 32

BIPM Maintained Ampere BIPM
    Maintained Ohm BIPM Maintained,
    124
Bond distances, **209**
Books Journals Publications
    CD-ROM products, **108**
Boolean Search Page Browse U. S. Pat-
    ent Classifications, **196**
Brazil, **11, 194**
Brazilian National System, **194**
Bristol, **50**
Brown Chemical, **8**
Brown University, **156**
Browse DOT Administrations, **119**
Brutto formula, **132**
Bryan Research, **58**
Buckman Laboratories, **8**
Bundoora campuses of RMIT, **131**
Business application software, **85**
Business Entities
    Listing of 497, **206**
Business Wire, **149**
Business-Pharmaceuticals, **51**
Business-to-business trade, **163**
Business-to-business transit times, **85**
Butadiene Rubber Chemigum HR
    Chemigum Powder Chemigum Car-
    boxylated, **22**
Buyers Guide
    chemical, **167**

C
C'T Magazine of Germany, **61**
C. F. Picou Associates, **59**
C. P. Hall Company, **13**
CAD Centre, **137**
California, **3, 70, 86**
Cambridge, **150**
Cambridge Crystallographic Data
    Centre Cambridge Structural Data-
    base System, **133**
Cambridge Scientific Computing, **58**
Cambridge Structural Database System,
    133
Cambridge University Julie Altmann,
    112
Cambridge's Chemical curriculum, **134**

CambridgeSoft Corporation, **58**
Cam-Lock flanges, **76**
Can I See More, **201**
Canada, **6, 34, 41, 46, 69, 76, 98, 99,**
    117
Canada every two years, **98**
Canadian Centre, **116**
Canadian Journal of Chemical Engi-
    neering, **98**
Canadian National Committee, **99**
Canadian Society, **98**
Canadian Society Honors John Moffat,
    107
Canberra, **168**
Cancer
    colorectal, **51**
Cancer therapies, **51**
Cancer treatment, **91**
Cancer treatments, **154**
Capabilities Product
    resinall Hattiesburg resinall Severn
    resinall, **40**
CAPD consortium, **138**
Capillary Columns, **62**
Capital costs, **13**
Capital HPLC, **59**
Carbon, **28, 37**
Carbon Black Division, **15**
Carborundum Company, **17**
Career Opportunities Industry Groups
    Web Page EMAX Publications, **66**
Carnegie Mellon University, **201**
Carnegie Mellon University-Computer
    Aided Process, **138**
CAS CAS Products, **150**
Case Western Reserve University De-
    partment of Biochemistry Gopher,
    189
Catalogs Company Home Pages
    Chemicals
    Company directory, **184**
Catalysis Society of New York 1996-
    1997 Program Catalysis, **107**
Catalyst applications, **93**
Catalyst-related services, **93**
Catalytic oxidation, **163**
Cayman Chemical Company, **9**

CCC, **133**
CCC building, **133**
CD New, **150**
CD ROM products of Japanese patents, **194**
CD-ROM Atomic Emission Conversion Software Network Licenses Formats, **67**
CD-ROM Europages Chambers of commerce Contact Europages Dialing, **199**
CEMS Institute, **144**
Census data, **202**
Census Lookup server, **202**
Central America, **72**
Central government, **11**
Ceramic coating, **73**
Ceremonial activities, **106**
CFC, **43**
Chairman of Board of Executive Editors Further information, **165**
Chartered Chemical Engineers, **103**
Chem3D Pro 3.5 ChemFinder Pro 3.0 CS, **58**
ChemExpo community, **170**
ChemExpo Forums, **170**
ChemExpo Industry News, **170**
ChemExpo Info Booth, **170**
Chemfab Corporation, **10**
Chemfinder Database Searching Online MSDS Project
Utah database, **189**
Chemical Abstracts Service, **189**
Chemical Abstracts Service of American Chemical Society, **182**
Chemical additives, **179**
Chemical applications, **41**
Chemical building block, **31**
Chemical Bulletin Boards Current Price Indications, **2**
Chemical change, **117**
Chemical characterization of surfaces, **125**
Chemical companies, **14, 75**
Chemical company, **15, 19, 33**
Chemical compounds, **78, 169**
Chemical data, **209**

Chemical Database Service, **170**
Chemical Distribution, **172**
Chemical end products, **53**
Chemical Engineering, **109, 132, 140, 144, 153, 181**
Chemical Engineering Departmental Information, **144**
Chemical Engineering Faculties 1994-1995, **171**
Chemical Engineering Faculty Directory, **171**
Chemical Engineering UFIAC-UF Industrial Assessment Center SUCCEED, **142**
Chemical engineering undergraduate textbook, **140**
Chemical engineers
technical association of, **98**
Chemical Feedstocks Chemical Intermediates Polymers Fabrics, **4**
Chemical Finder, **121**
Chemical group, **12, 19**
Chemical identification numbers, **121**
Chemical industries, **58, 114**
Chemical industry, **35, 80, 109, 111, 114, 167, 174, 183, 185**
Chemical industry personnel, **147**
Chemical industry's common interests, **112**
Chemical Information, **67, 173**
Chemical Institute of Canada, **99**
Chemical intermediates, **17, 31**
Chemical issues, **170**
Chemical Leaman Tank Lines, **60**
Chemical Management System, **73**
Chemical manufacture, **169**
Chemical Manufacturers Association, **99**
Chemical manufacturing, **42**
Chemical manufacturing facilities, **112**
Chemical markets, **114**
Chemical names, **121**
Chemical news, **170**
Chemical of interest, **189**
Chemical Physics Preprint Database, **137, 156**

Chemical Physics Preprint Server Journal of Molecular Modeling Journal, 139

Chemical problems, 24

Chemical process engineering, 177

Chemical process simulation software, 58

Chemical process vessels, 5

Chemical processing, 10

Chemical processing industries, 53

Chemical production, 7

Chemical products, 3, 6, 7, 14, 30, 38, 75, 186

Chemical reaction, 55

Chemical reaction capabilities, 42

Chemical reactions, 45

Chemical research, 99

Chemical science, 131

Chemical Sector's mission, 40

Chemical Shifts Clipart Available, 18

Chemical solutions company, 10

Chemical specialties, 9, 46

Chemical species, 56

Chemical Structure of Poly-Orange Tom-1 Toluenediisocyanate Polymer Poly-Orange, 11

Chemical supply business, 82

Chemical Technology, 98

Chemical testing, 66

Chemical trading groups, 2

Chemical transport industry, 76

Chemical transportation, 76

Chemical water treatments, 97

Chemical Week, 172, 180

Chemical WWW, 207

Chemical WWW Sites Chemical Engineering WWW Virtual, 83

Chemicals business, 7

Chemicals company, 33

Chemicals sector, 3

Chemicals sector's growth, 4

Chemicals/ Plastics Manufacturing Chemicals, 53

Chemist's Art Gallery, 173

Chemistry magazine, 109

Chemistry 4-D Draw, 60

Chemistry Conference THEOCHEM, 165

Chemistry departments, 150

Chemistry Departments of UK Universities, 112

Chemistry Departments Other Chemistry Resources, 142

Chemistry Division, 125, 126

Chemistry Division staff, 125

Chemistry drawing program, 61

Chemistry laboratory, 96

Chemistry of electronic materials, 125

Chemistry of solid state, 136

Chemistry papers, 158

Chemistry problems, 85

Chemistry Program of EPSRC, 170

Chemistry related topics, 158

Chemistry research, 158

Chemistry Resources, 184

Chemistry software, 77

Chemistry WWW sites, 77

Chemistry-related sites, 139

ChemOffice Pro 3.5 ChemDraw Pro ChemOffice 3.5, 58

Chemometrics, 90

Chemscape Chime PNG ChemWindow ChemIntosh ChemWeb CACTVS, 207

Cherwell Scientific, 151

Chevron Chemical, 10

Chicago, 1, 13, 173

Chile, 31

China, 23, 29, 34, 41, 51

Chinese Petroleum Corporation, 11

Chiral organic molecules, 49

Chiropractic, 132

Chlorination, 44

Chlorine dioxide, 91

Chromatography, 209

  capillary gas, 59

  liquid, 62

Chromatography chemistries, 92

Chromatography sample injection manufacturer of high pressure liquid, 85

Chromophore, 11

Chromosomes, 173

Chrompack-using, **62**
Ciba Giegy, **12**
Cleaners Waxes/Polishes Corrosion Preventatives Adhesives, **10**
Client/server, **87**
Clinical Blood Analyzers, **70**
Clipart optical equipment tuning New chemistry, **70**
CLTLs Value Added Services Looking, **60**
Club of Philadelphia Message, **107**
CMA, **99**, **100**
Coal, **114**
Coatings Surfactants Chemical Information Electronic Handbooks, **67**
CODATA Task Group, **123**
Collaborations Other Quality Related Resources, **96**
Combustion, **125**
Combustion Chemistry Laboratory, **128**
Combustion Research Facility, **128**
Commercial enterprise, **180**
Commercial interests of more, **111**
Commercial search engine, **200**
Commitment industry's, **99**
Commodity chemicals, **39**, **175**
Commodore 64 computers, **71**
Community of Science World Wide Web server, **175**
Companies-Kokkola Chemicals Oy, **35**
Company Information Products, **78**, **83**
Company Profile Merits of Experienced Equipment Success Stories, **74**
Company ranks, **3**
Company's chemical specialties, **46**
Compatabilization, **37**
Compliance Response Maritime Security Marine Personnel, **129**
Compounder of patented engineering thermoplastic alloys, **37**
Comprehensive database of meetings, **161**
Computation of structural formulae, **132**
Computational Chemistry, **160**

Computational Fluid Dynamics software, **67**
Computer Chemistry Center, **133**
Computer engineering, **148**
Computer Programming Ask PC Guy, **75**
Computer programs, **140**
Computer Science, **148**
Computer software, **57**
Computer solutions, **65**
Computer systems, **71**
Computer tools, **138**
Computer-Aided Process Design, **138**
Computing Self-Help Resources, **142**
CONDEA Vista, **12**
CONDEA Vista Company, **12**
CONDEA Vista's products, **12**
Conformation Sampling Random Walks, **139**
Congressional mandate, **190**
Congressional Mandates Organizational Structure Goals Statement of Values ATSDR, **191**
Connecticut, **27**
Consortium of research institutions, **175**
Constituent Societies, **99**
Constituent Societies of Chemical Institute of Canada, **98**
Construction industry, **22**, **152**
Construction management, **90**
Construction services, **64**
Constructor firms, **159**
Consumer do-it-yourself products, **41**
Consumer goods, **15**
Consumer hobby, **41**
Consumer products, **32**, **99**, **169**
Consumer Science, **132**
Consumption trends, **120**
Contents Latest epapers List of epapers Editors, **158**
Contract awards, **183**
Contract maintenance, **79**
Contractors engineering, **63**

Control Intelligent Feedback Algorithms Advanced Distillation Controls, **60**

Conversion factors of physics, **123**

Cool Sites OTI, **202**

Cooperations Inst, **133**

Cooperative agreement, **205**

Cooperative efforts, **31**

Corporate grades of Member, **103**

Corporate headquarters, **13**

Corporate Information News Financial Information Aerospace Sector Automotive, **3**

Corporate management, **40**

Corporate offices, **27**

Corporate Vision, **45**

Corporation
international chemical, **30**

Corporations
international, **31**
US, **149**

Corrosion control, **41**

Corrosion control coating, **72**

Corrosion protection, **53**

Corrosion rates, **62**

Corrosion resistance, **37**

Corrosion-resistant products, **56**

Cosmetic ingredients, **33**

Courses Low Cost Accessories Product of Fortnight Search instruments, **62**

Creates Chemical Equations, **87**

CRI Zeolites, **93**

Cron Chemical, **14**

Cron Chemical Corporation, **13**

Cron Chemical Group, **14**

Cron International, **14**

Crystal-crystal transition temperature of 625 degrees, **17**

Crystalline polymers, **17**

Crystallography, **209**

CS products, **58**

CSA, **149**

CSA bibliographic records, **149**

CSC, **98**, **99**, **173**

CSC Etc, **173**

CSD System CHANGES, **133**

CSD System Data Content Current known problems, **133**

CSIRO Publishing, **148**

Current Department citations, **119**

Custom formulations Exclusive contracts, **38**

Customer base, **8**, **26**, **48**

Customer basis, **26**

Customer referral list, **72**

Customer requirements, **38**

Customer satisfaction, **69**

Customer Service OSHA Software/Advisors Federal Register Notices Frequently, **127**

Customer-oriented companies, **23**

Customers capabilities, **28**

Customers direct access, **1**

Customers President's Message, **20**

Customers' needs, **28**

Customers' operations, **93**

D

DAELIM Engineers, **63**

Danish Chemical Society, **100**

Dansk Kemi
journal, **100**

Data Bank Goals, **146**

Data Standards Other OSHA Documents Technical Information US, **127**

Database Indexes Academic Pricing, **67**

Database of 150,000 companies, **199**

Database of chemical names, **189**

Database of sources, **198**

Daylight Chemical Information Systems, **63**

Daylight Depict service, **207**

Dedert Corporation, **64**

Delaware, **50**

Demos Pricing
isomers, **132**

Department of Commerce, **128**

Department of Energy, **119**

Department of Energy Reports Bibliographic Database, **119**

Deposition Overview of CSD System April 1996 Release, **133**

Deputy Director, **124**
Derwent, **176**
Derwent Information, **176**
Derwent Scientific, **176**
Desktop applications, **58**
Desktop workstations, **86**
Desulfurizing Unit, **51**
Detergent formulation, **143**
Deutsch Publications European Union R&D Fourth RTD Framework, **116**
Developing Specialty Chemicals, **24**
Development Buy Swap Sell Service Industries Employment, **179**
Developmental Chemistry, **131**
Diagnostic manufacturing, **42**
Diagnostic Reagents Biochemicals Custom Synthesis, **82**
Diagnostics
chemical, **125**
DIALOG Custom product, **177**
DIALOG DIALOG Subscription Form DIALOG Subscription Form, **177**
DialogFAQ DIALOG Publications, **176**
DialogLink Frequently Asked Questions
DIALOG databases, **176**
DIET 7 conference, **136**
Directions Publications Publications Search Feature Graduate Fellowship Applications, **125**
Director Meeting Programs 1996, **95**
Directory of 66,557,959, **201**
Directory of chemical companies, **184**
Directory of Chemical Engineering Research, **98**
Directory Technical reports Directory 1994, **177**
Disciplinary divisions, **105**
Disclosure of material information, **128**
Dishwashing detergents, **12**
Dispersant stabilization, **143**
Display of current work, **160**
Dissemination of information, **96**
Dissemination of new findings, **158**
Distillation, **28**
Distillation capabilities, **28**
Distillation equipment, **28**

Distillation project
customer's, **28**
Distillation unit, **28**
Distillations, **28**
Distribution companies, **27**
Distribution of final product, **158**
Distribution points, **123**
Distribution server, **137**, **156**
Distribution system, **31**
Distributor of quality chemical raw materials, **13**
Division InterCAP Graphics Systems Intergraph Computer Systems Intergraph Federal, **71**
Docs EXSYS Tech Support EXSYS Information Request EXSYS, **67**
Documentation International Patent Classification Information Patent Cooperation, **196**
DOE Contractors, **119**
DOE database, **119**
DOE Openness Initiative Information Resources, **119**
DOE's Office of Scientific, **119**
Dojindo Laboratories Catalog request Dojindo News
New, **15**
Dojindo Pharmacy, **15**
Dojindo's Company history, **15**
Donation of ranchland site, **88**
DOT Web site, **119**
DOT web sites, **119**
Dow Chemical Company, **15**
Dow Jones Industrial Average, **3**
Dow News Releases New Businesses Emulsion Polymers Working, **15**
Dow Specialty Chemicals STYROFOAM Liquid Separations INVERT, **15**
Download PTO Forms PTO Fees Order Copies, **128**
Dresser Engineering, **64**
Druck World-wide network of Druck companies
Company profile of, **64**
Drug delivery systems, **143**
Drugs Polymers, **67**

Duke University, **154**
Duothane one, **47**
DuPont Views Financial Information,
16
Durable coatings, **5**
Dye Corporation, **3**
Dyestuffs, **32**, **39**
E
E. L. Pacific's scope of services, **66**
Early Release of Annual Energy Out-
look 1997 Press Releases, **120**
Eastman Chemical Company, **17**
EC company
customer-oriented, **89**
Eclipse Software Technologies, **65**
Economic activities, **177**
Economic activity, **112**
Economic data, **203**
Economic growth, **204**
US, **123**
Economic organization, **177**
Economic problems, **177**
Economic Sciences, **108**
ECOSSE control course, **177**
Ecosse Process Engineering Environ-
ment, **177**
Edinburgh, **59**
Edition DuPont Stock, **16**
Editor Sponsors, **155**
Editorial Board, **157**
Editorial Board Reviews Information,
153
Education, **99**, **131**, **132**, **179**, **191**
Environmental, **110**
scientific, **94**
Education Division Membership Divi-
sion Publications Division Office of
Government, **95**
Educational opportunities, **96**
Educational programmes, **111**
Educational society, **98**

E
Egyptian Government List of Preferred
Sites INFOWEEK Magazine List,
182
Eh-pH diagrams, **55**

EIA Interactive Query facility Green-
house Gas, **120**
Eicosanoids, **9**
EJTC Operates Editors
Scope, **153**
Ekonol Polyester Resins, **17**
Electric Library, **198**
Electrical equipment, **92**
Electricity Demand Will Outweigh
Environmental Impact of Federal
Rule, **120**
Electrochemical cell equilibria, **55**
Electrochemical research and develop-
ment, **30**
Electrochemical Research Corporation,
30
Electrochemical science, **100**
Electrochemistry, **125**
Electrode-based measurement informa-
tion, **79**
Electron Microscopy Tomography
Visualization of Micelles Visualiza-
tion of Dynamics of Spreading, **173**
Electron Radius Cu X-Unit Deuteron
Magnetic Moment Deuteron, **124**
Electronic application system, **195**
Electronic archive, **137**, **156**
Electronic Chemical
Prior art Master list Design patent,
193
Electronic Conference, **153**, **160**
Electronic form, **162**
Electronic industries, **34**
Electronic mail, **153**
Electronic Materials Division, **15**
Electronic Materials Division Grant
Chemical Division Filled, **19**
Electronic medium, **164**
Electronic publication covering theo-
retical chemistry, **153**
Electronic publishing, **155**
Electronic structure, **85**
Electronic structure equations, **85**
Electronics, **10**, **84**, **102**, **177**
Electronics company
international, **91**
Electronics industries, **22**

Electronics materials, 33
Elf Aquitaine, 18
Elsag Bailey Home Page
    Product information Customer support, 68
Elsevier Science, 153
Elsevier Science B. V. Amsterdam, 160
Eluxyl technology, 11
E-mail Commands, 138
Email Directory, 175
Email Directory Fisher Scientific Locations About Fisher Scientific, 186
E-mail discussion groups, 206
E-mail messages, 198
Email Newsletter, 160
EMAX Solution Partners, 66
EMCI Query Form, 121
Emergency releases of hazardous substances, 191
Employment opportunities, 128, 186
Employment services, 108
Energy forecasts, 120
Energy industries, 64
Energy nuclear physics, 117
Energy production, 120
Energy Reorganization Act of 1974, 126
Energy Secretary Hazel R. O'Leary Access, 119
Energy Statistics EIA's Web Site Wins Award, 120
Engineering advantages of materials, 73
Engineering company, 58
Engineering Design Research Center, 138
Engineering materials, 37, 136
Engineering Mechanical, 193
Engineering Network News, 182
Engineering Network Prototype Development Workshop Computer-Aided Engineering Tools, 142
Engineering News-Record, 152
Engineering programs, 122
Engineering services, 59
Engineers Plastics, 179
ENR Shopping Mall Find, 153

Enterprise Management Software Solutions, 71
Entertainment sectors, 86
ENVIROFACTS program system databases, 121
ENVIRO-NET MSDS database, 186
Environment EPA Sector Notebooks American Institute, 121
Environment Institute's research heart of, 190
Environment Prototyping Miscellaneous, 179
Environment Today EMAX Industry Survey Results, 66
Environmental analytical laboratory, 54, 61
Environmental assessments, 90
Environmental benefits, 9
Environmental chemistry, 166
Environmental compliance assistance network, 121
Environmental control, 51
Environmental Education Society Activities Awards, 110
Environmental factors, 31
Environmental industries, 65
Environmental labs, 121
Environmental manager, 188
Environmental performance, 99
Environmental performance of manufacturing processes, 81
Environmental Planning, 80
Environmental programs, 170
Environmental protection, 51
Environmental remediation, 143
Environmental research and development, 110
Environmental RouteNet Free Demonstrations, 149
Environmental safety information, 188
Environmental services, 15, 58
Enzymes, 9
Enzymology, 169
EPA, 123
EPA data, 188
EPA specifications, 208
EPA's 1995 phase, 43

EPO
   languages of, **194**
EPO Annual Report 1995
   EPO publications, **193**
EPO's task, **193**
Epoxy Matrix Phase Detection Data
   Sheet Compliance, **81**
Epoxy resins
   manufacturer of, **34**
Epsilon Chimie Online Catalog Struc-
   tural Analysis Useful, **18**
Equipment Research, **179**
Ester plasticizers, **13**
Ether propylene project
   methyl tertiary butyl, **36**
Ethyl, **18**
Ethyl additives, **18**
Ethylbenzene unit, **47**
Ethylbenzene/styrene monomer plant,
   36
Ethylene, **51**, **204**, **205**
Ethylene/polyethylene, **36**
Europe, **2**, **14**, **19**, **23**, **31**, **41**, **48**, **49**,
   92, **190**
European chemical industry
   voice of, **101**
European context, **101**
European countries, **50**, **199**
European economic data Fairs, **199**
European economy, **199**
European Federation of Biotechnology,
   109
European market
   macro-economic analysis of, **199**
European Patent Office, **193**
European patents, **193**
Eurosciences, **117**
Events
   manuals, **133**
Every Investor
   SEC, **129**
Excel V Gas Chromatograph Sulf-Tane
   InfraTane TVP-1000, **68**
Expanded CAS Using CAS Registry,
   150
Experbib Expereact Chemicals Direc-
   tory Job opportunity Chemical, **169**

Experimentalists, **77**
Expert Systems EXSYS Products
   EXSYS Applications
   EXSYS, **67**
Expertise
   scientific, **175**
Exploration Expertise BP Homepage
   Tell Us, **8**
EXSYS Inc, **67**
Extremes-high pressures, **38**

F
F. Flow
   900-1000 degrees, **17**
Fachinformationszentrum Karlsruhe,
   182
Facilities Publications Search Guide,
   137
Factory premises, **91**
Factory trials, **26**
Factsheets
   toxic chemical, **189**
Far East, **19**
Farchan Laboratories, **18**
Fatty acids, **9**
FDA, **10**
Features Explorations Exhibits Ask
   Experts Interviews Bookmarks Mar-
   ketplace, **164**
Federal Agencies
   Events, **125**
Federal government, **124**, **161**
Federal regulations, **65**, **88**, **170**
Federation of European Chemical So-
   cieties, **100**
Feedstock, **114**
   chemical, **4**
Feedstock area, **179**
Feedstocks, **114**
   chemical, **114**, **144**
Fellowships Meetings Life-Cycle As-
   sessment Publications Ecological
   Risk Assessment Society, **110**
Ferrous metals, **1**
Ferruzzi enterprise, **5**
Fertilizer elements, **205**
Fertilizer plant, **36**

Fiberite molding compounds, 19
Fibers Chemicals Development, 4
Film samples, 82
Filter Dryers, 73
Filtration media, 39
Filtration Products, 14
Final Rules Investigations Inspection, 129
Financial resources, 91
Fine Chemicals, 4
Fingertight ferruless cartridge system, 59
Firestone Synthetic Rubber, 20
Firestone's anionic polymerization technology, 20
Fisher Chemical Catalog 95/96 Fisher, 20, 186
Fisher Scientific Internet Catalog, 189
Fisher Scientific products, 20, 186
Fisher-Rosemount flow measurement, 83
Fit Ball
    PROCEDE pro, 152
Flanders, 107
Flemish Chemical Society, 107
Florida, 27
Flow Simulation, 172
Flowsheet optimization, 138
Fluent Inc, 67, 68
Fluid Data, 68
Fluid Data News releases Employment Opportunities Dataline Newsletter history of, 68
Fluka Catalog, 21
Fluka Chemical Companies, 42
Fluorescent reagents, 77
Fluorinations of complex molecules, 29
Fluorine, 22
    elemental, 29
Fluoro-based chemical products, 5
Fluorochemicals range, 5
Fluoropolymer composite materials, 10
FMC, 21
FMC Corporation, 21
Focal point, 165
Food Graphic Arts Automotive Financial Leather, 176

Food ingredients, 32
Food processing, 10
Food Science, 132
Footwear, 22
Forensic science, 166
Forest industry adhesives, 33
Forestry Products, 33
Form Facilities, 142
Formaldehyde, 31
Forms Regulatory Notices, 129
Fortune 1000, 149
Fortune 500, 3
Forums EXSYS Hot News Search EXSYS TECOM AI, 67
Fourier transform, 77
Fourier transform infrared spectrometer, 78
Fourier transform NMR spectrometers, 88
France, 7, 11
Free Catalog, 55
French industrial company, 18
French IUPAC, 169
Frequently Asked General Questions, 120
FTIR Raman C13NMR VP-FTIR Mass Spec HNMR FTNIR, 67
FTP, 206
FTP search v3.3 Searching parameters, 199
FTP sites, 197, 199
Fuel additives, 11
Fuels chemistry, 125
Fullerene Structure Library USB Chemistry Department List of publications, 141
Fullerenes, 30, 141
    properties of, 141
Functional Pigments, 14
Fundamental Constants, 123
Fungicide, 51
Further Information Instructions, 133
FW Calculator
    Commercial databases, 169

G

Gallery Staff Directory Search Keywords Technical activities, 123

Gas Adsorption, 59

Gas chromatographs, 62, 86

Gas Chromatography PLOT columns HPLC columns Gas-Clean, 62

Gas exploration, 53

Gas Industry, 57, 154

Gas Journal, 162

Gas Research Institute, 46

Gas Utilization Technologies, 144

Gas Utilization Technologies Chemical Engineering Research Tools, 144

Gas-Based Petrochemicals, 204

Gasoline, 18

Gasoline company, 3

Gazetteer, 202

GE Plastics, 21

GE Specialty Chemicals, 21

Gel analysis, 71

General Assembly of WIPO, 196

General Electric Corporation, 21

General Information, 119

General Information Research and Development Activities Faculty Involved Current, 144

General Information Welcome Tours NIST Boulder homepage, 123

General Marine Safety Program Information Prevention, 129

Generation management, 8

Geneva, 196

Geology, 132, 147

Geophysics, 147

Germany, 6, 8, 82

Glance Customer Service Directory Chemical Abstracts Service Division, 95

Glance DuPont Career Opportunities DuPont Mexico DuPont News Releases, 16

Glance Investment Planned, 16

Glasgow Teaching materials Global Network Navigator, 137

Glass aramid, 37

Glassware, 53

Glossary of Terms EPA Glossary of Terms ATSDR Locations ATSDR, 191

Glycol Ethylene, 204

Glycol reprocessing, 28

Goodyear Chemical, 22

Gopher database, 189

Gopher file, 189

Gopher servers, 189

Gophers, 181

Goût, 36

Governance Contaminated Soils, 110

Governing Board, 113

Government UK, 136

Government agencies, 205

Government bodies, 111

Government Environmental Professional Organizations, 172

Government Printing Office, 119

Governmental clients, 88

Gower's Chemical Reference Series, 154

Graduate Studies Information, 142

Graphic systems, 7

Graphical molecule, 132

Graphics, 157, 188 scientific, 71

Graphics programs, 132

Graphics software, 71

Graphite components TiC-coated, 73

Graphite substrate, 73

GraphPad Prism, 68

GraphPad radioactivity web calculator Technical articles, 68

GraphPad Software, 68

Great Britain, 143

Greater Manchester, 49

Greenhouse Gas Emissions EIA Administrator Testifies Growth, 120

Gross national product, 102, 177

Groundwater investigations, 90

Group of world class chemical, 49

GSA, 10

Gulf Coast area, **30**, **43**
Gulf Publishing Company, **154**

H
H&S Chemical, **24**
H. D. Miller Sr, **76**
Halogen exchange, **44**
Handbook Other Useful Sites Arrang-
    ing Visit Vacancies, **136**
Harris Specialty Chemicals, **22**
Harvest system, **199**
HazDat Database
    Datasets/Resources, **191**
Head Office, **99**
Health, **5**, **99**, **145**, **169**
    occupational, **116**
    public, **125**, **126**
Health Act of 1970, **127**
Health Administration, **126**
Health assessments
    public, **191**
Health assessments of waste sites
    public, **191**
Health care, **7**
Health care company, **7**
Health consultations, **191**
Health effects, **190**
Health of hazardous substances
    public, **190**
Health research, **125**
Health surveillance, **191**
Heat transfer products, **72**
Heating fuels, **18**
Heavy Ions Brookhaven Center, **117**
Heavy Oil Cracking, **51**
Help Desk, **170**
Henry Dreyfus Chemical Informatics
    Program, **173**
Herceg Novi, **104**
Heteroatom NMR, **67**
Heterocycles, **61**
Heterocyclic Chemistry Conference
    Starts Invited Keynotes Synthetic,
    153
High Performance Liquid Chromatog-
    raphy technology, **92**
High Speed, **68**

High technology materials, **30**
Higher Education Bodies of United
    Kingdom, **137**
Highway Transport, **69**
Histology Particles, **82**
Historical origins, **94**
Historical records, **170**
History of 20 years, **204**
History of bulk transportation industry
    leadership, **74**
History of chemical engineering, **143**
History of magazine, **163**
History of technological innovation, **76**
History/information Information re-
    quest form
    Information resinall, **40**
Hobby
    spatulas magnets, **70**
Home maintenance, **41**
Home Page Feedback Form Survey
    Contact ASQC, **96**
Home Software List, **152**
Homepages, **178**
Homopolymers, **17**
Horizontal Palte Filters, **73**
Hot Sites, **182**
Hotel, **40**, **63**
House Course, **81**
Household laundry, **12**
Houston, **12**
Houston Ship Channel, **40**
HPC-11 Hydrogen Permeation Moni-
    toring System, **6**
HPI developments
    coverage of new, **159**
HPI plants, **159**
HSC Chemistry, **55**
Http, **200**
    URL, **175**
Huls America, **24**
Human Biology, **132**
Human Services, **125**
Hydrocarbon, **53**
    manufacturer of, **39**
Hydrocarbon chemistry
    halogenated, **1**
Hydrocarbon compounds, **78**

Hydrocarbon Processing, **159**
Hydrocarbon processing industries, **70**
Hydrocarbon processing industry, **83**
Hydrocarbon Processing Industry-
refining, **159**
Hydrogen sulfide abatement products
Sulfix, **6**
Hydroxy, **47**

I
IATA air requirements, **10**
IBM PC version of SigmaPlot, **71**
ICC President, **107**
ICHEMCO s. r. l, **24**
IChemE membership, **103**
Idemitsu of Japan, **36**
Illinois, **1**
Immunology, **161**
Imperial College, **150**
Importer of chemical raw materials, **48**
Improver
LiquidPower flow, **13**
Inc of U. S. A, **35**
Inc. BR&E, **58**
Inc. Chemsol Inc, **10**
Inc. Founded 1961 Latest Develop-
ments Polymers, **82**
Inc. Goes Worldwide, **26**
Index Find, **86**
Index of RSC web, **108**
Indexing Other Web Indexes Paper
Describing Webcrawler Postscript,
203
India, **11**
Indian Subcontinent, **29**
Indo China, **29**
Indonesia, **8**
Indus Group, **71**
Industrial activities, **19**
Industrial adhesives, **33**
Industrial applications, **8**, **13**, **84**, **206**
Industrial Applications of Quantum
Mechanics Oxford Molecular Group
History, **80**
Industrial body, **138**
Industrial chemicals, **12**, **14**, **29**, **48**,
100

Industrial chemistry, **23**
Industrial cleaners, **12**
Industrial coatings, **33**
Industrial effluents, **166**
Industrial equipment, **18**
Industrial hygiene, **82**
Industrial processes, **6**, **82**
Industrial products, **10**
Industrial Property, **194**
Industrial Property Information, **196**
Industrial Property System, **194**
Industrial research effort, **102**, **177**
Industrial samples, **66**
Industrial starches, **33**
Industrial systems, **29**
Industrial use, **38**
Industrial waste characterizations, **66**
Industrial Wastewater Engineering,
184
Industrial world, **17**
Industries of sizes, **65**
Industry association, **111**
Industry breakthroughs, **170**
Industry Communications Environ-
ment, **5**
Industry experience, **53**
Industry fundamentals, **32**
Industry groups, **111**
Industry Midstream Natural Gasbased
Petrochemicals Industry Downstream
Aromatic/Olefinic/Natural, **204**
Industry segments, **24**, **111**
Industry trends, **170**
Industry/government labs, **205**
Industry-related groups, **111**
Industry-wide calendar, **170**
Information
optics fluorescent biological markers
temperature calibration standards,
11
Information Centre Chemistry, **108**
Information Nuclear Reactors, **126**
Information Request Download Cron
Presentation, **14**
InfoSeek Corporation, **200**
InfoSeek's search, **200**
In-house applications, **63**

In-house information system
CrossFire, **168**
In-house turnaround times, **88**
Injuries, **127**
Inktomi Corporation technology white
paper, **200**
Innovation Submit research, **116**
Inorganic chemical products
stocks of selected, **118**
Inorganic chemicals, **118**
Inorganic polymeric modifier systems
marketing of new line of, **26**
Inorganic research chemicals, **42**
Installation of plant equipment, **39**
Installation of process facilities, **64**
Installation of tower internals, **78**
Institute of Chemical Engineers, **171**
Institute of Medicine, **124**
Institution of Chemical Engineers, **102**
Instructional course, **177**
Instrumentation laboratories, **96**
Insurance
liability, **97**
Insurance program
industry-wide, **97**
Integration of chemical information, **66**
Intelligence, **138**
corporate, **206**
Interdisciplinary research unit, **144**
Intergraph Corporation, **71**
Intermetallics, **30**
International advanced performance
materials company, **10**
International agreements, **194**
International association, **109**
International body, **102**
International Centre, **104**
International chemical company, **17**
International chemical physics com-
munity, **156**
International chemical trading, **27**
International conferences, **104**
International Contact Information
Product Support Collaborations Sci-
ence, **80**
International convention, **106**
International conventions, **106**

International Cooperating Companies
Multivariate Analysis Simca Con-
sulting, **90**
International cooperation, **100**, **104**
International Corrosion Council, **157**
International division, **33**
International Efforts Related Links, **144**
International events, **161**
International Events Funding informa-
tion, **144**
International government, **119**
International Legal Materials Informa-
tion, **128**
International licensing agreements, **26**
International magazine, **151**
International market, **63**
International markets, **31**
International network, **23**
International online information com-
pany, **181**
International operations, **13**
International ownership, **34**
International separations technology
business, **92**
International specialty chemical com-
pany, **46**
International Technical Polymer Sys-
tems, **26**
International theoretical chemistry
community, **137**, **156**
International trade, **2**
International trading, **33**
International Union of Pure and Ap-
plied Chemistry, **100**
Internet Business 500 JOM-A publica-
tion of Minerals, **182**
Internet Database Service Access, **149**
Internet HazDat Database, **191**
Internet resources
chemistry-related, **135**
Internet Services University master
Web server University, **137**
Internet Standards Value
World Collections of pointers
Chemical, **174**
Inventory
chemical, **73**

Inventory of chemical raw materials, 30
Investigations
  tank, 66
Investigations/feasibility studies, 90
Investment, 48, 146
Investments, 20
Ion Processes, 160
Ion Selective Electrode, 79
IRC Staff Scientific plan Seminars Papers www, 136
Irish Presidency Homepage-RTD Information Service English Francais, 116
Irradiation of food, 7
ISO 9001 compliance, 42
ISO 9002, 20
Isocyanate, 47
Isocyclic compounds, 168
Issue of Lab Animal Research Newsletter, 91

J
Jandel Scientific, 71
Japan, 11, 32, 46, 114, 155, 177, 178
Japan Information Center of Science, 182
Japan Science, 114
Japanese enterprises, 178
Japanese Technology Evaluation Center, 205
JASMS issues, 160
JCP Express, 156
JEOL equipment
  sales of, 72
JEOL subsidiaries, 72
JEOL USA, 72
JLM companies, 27
JLM Industries, 27
Job Opportunities, 88
Jobs Announcements Search Browse Examples Search, 191
John Ray Hazardous Chemical Database, 188
Joining Publications Education Other Programs, 96
Joining Working Party, 112
Joint venture, 30, 36

Joint venture opportunities, 183
Journal of American Society, 160
Journal of Chemical Physics, 156
Journal of Physical Chemistry, 158
Journal of Serbian Chemical Society, 159
Journal of Serbian Chemical Society-JSCS, 159
Journals
  online, 168
Journals' different publication schedules, 160
JPC features, 158
Jpeg images of teaching topics, 142
JST Service JST publications Information, 114
JTEC/WTEC assessments, 205
JTEC/WTEC's mission, 205

K
Karl Fischer Titrator Vaporizer Consistometer Moisture Balance Trip, 55
KBDS design support system, 177
KEDIACHEM group, 27
Keidanren, 177
Kg-10 Kg-100 Kg University 100g-1, 18
Khem modules, 73
Kinetics, 55
KMCO's pilot facilities, 28
Know EDGAR Database of Corporate Information SEC News, 129
Knoxville, 69
Knoxville-ATHAS Picture of ATHAS family Communication, 145
Knoxville-Molecular Based Study of Fluids, 146
Korea, 8, 43, 68, 204, 205
Korea Consumption of fertilizer elements, 205
Korea Overall supply, 205
Korea Production of fertilizer elements, 205
Korean Chemical Society, 106
Krueger Engineering, 72
Kyoto, 32

L

L'innovation et l'excellence technique, 36

Labtrader Magazine, 160

Lacquer thinners, 30

Lake Charles, 20

Language of chemistry, 58

Lanxide Coated Products, 73

Laser chemistry, 125

Laser Chemistry Gas-Phase Molecular Dynamics Photoinduced Molecular Dynamics, 117

Latex Company, 20

Latin America, 4, 19, 76

Launch of THEOCHEM-Alert Publication of Proceedings of 2nd Electronic Computational, 165

Leather chemical intermediates, 27

Leather tanning, 41

Lebanon, 67

Leophairatana family, 48

Letter Products, 15

Letters section, 158

LEXIS-NEXIS Products, 178

Library sources, 146

License Technology Transfer, 192

Life sciences, 165

Light Ends Fractionators Inferred Property Calculation Software-Distillation Cut, 60

LIGHTNIN Systems Division, 74

Linkers Pte Ltd, 29

Lipids, 9

Liquid chemical transportation, 69

Liquid Chromatographs, 86

Liquid fuels, 103, 104

Liquid Transport CRP, 74

Listserves, 147

Liverpool, 136

Logic Algorithm Dynamic Feedforward Algorithm Dynamic Multi-Variable Adaptive, 60

Logistics, 60

Lomas International, 29

London, 178

Los Alamos National Laboratory, 156

Louisiana, 11, 20

Louisiana Chemical Equipment Company, 74

Low-wage countries, 53

Loyola College, 205

LTL freight, 85

Lubricant, 11, 21

Lubricant additives, 18

Lubricants, 18

Ludwigshafen, 6

Lumber, 33

Lumber Manufacturers, 33

M

Magazine No Limit Big 3 CD-ROM, 162

MAGMAR Associates, 74

Magnesiurn, 1

Magnolia, 30

Magnolia Chemicals, 14, 30

Main Menu, 96

Major Portions of Book Learn, 206

Malaysia, 8, 23

Management Board, 157

Management of analytical services, 96

Manchester Science Park, 49

Manchester Staff List Researches, 136

Manual of Classification Index, 193

Manufacturer of adhesives, 33

Manufacturer of engineered polymer products, 40

Manufacturer of industrial coatings, 41

Manufacturer of polymers, 11

Manufacturer of specialty construction products, 22

Manufacturer's MSDS Data BNZ Materials Dojindo Laboratories liquids, 188

Manufacturers products, 14

Manufacturing company, 3

Manufacturing costs, 9

Manufacturing equipment, 39

Manufacturing equipment systems, 47

Manufacturing facilities, 21

Manufacturing objectives, 35

Manufacturing of specialty chemicals, 28

Manufacturing operations, 111

Manufacturing plants, 7, 16, 23, 76
Manufacturing process, 6
Manufacturing products, 47
Manufacturing sites, 15, 42, 91
Manufacturing technologies, 7
Marine markets, 41
Maritime petroleum, 76
Markers Liquid Crystalline, 11
Market introduction of organic metals, 93
Market survey Standardization organizations
    exhibitions, 199
Market-oriented research, 205
Markets high-technology systems, 91
Markov Chains, 139
Martin Marietta Energy Systems, 126
Maryland, 149
Mass Deuteron Molar, 124
Mass Spectrometers, 86
Mass Spectrometry, 160
Mass Transfer, 104
Massachusetts, 76
Master Batch Production Records, 49
Masterbatch business, 93
Material Safety Data Sheet management, 188
Material Safety Data Sheets, 187
Materials Science, 136
Materials Society Journal of ASM Science, 182
Mathematics, 108, 148
Mechanical Engineering Department of Middle East Technical University, 104
MedChem Project, 63
Medical Laboratory Science, 132
Medical products, 7
Medical publications, 164
Medical Sciences, 148
Medical/Life Sciences, 182
Medicinal applications, 26
Medicinal Drugs, 45
Meetings Conference diary Library Scientific activities, 108
Melamine Chemicals, 30
Membership association, 111

Membership dues, 148
Membership Information SETAC Foundation, 110
Membership services, 96
Mental health effects of petrochemical disasters, 145
Mental health outcomes, 145
MER's research and development activities, 31
Mercaptans, 78
Mercury Porosimetry, 59
MESSENGER Prices databases, 182
Metabolic pathways, 169
Metal Group, 15
Metal products, 35
Metallic brilliance, 73
Metallurgy, 132
Metal-matrix composites, 206
Methanex Corporation, 35
Methanol, 31
Methanol demand, 31
Methanol production facilities, 31
Mexican business units, 24
Mexican companies, 26
Mexico, 6, 9, 69
Mexico City, 11
Microbial enzyme-catalyzed reactions, 169
Microcomputer, 71
Microelectronics, 76, 143
Microelectronics manufacturing, 76
Microfilm, 4
Microprocessor designs MIPS, 86
Microscopes, 84
Microscopists
    electron, 82
Microscopy, 80, 81
Microscopy sample preparation supply market
    electron, 82
Military Spec chemical products, 10
Mill cleaning, 16
Miller Transporters' experience, 76

Mil-Spec Chemicals Featured Chemicals Quote Request Company Mission, 10
Milwaukee, 95
Mineral sources, 136
Minerals distributor, 29
Mining, 39
Ministry of Science, 159
Mission Statement Benefits of Phase-Transfer Catalysis Request, 81
Mississippi, 39
Mitsubishi Petrochemical Co, 205
Miwon Petrochemical Corporation, 31
Mixer Dryers, 73
MMC International Corporation, 76
MMC's primary products, 76
Mobil/Badger Third Generation Ethylbenzene process, 47
Modifier Resins, 21
Modifiers, 26
MOLCAS-3 quantum chemistry program package, 133
Moldmakers, 111
Molecular dynamics, 158
Molecular Modeling, 160
Molecular Modeling CD Clip Art, 71
Molecular modelling, 153
Molecular Physics Group, 156
Molecular Probes, 77
Molecular Simulations Inc, 77
Molecular structure elucidation, 132
Molecule Lab Equipment Dealers Labsavers Medical Equipment Service, 160
Monomers Microscopy, 82
Monsanto, 20
Monte Carlo Method Simulated Annealing XPLOR Home Page, 139
Montedison, 30
Month's Featured Items Request, 55
Mooney Chemicals, 35
MOPAC Pro CS Catalyst Register, 58
Motor carrier transportation, 60
Motorcycles, 63
Mount Olive, 6
Mountain View, 86
MSDS 127,000 3D, 184

MSDS data, 187
MSDS document, 187
MSDS Manager, 186, 187
MSDS pages, 189
MSDS Sheets, 189
MSDS transaction costs, 185
MSDS Unlimited software package, 188
MSDS Unlimited system, 188
MSI Contact Us Events Hotline Job Opportunities Navigating, 77
MTBE/propylene plant, 36
Multimedia publication, 160
Multiphase Flow Simulators, 57
Multistep chemical reactions, 55

N
NAE Members ONLY, 122
NAE Membership Information Frequently Asked Question Lifelong, 122
NAFTA region, 6
Nagase America Corporation, 32
Naphtha, 205
NASA Marshall Technology Test Bed NASA Ames Center, 88
NASA Stennis Space Center, 88
NASDAQ companies, 149
Nasdaq Stock Market, 41
National Academy of Engineering, 122, 124
National Academy of Sciences, 124
National Aeronautics, 205
National Chemistry Week, 98
National Institute of Industrial Property, 194
National Institute of Mental Health, 145
National Institute of Occupational Safety, 145
National Nuclear Data Center, 117
National Petrochemical Public Company
prime supporter of Thai government's, 48
National Representatives, 113
National Research Council, 124

National Science Foundation, **124, 205**
National Science Foundation Act of
1950, **124**
National service, **170**
National Starch, **33**
National Synchrotron Light Source
Brookhaven National Laboratory
fullerenes, **141**
National Technical Information Service, **119, 123**
National Toxicology Program, **125**
Natural gas, **31, 114, 144**
Natural gas resources, **144**
Natural resources, **110**
Nature science update Nature
advertisers, **161**
Nature Table of Contents, **161**
Navigation tool, **20, 186**
Navy ship, **40**
Négoce, **36**
Neste Chemicals, **33**
Net Search Free Trial Offer Download
Software Common, **198**
Netherlands, **1**
Neural Network, **88**
Neurosciences Research, **117**
New About Patents, **128**
New Access
Services, **149**
New Ashland Valvoline Guestbook
Safety, **5**
New Author Information Subscriptions
Contents Pages Corrigenda Selected,
148
New Carbon Fiber, **81**
New CAS Releases CAS Technical
Days
Training, **150**
New Catalog Acros Chemicals Catalog
95/96, **20**
New Catalog Acros Chemicals Catalog
95/96 Help, **186**
New ChemFinder Server CS Products
Technical Support CS
Software, **58**
New Company People Markets Products Environment, **38**

New Contact ASTM Technical publications, **96**
New England's premier laboratory, **54**
New Etc, **138**
New Event Calendars ACS, **95**
New Hampshire, **67**
New Jersey
100-150 mile radius of northern, **8**
New Latest Press, **70**
New Literature Request Form Application Guides, **77**
New Market, **91**
New Media Releases Publications Programs, **127**
New Mexico State University, **140**
New MSDS Archive, **188**
New Organization Doing Business, **88**
New Product Guide Message
manufacturing technology, **20**
New Products, **30, 71, 77**
New Recruitment Subscriber Area Patent Copy Ordering
Services, **176**
New Search hotlink Telnet Link, **177**
New Subscribe Company Info Products,
86
New Support Contact Prices About
Cherwell Customer Service, **152**
New Swiss Chemical Society, **106**
New Technology Alert Shameless Promotion of Month Refining, **83**
New Tradeshows Document Library
Thermal Analysis Products Accessories, **76**
New Varian's board
Search, **91**
New York branch of Nagase, **32**
New York Stock Exchange, **17, 42**
New Zealand, **31**
Newpapers, **147**
News
Site maps Workshop calendar Employment opportunities, **123**
News database, **161**
News information, **181**
News Releases
Inc. s, **41**

News Science-policy news, **161**
News services, **200**
News Submit URL Search Tips FAQ More, **202**
Newsgroups, **147**, **206**
Newsletter of international fission-track community, **162**
Next Wave Open Forum, **94**
Nicolet Instrument Corporation, **77**
NIH Tutorial, **139**
NIST mission, **123**
Nitric oxide reagents, **9**
Nitrosamine generation carcinogenic, **26**
NNDC services, **117**
Nobel Foundation home page, **208**
Nobel Prize, **208**
Nobel Prizes, **108**
Non-agricultural applications, **26**
Non-commercial federal entity, **128**
Non-deductible charge of $1.75, **148**
Non-environmental markets, **79**
Non-flammable high solvency, **1**
Nonlinear Regression Analyzing Radioligand Binding Data scientific data, **68**
Nonprofit corporation, **89**
Norlabs Inc, **34**
Norlabs product lines, **34**
North America, **23**, **24**, **31**, **72**, **92**, **99**, **155**
North American Catalysis Society, **106**
North American corporate services, **1**
North American sales office, **46**
North Carolina, **39**, **99**, **169**
NOVA, **34**, **35**
NOVA Corporation, **34**
Now Available ChromKeeper Simplifies Chromatography Publishing Free Chemfont, **87**
NRC Nuclear Materials Public Involvement, **126**
NRC Radioactive Wastes Contracting, **126**
NRC Rulemaking Strategic Assessment Initiative Search E-mail Phonebook, **126**

NSF Award Search Proposal Status Inquiry External Links, **125**
NSF NSF Location, **125**
NSF Regional Grants Conferences Federal Demonstration Partnership Federal, **125**
NSF's mission, **124**
NTIS price, **123**
NTP Data, **125**
Nuclear structure, **117**
Nuisance value, **78**
Number 2, **157**
Nutter Engineering, **78**

O
Oak Ridge National Laboratory, **126**
Occidental Chemical Corporation, **35**
Occupational Health, **116**
Occupational Safety, **126**, **127**
Octane analyzers, **68**
Offices Bulletin Board Seminars Locally Maintained Resources Other, **142**
OGJ Online, **162**
Ohio, **20**
Oil, **33**, **51**, **53**, **57**, **58**, **66**, **68**, **86**, **104**, **146**, **154**, **162**
international, **19**
Oil analysis, **66**
Oil drilling activities, **3**
Oil exploration, **51**
Oil industry, **19**, **78**, **146**
Oil journal, **163**
Oil products, **51**
Oil refineries, **78**
Oil refining, **33**, **114**
Oil-water separators, **76**
Olefins, **28**, **35**, **43**
production of, **15**
One of Top Users of Information Technology Conoco Aids Azerbaijani, **16**
Online industry periodicals, **178**
Online journals, **165**
Online news service, **180**
Online process analytical instrumentation, **68**
Online retrieval system, **195**

Online searchable database, 74
OnLine Trade Association, 174
Onstream Magazine Explore World
    flowchart, 4
Open Text Index, 202
Operating Companies, 41
Operational factors, 103
Optical Equipment Photo CD's Scien-
    tific Glassware Software 3D, 70
Optical quality, 73
Optics, 11
Order WIPO Publications Patent Coop-
    eration Treaty
    International intellectual property
        rights, 196
Ordering Directory Locations Employ-
    ment, 20
Ordering Etc, 132
Ordering Information Phone, 186
Oregon State University, 189
Organic chemical business, 26
Organic chemicals, 44, 81, 201
Organic Elemental Analysis, 59
Organic molecules, 49
Organic polymeric materials, 125
Organization Sections of NSCS Statis-
    tics Activities Awards
    NSCS history, 106
Organizational Structure Acquisitions
    Search US Search AIDS Patents, 128
Organo-acetylene compounds, 18
Organometallic chemistry, 61
Organometallic specialties, 38
Organosilicon compounds, 50
Orion Research, 79
Ormecon Chemie, 93
Oronite Division's deposit-control
    gasoline additives, 11
Oronite manufactures, 11
OSHA, 127
OSHA Directories, 127
OSHA documents, 123
OSHA hotlines, 123
OSHA Publications, 127
Osteopathy, 132
Other Elsevier Science Services, 165
Ottawa, 99

Outline of Report Order Form Execu-
    tive Summary Upstream Aromatic,
    204
Outstanding Aftermarket Service, 73
Over-the-road transportation of liquid
    specialty chemicals, 69
Overview End Use Consumption Fi-
    nancial Information Forecasts State,
    120
Overview Getting Started Subscribing,
    156
Overview of AllChem Operations
    Conferences Industries Served Na-
    tions, 2
Overview of Australian Plastics Indus-
    try, 179
Oxo products, 33
OxyChem's Petrochemicals business,
    35

P
Pace Incorporated, 28
Pacific Rim, 4, 92
Pahang, 36
Paint thinners, 30
Paper Industry, 111
Paperless Project, 195
Papermaking, 8
Papers Editorial Committee, 148
Paraformaldehyde, 14
Paraxylene, 11
    consumer of, 4
Park Scientific Instruments, 80
Patent, 127, 176, 181, 195
    Classification Class Patent number,
        193
    EPO home page Recent updates Re-
        quest, 194
Patent application, 194
Patent applications, 195
    Euro-PCT, 194
Patent information, 194
Patent Information About Derwent
    About Patents Products, 176
Patent offices EPO, 192
Patent offices of world, 192
PCs Other, 64

PDB file, 182
PDC Magazine Polycontent Polylinks Subscribe FAQ Plastics, 180
PDF index International science, 161
P-diethylbenzene plant, 47
Pennsylvania, 50
PennWell Publishing Company, 163
Pentaerythritol, 14
People Lessons Learned, 129
People www statistics MRes, 136
Peroxide catalysts, 50
Personnel spread, 127
Pesticide intermediates, 27
PET
    proprietary glass reinforced, 37
Petrarch silanes
    manufacturer of, 50
Petrarch specialty silanes, 50
Petrarch trademark, 50
Petrarch WorldwideMonitoring Frequently Asked Questions Website Search, 50
Petrochemical companies, 116
Petrochemical complexes, 43, 204
Petrochemical facilities, 145
Petrochemical industries, 53, 59, 136
Petrochemical Industries ABB's Oil, 53
Petrochemical Industries Solutions Customer Commitment ABB's Proven Record, 53
Petrochemical industry, 94, 146
    Korea's, 204
Petrochemical investments, 146
Petrochemical plants, 6, 78
Petrochemical productive installations, 51
Petrochemical raw materials, 11
Petrochemicals, 10, 35, 46, 63, 205
    market size of upstream aromatic, 204
    market size of upstream olefinic, 204
Petrochemicals business, 32
    OVA's, 34
Petrochemicals Industry Midstream Aromatic Petrochemicals Industry Upstream Olefinic, 204

Petrochemicals Midstream Olefinic Petrochemical Upstream Natural Gas Based Petrochemicals, 204
Petrochemicals products, 35
Petroleum, 19, 163
Petroleum Chemistry, 163
Petroleum companies, 138
Petroleum groups, 18
Petroleum industries, 18, 68
Petroleum industry, 163
Petroleum industry terms, 147
Petroleum Natural Gas Coal Nuclear Renewable Electricity International Energy, 120
Petroleum operations, 154
Petroleum products, 18
    sales of, 11
Petroleum technologies, 147
PETRONAS Fertilizer Sdn Bhd, 36
PETRONAS-petrochemical manufacturing, 36
PGP Keys, 126
PGU project, 36
Ph. D, 77, 87
Pharmaceutical chemistry, 166
Pharmaceutical company, 7
Pharmaceutical intermediates, 27, 45
Pharmaceuticals, 17, 23, 32, 46, 99, 169
Phase Diagnostic Particle Distribution Analyser International Reagents 3, 55
Phase Image of Graphite-Epoxy Composite Live Cell Movie, 81
Phase-Transfer Catalysis, 81
Phase-Transfer Catalysis Communications WANTED, 81
Philosophy Typical Projects GLP Compliance See Us, 88
Phoenix, 37
Phosphite Antioxidants, 21
Photochemistry, 61
Photography, 7
Photonuclear reactions, 117
Physical chemistry of molecules, 158
Physical Chemistry Online Markov Chain Monte Carlo Preprint, 139

Physical constants, 123
Physical Education degrees, 132
Physicals models, 67
Physics Department SUNY Stony
    Brook Long Island, 141
Pigment Group, 15
Pilot plants, 83
Pilot project, 173
Pilot's ability, 37
Plastic containers, 4
Plastic parts, 180
Plastic pellets, 48
Plastic pipe, 34
Plastic Raw Materials, 29
Plasticizers, 13
Plastics End Use Manufacturing ABB
    Sub-Sahara Africa, 53
Plastics industry, 21, 111, 179
Plastics Network, 179
Plastics Technology Center, 180
Platinum
    polysiloxane, 50
Points LABSYS Modules, 60
Pollution present, 190
Pollution prevention, 121
Pollution Prevention Animated Pollu-
    tion Prevention Technologies, 121
Polybutadiene
    molecular weight, 20
Polycarbon supercages
    properties of, 17
Polyester, 4
Polyester polymeric plasticizers, 13
Polyester products, 4
Polyethylene, 11, 48
Polyethylene pipe, 11
Polyethylene reports, 70
Polyethylene resin plants, 204
Polyethylene resins
    manufacturer of, 39
Polyethylene terephthalate plastic, 17
Polymer blends, 12
Polymer design, 41
Polymer industries, 13
Polymer industry news stories, 180
Polymer world, 26
Polymer-based products, 40

Polymers Animations of Protein Cello-
    biohydrolase I Visualization of Vol-
    umes, 173
Polymers Sunigum Acrylate Terpoly-
    mer Chemigum Nitrile Rubber-
    Acrylonitrile, 22
Polypropylene plant, 36
Polysciences GmbH, 82
Polystyrenes, 33
Polyvinyl chloride
    plastic raw material, 34
Polyvinyl chloride resins, 12
Pomona College, 63
Pontypool DACRON DuPont, 16
Posters List of Participants Conference
    Photograph E-mail discussions, 153
Posters Physical, 153
Potassium Chlorate, 14
Power plant flue gas scrubber, 40
P-oxybenzol repeat units, 17
PPG Industries, 38
PQ Corporation
    joint venture of, 93
Practical Guide, 81
Practical Phase-Transfer Catalysis In-
    creasing Plant Profits Subscribe, 81
Precision Weighing Balances, 82
Preface Overview Table of Contents
    Selected examples Subject, 140
Prepare Model, 182
Present A Paper Programs, 95
Present Submit Proposals, 95
Press Releases College Recruiting Sec-
    tion Experienced Job Openings In-
    dustry, 38
Pressure Chemical Co, 38
Pressure Temperature Tank Contents
    Press Releases, 64
Prevention Implementation En-
    viroene Business Sector Search
    National Pollution, 121
Prevention Roundtable Industry Con-
    tent Guides Partners, 121
Prime Pigments, 14
Private sector business conglomerate, 7
PRNewswire Operating Companies
    Trade Names 1996 Annual, 41

Probabilistic retrieval, 201
Process Industries, 71
Process Vacuum Services Inc, 83
Processing of chemical information
    Conferences, 174
Processors Raw Materials Suppliers
    Machinery, 179
Product Information About Products
    Service, 70
Production expertise of hundreds, 42
Production facilities, 8
Production facility, 48
Production information, 116
Production of high purity, 20
Production of organic chemicals, 81
Production Petroleum Refining Petro-
    chemical, 53
Production services, 180
Production sites, 6
Productivity of rich mixture of talent,
    126
Products
    market, 38
Products FAQ's Download Demo
    MSDS Sheets Customers, 185
Products Services About Varian News
    Jobs Index, 91
Professors Biegler, 138
Program Hot News Company Profile,
    62
Programme Fifth Framework Focus
    Research Themes Document Library,
    116
Programme Home Pages Green Paper,
    116
Programs Facilities Products
    Congressional testimony, 123
Programs Teaching Resources Elec-
    tronic Journals Organizations, 174
Progress Meetings News Undergradu-
    ate Prospectus Postgraduate Prospec-
    tus Student, 136
Project case histories Client list, 79
Properties
    chemical, 163
    fatigue, 37
Properties of surfaces, 136

Property
    industrial, 194
Proprietary catalytic technologies, 9
Proprietary coating process, 73
Proprietary manufacturing technolo-
    gies, 37
Proprietary materials, 37
Proprietary names, 188
Prostate, 51
Protect Human Health Participating
    Agencies, 125
Protection Centre, 157
Proton NMR, 67
Pseudospectral methods, 85
PTC Retrofit, 81
PTC technology, 81
Public access area of journal, 153
Public Health Service of Department of
    Health, 125
Public interest sources, 121
Public relations, 149
Public service, 174
Public Statements Information, 129
Public understanding of science, 94
Publication dates, 194
Publications Chemical Health, 125
Publications Communicating, 125
Purification products, 76
Purpose Overview Subscribing Listing,
    138
Pursuit search engine, 201
PVC compounds, 34
PVC plant, 34
Pyrotechnic Chemicals, 188

Q
Quaker Chemical Company, 38
Quantum Chemical, 39
Quasijudicial regulatory agency, 128
Questions Search Tips Help Index, 198
Quickstart Applications Services, 177
Quimica Anglo Chilena, 39
R
R&D facilities, 77
Radiation chemistry, 117
Radiation Chemistry Catalysis-
    Reactivity, 117

Radiation therapy, **91**
Radiotracer development, **117**
Ray L. Dudley, **154**
Reactor metallurgies, **28**
Receive Notification of New Preprint Entries Listing, **156**
Recent advances, **109**
Reducers, **13**
Refereed scientific publication, **157**
Reference Spectra Databases, **67**
Refineries, **6**
Refining Petrochemical Processes Major Advanced Control Projects Interface, **60**
Regional Distributor, **8**
Regional Representatives, **113**
Regional Student Conferences each year, **99**
Register Available training courses coverage of online, **194**
Register of European Patents, **194**
Registration Office United Kingdom Patent Office United States Patent, **192**
Regulatory agencies, **125**
Regulatory compliance, **65**
Reinforced Plastics, **19**
Related WWW Virtual Libraries Special Projects Chemistry Software, **184**
Relational database programs, **73**
Remspec manufactures, **84**
Report Updated Stock Quote SEC EDGAR Filings NAIC Green, **41**
Reprints
    Organization list New publication list Earlier publications, **145**
Request form, **64**
Research and development quantities, **3**
Research and development studies, **125**
Research Limited, **49**
Research Magazine, **41**
Research topics, **133**
Research Triangle Park, **99, 169**
Reservoir Engineering, **147**
Resin research, **34**
Resin series

casting, **47**
Resin systems
    production of, **47**
Resinall, **39, 40**
Resinall's production facilities, **39**
Resins, **33, 34, 37, 38, 39, 43, 47**
    Making Specific, **39**
    synthetic, **31**
Resins Fiber Glass Flat Glass Chemicals Search, **38**
Resource Locator Total Quality Coatings, **38**
Responsible Care, **99**
Restaurant, **40**
Resumes Membership, **184**
Retrieval Help Steps, **138**
Retrieval of Papers Help Submitting Articles Steps, **156**
Rightmost, **202**
RJF International Corporation, **40**
Roadway Express, **85**
Rochester, **87**
ROH symbol, **42**
Roller covering industry, **47**
Roller coverings, **47**
Root Inc one of world, **58**
Royal Charter, **107, 115**
Royal Society Heterocyclic Group, **104**
Royal Society of Chemistry, **150**
Royal Swedish Academy of Sciences, **208**
RPM shares, **41**
Rubber, **13, 26, 29**
Rubber industry, **20**
Rubber mold making, **47**
Rubber production, **26**
Russian journal Neftekhimiya translation of, **163**

S
SAF Bulk Chemicals, **42**
SAF Information, **42**
SAF Literature Manufacturing Facilities Technical Service, **42**
SAF Manufacturing Facilities About SAF Bulk Chemicals, **42**
SAF's capabilities, **42**

Safety Alerts Publications, **129**
Safety data management, **73**
Safety data sheets server, **40**
Safety Information News, **125**
Safety of products, **40**
Safety regulations, **53**
Sale Chemicals Wanted Chemical
    Equipment, **172**
Sales
    international, **30**
Sales Information Join team, **69**
Sales of R35-million, **44**
Sales offices, **2**, **23**, **76**, **91**
Salford Ultrafine Chemicals, **49**
Samplers, **76**
    gas, **76**
Samsung General Chemicals, **43**
Samsung Petrochemical, **43**
San Antonio, **88**
San Francisco, **71**
San Jose, **70**
Sandia National Laboratories, **128**
SAP-EHS Questions Answered Events
    Calendar Chemical Information So-
    lutions, **66**
Sapstain, **33**
Sarawak, **36**
SBIR contracts, **30**
SBR Pliolite Rubber, **22**
Scaleable architecture
    Inktomi, **200**
Scanning Probe Microscopy, **81**
SCIENCE ONLINE, **164**
Science Policy Office of Industry Rela-
    tions Office of Public Outreach, **95**
Science Science's Career Opportunities
    Meetings, **94**
Scientific American, **164**
Scientific American Frontiers Chil-
    dren's books
    Product selections, **164**
Scientific basis, **99**, **169**
Scientific data, **77**
Scientific information, **175**, **182**
Scientific information products, **176**
Scientific instruments, **85**, **86**
Scientific journals, **148**

Scientific papers, **158**
Scientific publication system, **157**
Scientific quality, **126**
Scientific research, **89**, **175**
Scientific research center, **88**
Scientific research centre, **136**
Scientific simulation software, **77**
Scientific societies, **94**
Scientific society, **94**
Scientific subjects, **109**
Scientific talent, **125**
Scientific vacancies, **161**
Scotland, **137**
Scotland Engineering Information
    Guide People Courses Research, **137**
Scottish Borders
    rural setting of, **91**
Sea Partners Program Other Sites, **129**
Sealants Lubricants Paints/Coatings, **10**
Search ACS Web, **95**
Search Engine Directory of Firms Meet
    ENR, **153**
Search Page Come, **60**
Search Plan, **202**
Search Service Frequently
    exhibitions, **182**
Searching Frequently Asked Questions
    Top 25 List, **203**
Seattle, **184**
Sector Engineered Materials Sector
    Feature Report, **3**
Securities laws
    federal, **128**
Securities markets, **128**
Select Chemicals Product List Material
    Safety Data Sheet, **2**
Semiconductor devices, **136**
Seminar room Guided tour
    lab, **141**
Seminars National, **144**
Serbian Chemical Society, **159**
Series Plioflex General Purpose E-SBR
    Budene
    Chemigum 80, **22**
Service Monte Carlo, **139**
Service unavailable Bad file request,
    207

Services About CS Free Software Chem
Links, **58**

Services Career Opportunities Publications Investor Relations, **30**

Services Case Studies Engineering Specialists, **78**

Services Chemical Employment Listings Frequently Asked Questions, **172**

Services Chemistry Gopher Servers Chemistry FTP Servers, **184**

Services Client Access, **83**

Services Compliance Assistance Vanguard, **127**

Services Customer Service Communications Employment, **178**

Services Customer Services User Groups International Home Pages, **71**

Services Customer Support, **150**

Services Employment Opportunities Buckman's Micro 101, **8**

Services Liquids NMR Solids NMR Sample Submission Frequently, **88**

Services Reference materials Data Calibrations Standards information, **123**

Services Society Alliances, **96**

Services Technical Committees, **96**

Seven Sales Representatives, **8**

Severn, **39**

Shanghai, **11**

Shaper Chemicals Ltd, **44**

Sheet Information NAIC Green Sheet Order Form Share, **41**

Shipping capabilities, **92**

Shipping operations, **33**

Shoes Construction Containers Equip, **176**

Short-Lived Positron Emitters High, **117**

Shrimp cultivation, **7**

SIC level, **118**

Silane, **50**

Silane chemicals, **22**

Silicates, **14**

Silicon Graphics, **86**

Silicon Ultralevers Silicon Nitride Microlevers Tipless Silicon, **81**

Silicon Valley, **83**
    capital of, **70**

Silicone compounds, **50**

Silicone greases, **34**

Silicones, **34, 50**

Simple Boolean parameters, **200**

Simple voltage supply, **64**

Simulation Sciences Inc, **86**

Singapore, **29, 34, 41**

SIRI MSDS NFPA codes
    Search, **188**

Site Sales Offices, **77**

Site Sudaan-Software, **84**

Sizings
    manufacturer of glue, **33**

Slower Growth Seen, **120**

Small Businesses Current SEC Rulemaking, **129**

Small Droplets of Chainlike Molecules, **173**

Small Molecule Diffusion, **173**

Small Scale Industries, **27**

SMART competition winner, **172**

SMART Stage 1 Stage 2, **172**

Societies Directory Heinz Heinemann s 40th Anniversary, **107**

Society Officers, **98**

SOCMA's reputation, **111**

Soda-Fabrik AG, **6**

Sodium Chlorate Powder, **14**

Sodium chlorite powder, **14**

SoftShell Online ChemWindow 4.0, **87**

SoftShell products, **87**

Software
    CFD, **67**

Software 2000, **87**

Software applications, **151**

Software Archive Faculty Lecturers NSF Career Planning Workshop, **141**

Software companies, **138**

Software company, **70, 85**

Software package, **55**

Software products, **65, 86, 90**
    CFD, **68**

Software solutions, **86**
Software tools, **71**
Solution Polybutadiene Rubber Natsyn Polyisoprene Rubber Solflex Solution, **22**
Solutions Sales, **86**
South Africa, **41**
South America, **72, 92**
South Central United States, **13, 14**
South East Asia, **48**
  markets of, **29**
Southeastern Consortium, **142**
Southwest Research Institute, **87**
Space Administration, **205**
SPE's 20 Divisions, **110**
Special Issues Single cell analysis Background information, **166**
Specialty Chemicals, **14**
Spectral data, **88**
Spectral Research Technologies company, **88**
Spectrometers, **84**
  NMR, **209**
Spectrometry, **160**
  Table of Contents listing of issues of International Journal of, **160**
Spectroscopic information, **117**
Spectroscopist, **89**
Spectroscopy, **109**
  optic infrared, **84**
Spectroscopy products, **77**
Sponsors Become A Sponsor Subscribe Companies, **160**
Staat und die Öffentlichkeit, **113**
Standard Operating Procedures, **49**
Standards Products, **96**
Stanford University, **154, 203**
Stanford University's HighWire Press, **164**
State of California, **89**
Static temperature, **88**
Statistical Mechanics, **160**
Statistical quality control, **95**
Statistical reports, **120**
Steel
  carbon, **28**

Stehenden Ingenieure und Naturwissenschaftler Beruf und Studium, **113**
Stereochemistry, **61**
Stick DIMPLE EndNote EasyPlot Cyrillic Demos Available, **152**
STN centers, **182**
STN Guide, **182**
STN Patent Databases Workshops User meetings, **182**
STN Representatives, **182**
Storage Computer Consultants Education, **172**
Strategic Information Services division, **149**
Strathclyde University, **137**
Structure Neutron, **117**
Struktol Co. Ltd, **46**
Struktol Company of America, **45**
Student Chapters, **99**
Student sections, **96**
Study of environmental issues, **110**
Styrene, **15**
Subject Selected Publications of Interest, **129**
Submarine atmosphere analysis, **125**
Submit Molecule Citing ECTOC Publisher Identifier, **153**
Submittal Making Changes/Replacing, **138**
Submittal Making Changes-Replacing, **156**
Submitted Paper Postscript, **138, 156**
Submitting Article Submission Commands Format of Papers, **138, 156**
Subscribe Daily Economic News Frequently Requested Statistical Releases, **129**
Subscribe Grand Tours About Us, **162**
Subscription basis, **180**
Sulfur
  Elsag Bailey Process Automation N. V, **68**
Sulfur recovery units, **78**
Sumitomo Chemical, **46**
Summary Fiscal Year 1994 Agency Profile Background, **191**

Superabsorbent polymers, 25
Supercomputers, 67
    Cray, 86
Supplementary information, 161
Support Associates Access, 83
Support Electronic Commerce Commit-
    tee Information, 125
Support General Information AIChE
    Student Chapter Research, 144
Support Information, 70
Support Process Tools Technical Pa-
    pers Job Opportunities, 83
Surface Science, 136
Surface Science Symposium, 143
Surfaces Visualization, 173
Surfactant, 143
Surfactant research, 143
Surfactants, 2, 14, 39, 143
Surfactants market, 37
Swedish Patent, 192
Swellable
    water, 25
Swiss Chemical Society, 106
Switch Integrator Tensiometer Vacuum
    Pump Sieve Shaker, 55
Switching valves, 85
Switzerland, 106, 196
SwRI News, 88
SwRI Publications Search Site, 88
Sybron Chemicals environmental prod-
    ucts, 47
Sybron Chemicals Inc, 46
Symposium Series, 109
Synair Corporation, 47
Synergous topics, 64
Synthetic capabilities, 38
Synthetic carpets, 51
Synthetic fuels industry, 114
Synthetic methods, 61
Synthetic organic materials, 51
Synthetic polymers, 33
Systems Intergraph Public Safety Inter-
    graph Software Solutions Optronics,
    71

T
Table of Contents of issues Forthcom-
    ing Articles Guide, 166
Taipei, 11
Taiwan, 11
Talks Visual Sources, 174
Tampa, 27
Tank containers, 3
Tank linings, 72
Tank trucks, 3
Tanker services, 69
Taylor-made products, 25
Technical Affairs, 111
Technical assistance, 96, 154
Technical assistance bulletins, 120
Technical association, 98
Technical Association of Pulp, 111
Technical centers, 180
Technical conferences, 110
Technical Description of Submit, 203
Technical Desktop, 71
Technical development, 20
Technical expertise, 38
Technical function, 194
Technical guidance documents, 120
Technical Info, 127
Technical information, 21, 100, 114,
    119
Technical interests, 99
Technical liaison services, 74
Technical magazines, 163
Technical matters, 161
Technical news, 152
Technical papers, 177
Technical polymers, 23
Technical reports, 119
Technical requirements, 165
Technical Research Council of Turkey,
    104
Technical resources, 40
Technical service center, 13
Technical services, 84
Technical standards, 96
Technical Support Graphics Gallery, 77
Technical talents of personnel, 144
Technikwissen-als
    Er fördert den Transfer von, 112

Technological experience, 35
Technology Corporation, 114
Technology Japanese Information, 114
Technology of Serbia, 159
Technology Symposium Getting Started Manual Congressional Symposium, 67
TeleChem's market knowledge, 48
Telecommunications, 63, 84, 86
Telephone, 167
Terephthalic acid plant, 43
Terminologies, 147
Terra-Sorb Superabsorbent polymers, 25
Testing Information Documents, 125
Tetra Tech's specialties, 90
Tetrahedron Alert Other TIS Services Tetnet Notes, 165
Tetrahedron Information System, 165
Texas, 61, 112
Texas Chemical Council, 112
Texas wildcatter's dream, 87
Textile, 33, 39
Textile industries, 29
Textile preparation, 47
Textiles, 22
    physical characteristics of, 46
Thailand's Eastern Seaboard, 48
THEOCHEM Supplementary Material, 166
Theoretical Chemistry, 156
Thermal expansion, 37
Thermal/chemical resistance, 19
Thermochemical database, 55
Thermoplastics, 17
Thermoset molding compounds, 19
Tiger Chemical Company, 48
Tiger Chemicals
    business activity of, 48
Tiger Map Server, 202
Tin, 50
TIS products, 165
Titanium carbide, 73
To-day ICHEMCO, 25
Toiletry Industry, 175
Tokyo, 155

Tom-1 Toluenediisocyanate NLO Table of Contents DAST DANS, 11
Toothbrushes, 17
TOP 40 companies, 29
Topic Information, 128
Topics FAQ Submit articles Editors Volunteer, 155
Torpene chemistry, 22
Total Quality, 38
Toxicological information, 125
Toxicology, 166
Toxicology research, 125
Toxicology research institute, 99, 169
TPI Concrete Co, 48
TPI's extensive operations, 48
Trade association, 111, 112
Trade association news, 170
Trade association of businesses, 112
Trade associations, 99
Trade Names, 41
Trade organization, 97
Trademark, 181
Trademark applications, 195
Trademark Office, 127, 193
Trademark Office World Intellectual Property Organization Other Intellectual Property, 192
Trademark Related Web Sites Document Formats, 128
Trademarks Patent, 128
Trademarks US, 128
Tradename, 186
TradeWave Corporation, 174
Tradewinds Publishing Company, 174
Traditional Transportation Fuels 1994- Volume 2, 120
Training Information Criteria, 81
Training Toolmakers, 179
Tramper, 69
Transfer Agent, 41
Transportation system, 69
Treaty information Laws, 196
Tribology, 125
Trichloroethane, 1
Trinidad, 31
TRInternational Inc, 48, 49
Tsukuba, 205

Turpentine, 22

U
U of Akron, 188
U. C. Berkeley, 200
U. S. A. Business activity, 48
U. S. Congress, 126
U. S. Department of Energy, 117
U. S. Department of Energy's national laboratory system, 116
U. S. Environmental Protection Agency, 189
U. S. EPA, 121
U. S. EPA Test Methods, 121
U. S. Government, 124
U. S. MSDS, 190
U. S. Nuclear Regulatory Commission, 126
U. S. Senate, 124
UCB Group, 49
UK Department of Trade, 172
ULCC Forthcoming conferences, 112
ULCC Membership list Computer Programs, 112
Ultrafine Chemicals, 49
Ultrafine's team, 49
Umbrella organization, 99
Umeå University, 90
Umetri Statistical Experimental Design Modde Courses Download Software, 90
Unauthorized Forbidden Not, 207
Undergraduate Students Courses-Fall 96 Classlist Request, 142
Unified Search Page Chemical Companies chemical industry sites, 172
United Chemical Technologies, 50
United Nations system of organizations, 196
United States, 7, 14, 31, 41, 65, 69, 76, 89, 102, 117, 118, 163, 177, 205
United States Department of Energy multiprogram national laboratory, 127
Universities of Leeds, 150

University analytical instrumentation laboratory, 96
University campuses, 99
University College, 168
University laboratory managers, 96
University of Alabama, 88
University of Bayreuth-MOLGEN-Automatic Structure Elucidation Mathematik, 132
University of Chicago, 116
University of Edinburgh, 59
University of Erlangen, 133
University of Florida Chemical Engineering Department Process Improvement, 142
University of Liverpool Information STM, 136
University of Manchester, 49
University of Manchester Manchester UMIST, 136
University of New South Wales, 168
University of Oklahoma, 143, 144
University of Oklahoma faculty, 143
University of Pittsburgh Medical Center, 145
University of Strathclyde-Computer Aided Design Centre, 137
University of Strathclyde-Computer Aided Design Centre Strathclyde University, 137
University of Tennessee, 145, 146
University of Texas, 183
University of Texas information, 146
University of Utah Chemistry Department, 187
University of Utah Department of Chemistry, 189
University of Utah Department of Chemistry MSDS database, 189
University of Utah MSDS database mirror of, 186
University of Waterloo Library, 181
University research, 80
Urea, 36
Urea Nonlinear Optical Materials Biological PNA MNA, 11

Urethane chemical company
rubber, **47**
Urethane processing, **47**
Urethane resins
Synair's repertoire of, **47**
US Code Section 35 IPNS Archive of
stories, **193**
US Patent, **192**
US Patents, **37**
Use of Safety Information Resources,
188
Useful Order A Copy Table of Contents
Prelude A, **206**
Usenet news groups, **197**
Utah database, **189**
UTI measurement devices, **76**
Utility model applications, **195**
UV/VIS Heteroatom NMR Natural
Products, **67**
UV-VIS atomic radiation, **88**

V
Valve accessories, **85**
Vapor Pressure analyzer 8280 Hydro-
carbons-in-Water monitor FLO-
CAL, **68**
Vente, **36**
Vermont SIRI Material Safety Data
Sheet collection, **188**
Vernio 1987, **4**
Victims of Disease, **16**
Video clips, **137**
Video materials, **137**
Vinyl, **12**
Vinyl acetate monomers, **23**
Vinyl modified styrene/butadiene co-
polymers, **20**
Viruses Based, **173**
Visualization Group, **173**
Volt Bohr Magneton Bohr Radius
Boltzmann Constant Classical, **124**
Volume 43, **171**
Volume 9 Number 1, **157**
Vt. SIRI Safety File Library of text, **188**
VWR Releases First VWRbrand Cata-
log VWR Introduces Premier, **91**

W
W. Wilbeth Road, **20**
WAIS, **199**
WAIS server
Inc. s, **199**
Wall Street Research Net, **203**
War About DuPont DuPont, **16**
Warehousing operations, **13**
Wastewater sites, **184**
Water analysis, **66**
Water studies, **66**
Water technology companies, **66**
Water treatment, **8**
Water treatment chemicals, **39**
Water treatment companies, **97**
Water treatment facilities, **78**
Water treatment industry, **97**
Water treatment products, **2**
Waterhouse, **92**
Wave of Future, **157**
Web Based News Groups
Test, **97**
Web page, **157**
Web pages, **167, 201**
Web reports, **177**
Web Servers, **192**
Web sites, **185**
Webcrawler Hints, **203**
Webcrawler Search Page News About,
203
Webpages, **181**
Website, **155, 179**
Nature's, **161**
Website Intergraph News About Inter-
graph ANA Tech
Search, **71**
Welcome Industry Related Sites, **30**
West Coast business, **89**
Western Hemisphere, **30**
Widener University Chemistry De-
partment Patents Fullerene Gallery,
141
Widerange, **148**
Windows application organizations,
186
Winning Team, **60**
WIPO Arbitration Center, **196**

Wolfson Chromatography Unit, **59**
World Association of Theoretical Organic Chemists, **113**
World Association of Theoretical Oriented Chemists, **113**
World Intellectual Property Organization, **196**
World Market Products exhibitions, **161**
World Technology Evaluation Center companion, **205**
Worldwide Monitoring surface modified organosilicas, **50**
WorldWide WebLabs, **180**
Worth Up, **75**
WWP Market Intelligence Reports monitor engineering/construction undertakings, **183**
WWP Quick Site Tour Region Industry Frequently Asked, **183**

X
X-Ray Diffraction Studies Solar Neutrinos Nuclear Chemistry-Relativistic, **117**

Y
Yanshan Petrochemical Corpporation, **51**
Young Engineers event, **64**
Yugoslavia, **104**
Yukong, **51**

Z
Zeneca, **51**
Zeolite catalysts, **93**
Zeolite powders, **93**
Zeolite products, **93**
Zeolyst International, **92, 93**
Zipperling Kessler & Co., **93**
Zhuhai Skyhigh Chemicals Co., **52**
Zinc, **50**
Zone Refining, **42**